WORKING IN PARTNERSHIP WITH PARENTS: THE PARENT ADVISER MODEL

WORKING IN PARTNERSHIP WITH PARENTS: THE PARENT ADVISER MODEL

Hilton Davis*, Crispin Day and Christine Bidmead

Centre for Parent and Child Support, South London and Maudsley NHS Trust, London, UK and Guy's, Kings' & St Thomas' School of Medicine, London, UK.

*For correspondence: Centre for Parent and Child Support, Munro Centre, Guy's Hospital, Snowsfields, London SE1 3SS, UK

Tel: 020 7378 3235 Fax: 020 7378 3243 E-mail: hilton.davis@kcl.ac.uk

Harcourt Assessment

The Psychological Corporation

Published by Harcourt Assessment, 1 Procter Street, London WC1V 6EU.
Printed in the United Kingdom.

07 06 05   7 6 5 4 3

This book is dedicated to our families. Without their support in every sense the book could not have been written.

To Liz, Owen, Cara and Rachel.

To Caroline, Joseph and Theo.

To John, Richard, Christopher and Ann-Marie.

CONTENTS

PREFACE

This book is about helping parents. It is intended to be read by anyone working with children and their families, and is relevant to all the main children's agencies, whether voluntary, health, education, or social services. It is based upon the Parent Adviser model, which was initially developed to enable non-mental health workers to provide broader psychosocial support for families of children with severe disabilities. This model has subsequently become the basis for work with families of children with or at risk of a wide range of problems. This has included intervention work with parents of children with chronic illness and emotional and behavioural problems, and promotional and preventive work with families at risk of psychosocial problems and abuse and neglect.

The model arose originally from parents' concerns about professionals not listening to them, not treating them with respect and not caring for them as individuals, as people with competence of their own. It came from dissatisfaction with the communication skills of professionals, whose focus was almost exclusively on the management of children's problems, without taking account of parents and their adaptation to the problem situation. The parental role is central to the care of children, yet there seemed little realisation that this might suffer, if parents feel misunderstood, unvalued, ill-informed and in conflict with the advice they are given. They may comply with advice if they are reasonably adapted to the problem situation, understand what has been said, and are willing and able to do it. It is less likely, however, if they are depressed, low in self-esteem, have relationship difficulties, are isolated socially, or do not have the resources, all of which can accompany significant and chronic problems in children. Perhaps more important, in such situations parents are likely to have difficulties in interacting with their children and this can adversely affect their children's development and well-being.

Being a parent is not an easy task in any circumstances. With additional, extraneous stresses it can become very difficult. Help is, therefore, not just about giving advice, which is notoriously variable in outcome. Ideally, it is about enabling parents to use their own resources to find ways of adapting to and managing problems in the long-term. It is about engaging parents fully and being with them in a relationship that is potentially supportive in itself. It involves hearing the whole story, seeing the full picture, knowing their main worries, learning their strengths, and taking all these into account in enabling them to find ways of managing the problems that confront them and their children. Help might include giving information, advice and possible strategies, but these must still involve parents, as they have to be tailored to their needs. However, involving them as partners in the process, has the advantage of enabling them to use their skills and expertise fully, and hence maximising the chances of them finding solutions of their own.

The Parent Adviser model was developed as a way of making sense of the helping processes generally and enabling helpers to explore and increase their understanding and skills. It is not an alternative to the professional and technical expertise of the many people working with children and their families. It is the vehicle by which this might be delivered more effectively, while maximising the parents' contribution to the specific problem area, and facilitating their general well-being. The intention is to provide help while at the same time enabling the parents' problem solving abilities, self-esteem, and self-efficacy, facilitating their interaction with their children, and hence fostering their development and well-being.

The book elaborates the ideas of Cunningham and Davis (1985) in the area of childhood disability and Davis (1993), who included chronic paediatric illness. The ideas have developed and are presented here in order to help parents generally, whatever the problems in their children, and especially in the context of any endeavour to promote parenting and prevent difficulties. It is written as a text to accompany the Parent Adviser training course, but should be of interest to anyone wishing to explore the ways in which they communicate with parents (e.g. teachers, nurses, medical staff, child care staff, social workers, or volunteers). However, a book can only provide descriptions of the frameworks relevant to this work, and cannot train the use of these and the personal qualities and skills which are the essence of this work. Practical training is, therefore, essential and should be pursued if at all possible, followed by supervision to ensure support in dealing with the many problems that are heard when people take the trouble to listen.

We have tried to make the book as short, clear and simple as possible. The ideas presented are not definitive or absolute, but frameworks we have found useful in understanding how to help others. They are presented for the reader's consideration. It is hoped that they will stimulate constructive exploration and lead to each individual developing a more elaborate and effective understanding.

The book can be read straight through, since we have tried to structure it for the training course, taking account of the most effective order for learning. We have also tried to make each chapter self-contained so that the ideas may be explored separately. There is an introductory chapter to set the context, to describe an overall system of care, and to provide an overview of the Parent Adviser model and its applications. This is followed by a chapter considering the problems and needs of parents and families and the overall aims of helping. Chapter 3 presents a model of the helping process, followed by a chapter on the nature of the parent–helper relationship and how this facilitates the process. Chapter 5 considers the basic qualities and skills of helpers, while Chapter 6 applies these to the first meeting with parents. Chapter 7 describes the skills of exploring people's problems, and Chapter 8 takes this further, by looking at the processes by which people make sense of their world, and the implications of this model for the helping process as a whole. Chapter 9 is about the skills of helping parents change the ways they construe situations and Chapter 10 is a general consideration of goal setting and problem management.

These first chapters constitute the core of the book and are the basis for communicating effectively with parents. However, it goes on to consider the context for the application of these ideas, firstly by exploring the area of parenting and then finishing with questions about implementation. Chapter 11 sets the scene by outlining the task of parenting, presenting a model of parent–child interaction as the essence of the task, and considering the ways in which problems arise. Chapter 12 and 13 are concerned with parenting in the first twelve months, and explore strategies for promoting and enhancing the parent–infant relationship. Chapters 14 and 15 look at the qualities, skills and strategies for parents of children up to 7 or 8 years. Finally, chapter 16 deals briefly with the implementation of the Parent Adviser model as a whole, and picks up final issues to do with training, supervision and service organisation.

Since this book is relevant to people from many different backgrounds, for simplicity we have adopted the convention of using the term, 'helper', to refer to anyone working with parents, unless we wish to make a point specific to a particular profession. Although we are using the term, 'parent', we realise that children can be raised by carers other than their biological parents. However, since we believe that what we have to say applies equally to adoptive parents, for example, or foster parents and other carers, we will include these by implication whenever we say 'parent'.

As a reader, whatever your professional or personal background, we sincerely hope you find the book interesting and useful. Although you will have thought about these areas already, we hope you are stimulated to think further, to develop a greater understanding of your role in relating to parents and to enjoy it more.

Helping is not easy and can be particularly stressful when faced with one's own feelings of inadequacy in not being able to solve other people's problems for them. By thinking about the broader helping processes, we hope you gain an appreciation of the value of listening. It accords respect, dignity and belief in parents. It can make them feel proud of themselves and more able to cope, especially if you stay with them in their difficulties. Because you care, you will still feel the need to solve their problems, but unfortunately, there are few, if any problems that can be solved without the direct involvement and effort of the parents themselves. It would be good to be all-knowing and all-competent as helpers, but few of us are. Self-doubt and humility are important, because they imply the need to respect parents, to work with and for them, to use their knowledge and expertise, and, above all, to listen to them. If you ask parents what they should do, and you listen to their replies, they will contain at the very least the elements of a way forward.

Hilton Davis, Crispin Day and Christine Bidmead
Centre for Parent and Child Support, Guy's Hospital, London. July 2002.

ACKNOWLEDGEMENTS

Many people have influenced the ideas in this book, including many colleagues, the parents and children with whom we have worked over the years, participants on the Parent Adviser Courses, and those who have worked as Parent Advisers. We are extremely grateful to them all. We will not acknowledge them individually here, but we sincerely hope they know who they are and that we have already made our feelings known to them. Thank you.

We are particularly grateful to the Guy's and St Thomas' Charitable Foundation whose funding enabled this book to be written.

We should like to express our grateful thanks to Ms Linda Fone, the administrator of the Centre for Parent and Child Support, for her help in completing the book.

CHAPTER 1
SETTING THE SCENE

Although children are our future, parents have not been accorded the importance they deserve within our society. The care of children has been regarded as a low status, menial occupation. Specific support for the parenting role is limited, in spite of the prevalence of psychosocial problems such as postnatal depression, the effects of this on children, and the high levels of emotional and behavioural problems in children. In the UK, health visitors have long provided a universal preventive service, but emphasis upon psychosocial problems is still dependent upon individual interest. Recent evidence indicates that parenting support is still not systematically available (Henricson, Katz, Mesie, Sandison & Tunstill, 2001).

The Parent Adviser model was developed to acknowledge the importance of children and the role of parents within our society, and the need to provide psychological and social support. It recognises that many people have a potential role in providing help and support, while at the same time taking account of the expertise and self-determination of parents.

This chapter will briefly outline the context for the development of the Parent Adviser model, beginning with our basic assumptions about children and parents, and the task and difficulties confronting them. We will go on to describe concerns about service provision, before discussing a general tiered model for the organisation of helping services. In principle this is an overall system of care for children and families, indicating a clear psychosocial role for all people working with them. It is here that the Parent Adviser model has its place in providing support for all families preferably before problems develop. We will finish with an overview of the model, illustrating its application and evaluation.

Children and their Parents

Each child is a person at birth, an individual with a unique personality (Buss & Plomin, 1986) and the abilities to engage immediately in complex social interactions (Murray & Andrews, 2000). The long developmental journey involves children in the task of learning about and adapting effectively to the world in which they live. Parents and others are the guides on this journey, mediating between the child and the outside world. The importance of this task is reflected in the fact that from birth the child is highly responsive socially and preadapted to attract and interact with the parents. Without the baby's contribution, the caretaking process would breakdown. Infants are not passive recipients of their parents' care, but active determinants of what parents do and how they do it. They are partners in the business of development, with the outcomes dependent upon the complex interaction between them, mediating the influences of the wider context in which they live (Bronfenbrenner, 1979).

The parents' task is to get to know and adapt to their children, nurturing what they bring into the world, and enabling their development and well-being. The importance of the task is again reflected in and ensured by the strong emotional bonds that form. Parenting can be characterised as a continuous interactive cycle in which the parent monitors the child, attempts to understand him/her in all aspects, and responds accordingly, with the child mirroring this in monitoring the parent, developing an understanding of what he/she observes and again responding (see Chapter 11).

Being a parent is a demanding role, involving enormous commitment, time and energy, in addition to all other roles undertaken in and outside the family. It is a full-time and permanent post, including life-long concern, if not responsibility, for one's offspring. There is rarely explicit preparation for the task, and opinions on how to do it are as numerous as the people involved. The lack of immediate, direct and unambiguous feedback on one's performance as a parent makes it all the more difficult to know what is appropriate and effective. It is complicated by the fact that children change so rapidly, and one's understanding of them as a parent often lags behind their developmental progress.

Problems Disrupting Parenting

The implied difficulties of adapting to the task of parenting is borne out by the extent of problems families encounter. Postnatal depression, for example, occurs in 10 to 15% of mothers (Oates, 1994) and clearly illustrates the adaptive stresses of becoming a parent. However, it also indicates disruptive changes to the interaction between the parent and child, including lack of synchrony and increased distress (e.g. Murray, Kempton, Woolgar & Hooper, 1993) and significant long-term negative effects upon the emotional and cognitive development of the child (e.g. Hay, Pawlby, Sharp, Asten, Mills & Kumar, 2001).

Unfortunately, there are many other additional factors that can disrupt the parenting process, and hence the child's subsequent well-being. These include difficulties in the child (e.g. prematurity, illness, disability, and negative temperamental characteristics), in the parents (e.g. ill health, mental health problems, lack of social support, and parental disharmony), and more generally (e.g. adverse life events, poverty, housing difficulties, war, and other environmental threat). The extent is shown in a study of deprived inner city environments (Davis, Day, Cox & Cutler, 2000) where 80% of families were experiencing at least one such problem, and nearly 50% three or more. For example, approximately 20% of mothers were judged to be socially isolated and a third had mental health problems. Other population studies have suggested that as many as 18% of children experience chronic illness or disability (e.g. Cadman, Boyle, Szatmari & Offord, 1987).

Psychosocial Problems in Children

Since these problems disrupt parenting, it is not surprising that a worrying number of children experience emotional and behavioural problems as a result. A national survey in the UK (Meltzer, Gatward, Goodman & Ford, 2000) indicated that one in ten 5–15 year-olds has a psychological disorder, with higher rates (14–20%) in less affluent families. Looking at specific problems, rather than disorder categories, studies in deprived areas have found as many as 48% of children with at least one psychosocial problem that impaired the quality of their daily life, and 19% with three or more (Attride-Stirling, Davis, Markless, Sclare & Day, 2001).

Such problems can be extremely distressing at the time for the children and young people or for their parents. They are also likely to have adverse implications for other people such as teachers and the children's peers. However, psychosocial problems in childhood have long-term implications in being associated with increasing youth crime (Rutter, Giller & Hagell, 1998), with adult mental health problems (Angold & Costello, 1995) and consequently with costs within society more generally both economic (Scott, Knapp, Henderson & Maughan, 2001) and otherwise.

Help Seeking

Although there are many parents and children with problems, it does not follow that all of them want help from available services, nor that they get it if they do. Davis, Day, Cox and Cutler (2000) found that only 25% of a random sample of parents expressed a need for help when asked. They tended to have more problems disrupting their parenting and more severe problems in their children than parents who felt they did not need help. Nevertheless, there were people who had many problems, yet did not express a need for help, and some with very few problems who did.

Other studies (e.g. Offord, Boyle, Szatmari, et al, 1987) have indicated that about 80% of children with significant psychosocial problems do not obtain help from specialists, such as child mental health, counselling or social services. Those who do, may have had their problems for a long time, and as many as 42% of parents of children with significant psychosocial problems have never sought professional help of any nature (Attride-Stirling, Davis, Day & Sclare, 2000).

It would seem, therefore, that there are many families with problems; fewer, but still a large number, who would like help, but comparatively few who are successful in obtaining specialist support. This is partly to do with stigma and the feeling that you are a failure, if, as a parent, you have problems. However, it is also to do with inadequate resources and a severe shortage of child mental health services. For example, only 5% of the money allocated to mental health services in the UK is directed at children (Audit Commission, 1999). The amount spent varies considerably from place to place, but is not related to the needs in the population (Kurtz, Thornes & Wolkind, 1994). There is considerable variation in the numbers and type of staff available, but again this is not related to need. Accessibility to services that do exist is poor; families are usually dependent upon others for referral (e.g. GPs), centres are often some way from home, and there are usually long waiting times for a first appointment.

In the absence of specialist help, many parents seek support from a variety of local professionals, including GPs, community paediatricians, health visitors, child care staff, school nurses or teachers. Again, however, there are problems, the most obvious being the lack of time, since public services tend to be overwhelmed with work. There is also a disinclination in these helpers to take on psychosocial problems, at least partly because of a lack of training and confidence. There is certainly a need for professional communication skills to improve, as is evident from the level of parental dissatisfaction (e.g. Davis & Fallowfield, 1991). For example, Attride-Stirling et al (2001), found that parents complained of poor, inappropriate or ineffectual help, people not listening to them, not caring, being insensitive and occasionally rude. They said they wanted: 1) accessible, convenient and effective services, provided by people who would listen without judging them; 2) reassurance to help restore their self-confidence; and 3) an acknowledgement of their own strengths.

This situation is changing with a growing awareness that many problems in our current society (e.g. social exclusion, mental illness, family breakdown, increasing crime, drug addiction) might be related to children's development and that early intervention and prevention might have a role in this. Governments and public services in a number of countries are beginning to consider and fund preventive and early intervention strategies (Home Office, 1998; McCain & Mustard, 1999).

The UK government, for example, has been developing interdepartmental policies and initiatives for the early support of the family, including a National Family and Parenting Institute, telephone help lines for parents, and the development of Sure Start centres to co-ordinate early services for children and parents in deprived areas. A wealth of specific strategies are now available, as described by Pugh, De'Ath, and Smith (1994), for example. These include direct parent training (e.g. Sanders, 1999; Sutton, 1992; Webster-Stratton, 1992), training health visitors to deal with behavioural problems (e.g. Stevenson, 1990), befriending schemes (e.g. Friends United Network; Homestart, Newpin) and home visiting (Gomby, Culross & Behrman, 1999).

However, such support is not systematically available to most families (Henricson, et al, 2001), the level of support varies enormously across areas, and most services are funded by charitable sources and staffed by volunteers. The resources in this area are insufficient, and particularly services of a promotional or preventive nature (Mental Health Foundation, 1999).

Service Development Strategies: A Tiered System
Given the high levels of psychosocial problems, the serious implications of these (e.g. costs of crime) and the lack of systematic high quality support services, there is urgent need for radical change.

Although an increase in specialist mental health resources would help, inadequate funding and the lack of trained personnel make this a partial solution at best. An alternative strategy is to use all available resources more efficiently to develop a network that forms an effective system of care, and not a set of discrete workers with entirely different and seemingly unrelated roles. A system of care refers to a universal service that works with parents systematically to promote the psychosocial development of their children, to prevent problems from arising, to identify special need early, and to enable effective strategies at the appropriate level of specialisation.

Our aim has been to develop such a system for all families, whether or not their children have problems and regardless of the nature of their difficulties. We assume that all families need support at some point, and the ability of professionals to communicate effectively is crucial in providing it. These are needed not only to convey information and identify solutions, but to engage them in the first place, to enable them to express and explore problems openly and to develop self-efficacy. This applies to families with or likely to have children with emotional and behavioural problems, as much as to those with children with chronic illnesses, disabilities, or even academic problems (e.g. dyslexia). All are associated with increased psychosocial difficulties in the children, as well as higher degrees of stress in the parents, increased parental mental health problems, marital difficulties, and social isolation (e.g. Cunningham & Davis, 1985; Furneaux, 1988; Eiser, 1990).

We have begun developing a system in London (Day, Davis & Hind, 1998;

Day & Davis, 1999), similar to the model recommended by the NHS Health Advisory Service (1995). It assumes: 1) different levels of need in terms of number, type, duration and complexity of problems in children and their families; 2) a requirement for different degrees of mental health specialisation; 3) a psychosocial role for all people working with children and families, and hence the need for interagency partnership and co-operation; and 4) emphasis upon promotional and preventive work.

Our system in South-East London consists of four co-ordinated service tiers and is represented in Figure 1.1. This shows the four tiers cutting a triangle at different levels. The triangle is used here to indicate the total child population in an area with the implication that Tier 1 is intended to deal with all children, and each subsequent tier dealing with smaller proportions. Tier 4 as the most specialist level is therefore dealing with comparatively few children and families with the most complex needs.

FIGURE 1.1 TIERED SYSTEM OF CARE

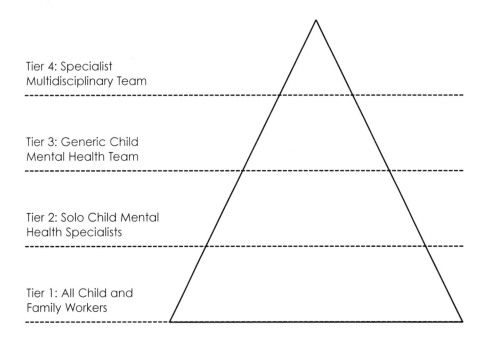

Tier 4: Specialist
Multidisciplinary Team

Tier 3: Generic Child
Mental Health Team

Tier 2: Solo Child Mental
Health Specialists

Tier 1: All Child and
Family Workers

TIER 1: ALL CHILD AND FAMILY WORKERS

In principle this involves everyone working with children and families, including midwives, health visitors, school nurses, GPs, community paediatricians, nursery nurses and other early years staff, social services personnel, teachers and people from the voluntary agencies. They are confronted by psychological and social issues all the time, and, in fact, take the main burden, at least in the first instance, of care.

This service model acknowledges that they are the first level of service in the provision of psychosocial support, that might be promotional, preventive and/or reactive in nature. If organised and trained properly, many more people in this tier become available to provide help. There would be broad support from pregnancy onward. All helpers would feel equipped to deal with many problems at lower levels of need at the earliest possible stage. For example, they would be able to encourage more effective adaptation at relevant transition points, and to prevent the development of more persistent and severe problems. At the very least, the role involves initial exploration of problems and assessment, even if the result is a referral to more specialised services. Such a system enables the development of a network of interlocking support services across all agencies (health, education, social and voluntary) at all stages of the development of families and their children, with the potential for it being long-term, continuous and intermittent.

These developments require all services to share a vision, have clear policies about the importance of psychosocial support and their role in it, and to be well co-ordinated. In principle, individual workers should be selected for the qualities and skills needed to relate to and communicate effectively, as well as for the technical expertise associated with their specific profession. They need to be trained in the qualities and skills of engaging families and working with them effectively in partnership. They need managerial permission and the time to work in this way, but also on-going supervision to maintain and enhance their skills and motivation and support them under all circumstances. It is precisely this situation for which the Parent Adviser programme was developed, as will be described towards the end of the chapter.

TIER 2: SOLO CHILD MENTAL HEALTH SPECIALISTS

This tier consists of a set of child mental health specialists, who might have a background in a variety of professions (e.g. social work, psychology, nursing, medicine or teaching) but with additional mental health training and experience in child mental health specifically. In our system, they are based in the community and work individually on a regular weekly basis in all the places children and families are most likely to be found (e.g. health and early years centres, GP surgeries, and schools).

Their role is to work in partnership with Tier 1 to provide specific support, explicitly negotiated with them, and tailored to the need in their particular setting (e.g. health centre or nursery). This usually involves the provision of direct more specialist help for families, whose needs are beyond the capacity of Tier 1. The advantages of this include seeing families locally, more quickly, and at an earlier stage in the development of problems. It also enables close liaison with Tier 3 in relation to families where the complexity of problems necessitates even greater specialism.

However, an equally important aim of the Tier 2 role is to do whatever is necessary to enhance the ability of Tier 1 to provide effective psychosocial support themselves. This can be done by joint-working, consultation, training and supervision. Consultation can be both formal or informal and is available to all Tier 1 staff in relation to the problems of specific children and families, and strategies for their management, as well as issues of more general service development. There are always many possible options for training and these are decided in collaboration with Tier 1 locally. However, we believe that the Parent Adviser model should be the core of the training, so that the ability of Tier 1 staff to provide effective help themselves is increased. Following systematic training of this nature, there is always the need for subsequent, ongoing, supervisory support, which can also be a vital part of the role of the Tier 2 child mental health specialist.

TIER 3: GENERIC CHILD MENTAL HEALTH TEAM

Tier 3 consists of a multidisciplinary child and adolescent mental health (CAMH) team, whose role is to help children and families with needs beyond the resources of the solo child mental health specialists at Tier 2. Such teams exist already in most areas of the UK, although they are extremely variable in size, composition, organisation and function. In general, they include clinical psychologists, child psychiatrists, specialist social workers and nurses, psychotherapists and family therapists, and might realistically involve specialist teachers, speech therapists and occupational therapists.

TIER 4: SPECIALIST MULTIDISCIPLINARY TEAM

This is the final level of service to be differentiated in this system of care and consists of highly specialised multidisciplinary teams dealing with children and families with the least frequent, most severe and complex problems. The existence of such teams varies from place to place and developments are needed to deal with disorders such as autism, attention deficit, anorexia, psychotic problems, children looked after by the local authority, or youth offenders. Their development would be aided considerably if all relevant services (e.g. paediatrics, education and social care) were tiered similarly (Finch, Hill

& Clegg, 2000). The composition of Tier 4 teams tend to be similar to Tier 3, although they usually serve a much larger geographical area.

Close communication, co-operation and careful organisation are crucial at all levels in this system, so that they function effectively. Although one might assume that each tier is accessed by the one before it, liaison between them all is essential, so that, there can be a two-way movement of families. For example, a child with severe autism might be referred by a health visitor in Tier 1 to Tier 4, whose role would in part be to enable the health visitor to provide ongoing support for the family during the specialist intervention and subsequently.

Although Tier 4 and Tier 3 may be seen as more exclusively and directly therapeutic than Tier 2, they still have consultancy, training and supervisory functions with the other tiers. In fact, it is crucial for the success of the system that the different levels work closely together to provide appropriate support for each other at all times. The notion of partnership is again relevant, in that each tier has to complement the work of the others, and this requires time, effective relationships and negotiated agreement.

The Parent Adviser Model

As indicated earlier, Tier 1 personnel require training to enable them to be effective in supporting parents. It is frequently assumed that this means having information on child development, childhood problems, and specific methods or techniques for managing children's behaviour. Clearly these are enormously important and there is a large and useful literature available on this (e.g. Graham, 1998). Currently, a growing emphasis is being placed upon the provision of parenting skills training via a range of professional and voluntary agencies (e.g. Smith, 1996), varying from the humanistic (e.g. Sokolov & Hutton, 1988) to social learning theory (e.g. Webster-Stratton, 1994). Again although the evidence is that such methods are effective (e.g. Barlow, 1997; Barlow, Coren & Stewart-Brown, 2002), it cannot be assumed that anyone can simply impart this information and these skills to parents and that all the problems will be avoided or managed effectively. This neglects the complexity of the psychological and social context of the helping process and the more general qualities and communication skills needed by helpers to negotiate it. It may also underestimate the extent to which current professional communication skills have to be unlearnt in order to do this kind of training effectively.

As indicated earlier, not all parents seek help and many will certainly not attend groups. Even when seeking help, parents' problems might not be what they seem initially and detailed exploration becomes necessary through skilled communication. Communication is not simple, and parents are often dissatisfied with how they are treated, as discussed earlier. What is more, many people do not take the advice they are given by professionals; studies have shown that nearly 50% on average do not adhere appropriately to treatment regimes and this is highly related to satisfaction with communication (Davis & Fallowfield, 1991).

To provide help and ensure an overall system of care, one cannot simply have a set of solutions. Helpers have to take into account the psychological and social context from the families' viewpoint and the interpersonal processes involved. This means firstly engaging them, earning their respect, identifying and exploring their particular issues and then moving on with them to appropriate problem management. This requires high level communication skills and thought not just to the immediate problem and its resolution, but to the future adaptation of parents and their children more generally. This involves attempting to enhance their self-efficacy and continuing skills of problem management. This is rarely taught systematically in professional training, and the characteristics and skills involved are frequently taken for granted.

The Parent Adviser model was developed to enable all potential helpers at Tier 1, to provide a more effective and broader service, and to work together with others to enable a complete system of care. The intention is to enable them to understand the processes and skills of helping, so that they can use their own technical expertise more effectively by taking into account the interpersonal processes, yet also deal with the psychological and social issues that are invariably present when people have a problem.

The overall aim of the model and the associated training is to provide an explicit, relatively simple set of frameworks for understanding the psychosocial nature of the helping situation and to give intensive practice and feedback to enable potential helpers to develop and use the qualities and communication skills needed to facilitate the processes involved. The frameworks, which are shown in Figure 1.2, were mainly derived from the psychotherapy and counselling literature, including cognitive and behavioural work. They also incorporate ideas from the study of child development and parenting. They have been particularly influenced by the work of George Kelly (1991) on how people adapt to their particular circumstances, Carl Rogers (1959) in terms of the fundamental characteristics of helpers, and Gerard Egan (1990), who has presented a systematic understanding of the helping process and skills involved. Each framework takes what is essentially a complex area and provides a relatively simple structure by which the helper can think about and make sense of what he/she is doing with parents.

These frameworks are listed below, although not necessarily in the order in which they appear in the book.

FIGURE 1.2 FRAMEWORKS OF THE PARENT ADVISER MODEL

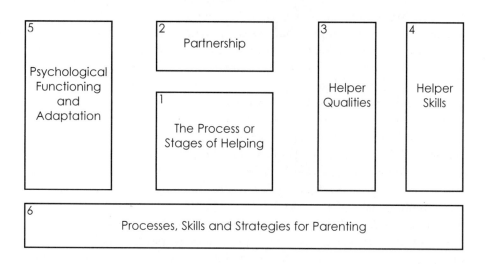

The first is concerned with the overall process of helping (see Chapter 3). This is presented as a series of interrelated stages or tasks, beginning with the development of the parent–helper relationship and moving through to the implementation of strategies and evaluation of the results. The second framework addresses the first stage of the helping process and assumes the most effective parent–helper relationship to be a partnership, which has important implications for the process as a whole (Chapter 4). The third framework considers the basic helper qualities required to facilitate the processes of helping (see Chapter 5). These include a set of six general qualities, which can be understood as broad attitudes or general expectations (e.g. respect). They are assumed to be fundamental in determining whether parents relate to the helper and the eventual outcomes.

These qualities are expressed through a vital set of communication skills (e.g. active listening), and these constitute the fourth framework of the model. Attending and listening are described in Chapter 5, but the other skills are covered as relevant to the helping process in Chapters 6 to 10.

The fifth framework is intended to provide a model for understanding the processes by which parents and children make sense of their world, and adapt to the people and events in their lives (Chapter 8). It is assumed that they do this by developing a personal model of their world on the basis of previous experience, and then use this as a way of making sense or anticipating events. Helping is therefore seen as a process of exploring these personal models with the aim of elaborating their effectiveness and usefulness.

The sixth framework is specifically concerned with a model of parenting (see Chapters 11–15) and derives in part from the previous frameworks. This framework is more complex, but has the Parent Adviser model as the basis of it. By this we mean that all the previous frameworks (i.e. of the helping process, partnership, helper qualities, communication skills, and adaptation) are directly applicable to parenting in the sense of providing guidance for parents and their helpers. We will focus upon the parent–child relationship and will assume that parent–child interaction is fundamental to the parenting task. We will elaborate this basic framework by the inclusion of a range of skills and strategies involved in parenting at different ages from birth onward. These have been derived from a number of different approaches, but are given coherence by reference to the underlying interactive nature of the parenting task.

Overall the Parent Adviser model is an attempt to take account of the needs of parents and children, the process of helping including the parent–helper relationship, the qualities and skills involved, the nature of parenting, and again the qualities, skills and strategies involved in being a parent. The aim is to work with parents in partnership, to bring new ideas if necessary by way of information and strategies, but to involve parents intimately, so that their experience, expertise and ideas are used to the full, and so that they take credit for what happens, feel good about themselves, feel effective, and are more able to deal with future problems themselves.

Nothing here is intended to deny or diminish the specific technical expertise of existing Tier 1 professionals. Their knowledge of diagnosis, assessment and intervention is crucial. However, unless a working relationship is established and methods are effectively communicated to the satisfaction of the parents, this expertise is of little value, and the opportunity for the provision of emotional development and support is lost. Much of what enables people to cope with life generally and deal with specific problems stems from their self-constructions (e.g. self-esteem and self-efficacy) and professionals are in a very powerful position to enhance these considerably, rather than undermine them.

The model makes the point that to use technical expertise appropriately, it is essential that helpers have an understanding of and the communication skills to facilitate the helping process. The personal qualities of helpers make the difference between intervention success and failure. Systems are only as good as the weakest link; good systems fail because of the lack of these qualities, and rather unlikely systems can work, because of the human qualities shown by the people involved. It follows that helpers should be selected carefully, as much for their personal qualities and skills as for their technical ability.

These ideas have been used as the basis of a short training course that has been developed and used over the years and is described in manual form by Davis, Day and Bidmead (2002).

Applications of the Parent Adviser Model

Several Tier 1 services have been set up using the Parent Adviser model. The first was a service to provide long-term support for families with children with severe and multiple disabilities. Health visitors, physiotherapists, nursery nurses, teachers, social service personnel and parents were trained in the model and then worked by home visiting over extended periods beginning weekly and then gradually increasing the intervals between visits to about once a month. A detailed description can be found in Buchan, Clemerson and Davis (1988) and Davis and Ali Choudhury (1988).

A similar service was set up to provide help for families of pre-school children where there were emotional and behavioural problems in the children, parenting problems or personal problems in the parents (e.g. depression). The service was home-based and staffed by health visitors and community paediatricians. This original pilot project was described by Davis, Spurr, Cox et al (1997), but has since grown as a major aspect of the tiered system we have been developing (Day et al, 1998). We have undertaken wide-scale training of most health visitors in the area, as well as large numbers of early years staff, teachers, school nurses and others. This has included work with the families of older children in primary and secondary schools, and there have been further independent developments, including work with families of young offenders (Davis & Day, 2001) via the voluntary sector and through a youth offending team.

However, we have been particularly concerned to develop specific promotional and preventive services and three systems have been set up so far involving the Parent Adviser model. The first (Avon Premature Infant Project, 1998) was a service for families of preterm infants born at 32 weeks or less. Nursery and state enrolled nurses were trained to visit families at home once the children had been discharged from hospital. Again initial visiting was weekly, gradually reducing to monthly and remaining at this intensity until the intervention finished at about two years. The second, the European Early Promotion Project, is a universal service for all families in a designated area (Puura, Davis, Papadopoulou et al, 2002). It is staffed by health visitors, who visit all prospective parents approximately four to six weeks before and after the birth of their child to conduct specially designed interviews intended to promote the psychosocial adaptation of the parents and hence their children. Families identified as at risk of child mental health difficulties are then engaged in a series of weekly home visits using the Parent Adviser model to attempt to reduce the risk factors (e.g. postnatal depression) and particularly focusing upon enhancing the parent–infant interaction (see Chapter 13 for more detail). The third service has been set up by a team based in the Health Services Research Unit in Oxford. This involves midwives screening during pregnancy for families in which children are at risk of abuse and neglect. Those identified are then allocated a health visitor trained as a parent adviser, who attempts to visit the families at home on a weekly basis throughout the remaining period of the pregnancy and continuing until the child is 12 months.

EVALUATION OF EFFECTIVENESS

Before finishing the chapter, it is important to address the question of the effectiveness of the Parent Adviser model in producing anticipated benefits for helpers and especially for families. Is there any point in changing the ways we have worked in the past and adopting the model being proposed here if there are no benefits?

This is a difficult question, because of the complexity of the intervention, which is not standardised, but tailored to individual families. It also involves many possible sources of benefit, varying from the potential effects of relationship building to devising many different strategies according to the nature of the specific problems for the parents and their children. The answer hinges around knowing a great deal more about the processes of intervention than is possible from the current research literature. Nevertheless, a very reasonable case can be made for the use of the Parent Adviser model and there is evidence to suggest that it is a promising approach in a number of areas.

We can argue for the approach on theoretical, ethical and humanitarian grounds, and in terms of the need, given the high frequency of psychosocial problems in families, service inadequacies, problems with professional communication, and parents' own expression of need. However, there is a need to provide empirical evidence of the effects of any approach in terms of beneficial outcomes.

Indirectly this can be gathered from a number of sources. These include: 1) studies indicating health care benefits as the result of improved professional communication (e.g. less professional stress, more accurate diagnosis, greater compliance, improved outcomes both physically and psychologically for patients) (Davis & Fallowfield, 1991); 2) studies showing benefits to women with postnatal depression as the result of interventions that are related to the Parent Adviser model (e.g. Holden, Sagovsky & Cox, 1989; Cooper & Murray, 1997); 3) the results of home visiting studies showing long-term benefits to both parents and children (Gomby, Culross & Behrman, 1999); and 4) the extensive body of research on psychotherapy and counselling showing consistent positive benefits (e.g. Lambert & Bergin, 1994), including the effectiveness of paraprofessionals in providing social support for example (Pless & Satterwhite, 1972; Pless & Nolan, 1991).

More directly, there is evidence from our own studies of the Parent Adviser training course. It has been shown to be valued consistently highly by participants (e.g. Rushton & Davis, 1992; Davis et al, 1997; Lea, Clarke & Davis, 1998), who clearly benefited in terms of increased theoretical knowledge of the helping processes, improved self-assessments of themselves as helpers, and improved qualities and communication skills.

However, and perhaps most important, there is also evidence of benefits for families who have been supported by people trained as parent advisers. For example, Davis and Rushton (1991) evaluated the outcomes for families of children with severe intellectual and multiple disabilities. In comparison with randomly allocated controls, the mothers in the intervention group showed significant improvements in psychosocial adaptation at the end of the study, and their children had fewer behaviour problems and made significantly better developmental progress. Similarly, significant but small effects on children's developmental progress at two years were also found in an independent study of families supported by parent advisers at discharge from a special care baby unit (Avon Premature Infant Project, 1998). Most recently, Davis and Spurr (1998) found significant benefits for families of pre-school children with emotional and behavioural problems in terms of the acceptability of the service to them, the adaptation of the mothers (e.g. decreased levels of stress and depression, increased self-esteem), improvements in the home environment and in the behaviour of the referred children.

In Conclusion

Although children are vital for our future, there are many problems in modern society that can disrupt parenting and have significant effects upon the development and well-being of children and young people. This is clearly indicated by the large number of children experiencing psychosocial problems and the serious implications of these for their future in terms of social exclusion, crime and adult mental health. Nevertheless, although the situation is improving, there is little systematic support universally available to parents, and certainly little that could be described as promotional or preventive.

We have argued in this chapter for the development of a system of care in which all services currently working with children and families might provide more effective support, taking into account the psychosocial aspects of life, as well as those related to health, child care and education. The Parent Adviser model has been developed as a basis for this, and provides ways of understanding the psychological and social aspects of helping, and the interpersonal skills necessary to engage parents and enable them to help themselves and their children. The model has been used in a number of settings with promising results, and this book is intended to present the model in detail, beginning in the next chapter with a consideration of the problems facing parents and the aims of helping.

Our ultimate aim in producing this book is to enable services that will facilitate the well-being of all children, their ability to manage problems and to derive a measure of happiness and security, so that they might achieve their potential, and contribute positively to society. Since parents are probably the most important element in their children's achievement of these aims, we believe that there is little choice but to work with and through parents, or their substitutes, if there is to be effective and appropriate support available for them at all stages of their early lives.

CHAPTER 2
PARENTS' PROBLEMS AND THE AIMS OF HELPING

It is clear from the last chapter that there is the need for a general system of care in order to support parents and provide effective options for help at all stages of the developmental process. Parents deserve such help, since healthy and well-adapted children are important for our future and the task of parenting is demanding within modern society. They need support, because there are many circumstances that disrupt the ability to provide a secure and facilitative environment for their children, and there are unacceptably high numbers of children with psychosocial problems. They also want help and many parents express a need for support in dealing with problems in their children.

Parenting is a process of continual adjustment, potentially fraught with uncertainty. It involves a never-ending attempt to make sense of and adapt to a constantly changing situation, and yet it is often assumed to be natural. Little systematic preparation is provided, especially for those most in need, and subsequent accessible help is not universally available.

Since the book is concerned to provide basic frameworks for a system of care involving all people working with children and their parents, it is appropriate to begin by considering the kinds of problems parents are likely to face. If we want to help, then we must know the difficulties in order to have an idea of the needs, and what we might realistically attempt to achieve. Before doing this, however, we should like to make some general points.

Firstly, we are not assuming that every parent has problems with which they need help all the time. All parents are unique; they respond in their own particular ways to their individual children in the very different circumstances of their family and social context. Most cope well enough most of the time using their own resources and those of the social network surrounding them. However, there will almost always be occasions on which they need extra support, and it would certainly be reassuring if they knew this was easily available before problems arose.

Secondly, the potential range of problems confronting parents are not separate, individual issues, but highly interrelated. Having difficulties in one aspect of life (e.g. at work, with a partner) is likely to affect the ways parents interact with their children, because the different problems are all mediated by the parents' psychological system. We naturally look for simple causal explanations, such as a father's hostility or infidelity causing his wife to be depressed, leading to her being unresponsive to the children and causing them subsequent distress. However, although this might be valid, the direction of cause and effect is not necessarily clear. Each problem is likely to influence and be influenced by all the circumstances impinging upon the family at a particular time. Taking just the last part of this causal chain, although we might assume that the mother's behaviour may have distressed the children initially, their distress is equally likely to further disturb and/or depress the mother, which might increase the upset in the children, and so on in a cycle. Each problem area can have multiple effects upon all other parts of the personal and family systems involved, and the effects are specific to their situation.

Thirdly, if we define a problem as, for example, a difficulty or a disturbance of function that might require help (e.g. a child being aggressive), there is a question of whose views are to be considered. A teacher might see a boy's aggression as problematic, whereas the parents might deny such behaviour at home, blaming it not on the child, but on the school system, other children or the teachers. In contrast, parents with worries about their children in relation to hearing or general development might not be taken seriously by the GP, for example, or paediatrician.

The views of both parents and professionals are important, but for parents to be helped, their views are paramount and must always be taken seriously. If parents are worried, then they have a problem. If they disagree, there is a conflict, which is problematic in itself. They know their own situation better than anyone else, and their expertise must be used. Perhaps most important, however, is that they are actually almost entirely in control of what happens in the whole of the process of helping. To illustrate, they may have problems, but not recognise them. They might recognise them, but not seek help. They might seek help, but not from the available services. They control what information is available to the helper, guided by their feelings about the helper, and compliance with advice is almost entirely in their power.

Finally, without a clear picture of all the problems confronting parents at a particular time, the help they receive may be compromised. Whatever the help (e.g. prescribing medicine or conducting a developmental assessment) the range of problems confronting parents and children will influence the situation, whether the helper knows it or not. If the helper is aware of the overall situation, their specific circumstances can at the very least be taken into account in the helping process. This does not necessitate dealing with all their problems, which is impossible, but it does mean acknowledging and caring about them, listening to them and at the very least considering their implications for the helper's role. By doing so, one may have valued the parents, helped them to be clearer about what is happening to them, and provided a more considered response.

With these points in mind, we will now illustrate the problems facing parents and their possible needs. We cannot be exhaustive, but will cover the most common issues that arise if one listens effectively to parents and is trusted.

Problems in the Child

Since virtually all parents want the best for their children, any distress or disturbance in the child may be problematic for her/his parents. This occurs on a day to day basis and might include slight injuries, being reprimanded at school, or not fitting in with friends. For the most part, these are easily resolved and do not persist. However, there are many ongoing problems that do arise in children, and have considerable implications for them and their parents. These include, for example, a range of chronic illnesses and disabilities, an array of psychosocial problems, including emotional, social and behavioural difficulties, and educational issues, usually related to perceived failure.

As many as 18% of children are judged to have persistent ill health at any one time (e.g. Cadman et al, 1987). These vary in severity from mild eczema and asthma to life-threatening and painful disorders such as heart disease, cancer, cystic fibrosis, sickle-cell disease, and HIV/AIDS. Regardless of severity, all of them have significant implications for parents, practically, financially, socially and, of course, emotionally.

Somewhere in the region of ten percent of children have life-long disabilities, which again have widespread and significant implications for both them and their families. These include, for example, children with visual (2–3.5%) or hearing impairment (about 1.6%), and a range of motor disabilities such as cerebral palsy (about 0.3%). A large number of children (2–3%) have intellectual impairments, including those associated with Downs syndrome, for example, autism, or brain damage from various causes such as birth anoxia (i.e. being starved of oxygen), trauma (i.e. where the head has been physically injured) or infection.

In addition, there are large numbers of children who despite normal general intellectual levels, have serious academic problems in acquiring the range of basic educational skills. For example, as many as ten percent of children have significant difficulties in acquiring the skills of reading (e.g. Maughan & Yule, 1994). Again, as with the previous problems, there are widespread implications of these difficulties for the children, emotionally and socially, and for their parents.

The final category of problems we should like to mention are the children with psychological and social problems. As previously mentioned, one in ten children with such problems in the UK are likely to be sufficiently disturbed or impaired to meet the criteria for a recognised psychosocial disorder (Meltzer et al, 2000). This figure rises considerably in families experiencing deprived socio-economic conditions, with prevalence rates reaching as high as 20%. It is also worth noting that many more children have psychosocial problems than reach the thresholds set by diagnostic criteria (e.g. Davis et al, 2000) and these may still have considerable effects both upon their own lives and their parents. Children with conduct disorder, for example, one of the most common categories of these disorders, are not necessarily distinguished from children with conduct problems that do not meet the diagnostic criteria for a disorder, in terms of impairment, treatment approach or outcomes (Kazdin, 2001).

Although we have described these various problems separately, as already implied, they are interrelated, and there are many children with multiple difficulties. For example, children with chronic illnesses and disabilities, and especially those with brain disorders (Goodman, 1994), are much more likely to exhibit emotional and behavioural problems, as a result of their other problems. Children with conduct disorder are more likely than usual to have educational difficulties, with approximately two-thirds estimated to need intervention (Earls, 1994).

In terms of the needs of parents, there is a very high likelihood that they will all need help of various kinds with most, if not all, of these problems in their children. This statement, however, should be interpreted carefully, as the process of seeking help is not straightforward. This is especially true in relation to psychosocial problems, where many parents might acknowledge problems in their children, but not express a need for help from professionals (Attride-Stirling et al, 2001). Those acknowledging the need for help will require a range of assistance from assessment and diagnosis to intervention, including, for example, specialist treatment or teaching, advice on what to do themselves, and practical aids.

Whether or not something can be done about any of these problems, a particularly important need for most parents will be to have an explanation of them. They are likely to want to know about causes, and particularly their own role in this, and what they might have done by way of prevention. One parent, for example, described being particularly upset when given the diagnosis of severe conduct disorder in her son, not because of the lack of treatment options or the very poor prognosis, but because she was not given the opportunity to explore the reasons for the disorder.

All such problems have implications for parents themselves, the stresses upon them, the practical aspects of their daily lives, their relationships with their children, their parenting, the relationships within their immediate family, and their wider social network (see Davis, 1993). Associated with these problems in children, therefore, are a range of possible parental needs with which help might be required. We will go on to elaborate these in turn, without assuming that they only arise in the context of children's problems. They may be caused by problems in the child, but are equally likely to arise independently as a result of other factors and as indicated earlier may themselves be causes of problems in children.

Problems in the Parents

Bringing children up requires a considerable degree of personal strength and equanimity in parents, given the need to understand and meet the needs of another person for long hours in a day and over many years. Like all adults, parents vary considerably in how strong they are psychologically and physically, how able they are to deal with stress and the variety of personal problems which we all have to manage. These include the whole range of emotional, practical and relationship issues, as well as physical health problems and of course disabilities they might have of their own.

Most parents manage to cope with these issues most of the time, and even if they affect their parenting or their children to any extent, they do not do so over extended periods, nor excessively. There are times, however, in the lives of most parents, when such problems do impact more heavily upon all aspects of their lives, and when they might clearly need more or less specialist help. There are also some parents whose problems are extreme and long-term, whose own childhoods may have been unhappy, and who clearly might benefit from personal help early in their parenting careers in order to prevent their children being badly affected.

Of particular concern are the range of debilitating adult mental health problems, with the most common being depression. This is especially evident, for example, in women with children under five, and in those lacking a close, confiding relationship (e.g. Brown & Harris, 1978). There are, for example, very high numbers of women who suffer postnatal depression. It is found in about 10 to 15% of women, beginning by definition in the postnatal period, usually within the first 12 months. It has been studied extensively in recent years and is still not really understood in terms of its causes. These are likely to vary from person to person, and may range from the physiological (e.g. hormonal changes) to the social (e.g. specific stresses and absence of social support). What is clear, however, is that, such problems are amenable to psychological intervention, including home visiting by trained nurses (e.g.

Wickberg & Hwang, 1996; Holden et al, 1989). They also signal urgent need, since there are definite adverse emotional, behavioural and intellectual influences upon children in the immediate situation and long-term (e.g. Hay et al, 2001).

Although less common, other disorders such as schizophrenia and drug or alcohol abuse are equally, if not more serious. They may produce highly disturbed behaviour in the parents, resulting in potentially very frightening and abnormal situations for the children involved, and even the occurrence of direct neglect or abuse. Another situation in which very similar concerns about children arise is where parents have general learning difficulties and lack the ability to provide consistently for the needs of the children on their own. All such disorders have to be taken very seriously by services, and although there is a need for specialist expertise, Tier 1 community staff, such as health visitors, are in an ideal position to spot difficulties early on and to provide longer term monitoring and support.

Although much less extreme, more common problems to be encountered in working with parents are to do with self-esteem and self-efficacy. These characteristics are no doubt related to the development of more serious disorders like depression, but they are powerful influences upon the parents' ability to manage their lives generally and their children specifically. Self-esteem relates to one's feeling of self-worth or value, and self-efficacy (Coleman & Karraker, 1997) to the general expectation or belief in one's own ability or power to influence events in our lives.

People vary considerably in these characteristics, but low levels may result from many different stresses and difficulties. This might include the difficult nature of the task of parenting per se, the low status it is accorded in society, and many other stresses (e.g. financial hardship) discussed later in the chapter. However, self-constructions are central issues, when parents are forced to seek external help, and when they feel they are failing to manage or to help their children as they should. Because of their importance, raising self-esteem and self-efficacy is a general need in relation to working with parents. They should be given careful consideration by anyone helping parents, not only because it can easily be undermined further by one's own expertise as the helper, but also because it is essential for long-term functioning in the role of parent.

Parenting
One can assume that the majority of parents interact sufficiently well with their children, that they enable effective development. This is supported by evidence from Van Ijzendoorn & Kroonenberg (1988), for example, who found secure attachments in 65% of children on average in a series of cross-cultural

studies. However, quite clearly this also indicates that there are a large number of parents with difficulties in providing for their children secure and sufficiently stimulating environments in which to develop appropriately.

This might arise for multiple reasons, including all the problems listed in the other sections. Some children are easier to manage that others, with some being particularly difficult in temperament (e.g. Thomas & Chess, 1977) and therefore much more difficult to manage. Likewise, parents will range in their abilities, because of their own emotional problems or stressful circumstances, and the more problematic the child, the more demands are put on the abilities and resources of the parents.

Of particular importance are the circumstances of parents' own childhoods, which might be the only preparation that they have had for the parenting role. Parents who have had adverse experiences in childhood, including lack of affection, harsh or inconsistent discipline, neglect or even abuse, may have subsequent difficulties in understanding the needs of their children, the processes of development and the importance of their relationship with them. They might, for example, have unrealistic expectations about children in general or in relation to particular issues, and not realise the importance of responsive parent–infant interaction in terms of ensuring the identification and appropriate fulfilment of the needs of their children.

Whether they realise it or not, there are parents who are likely to need extensive support and even education in understanding the developmental needs of their children and training in the skills of meeting these appropriately. However, most parents are likely to need some kind of help in parenting skills at some point in their children's upbringing, particularly in the early stages when there might be specific problems with excessive crying, sleep difficulties, or tantrums, or where there are significant problems in the child (e.g. learning difficulties) that might benefit from specific skills and techniques. Adolescence is characteristically another developmental period that parents can find particularly hard, probably because of rapid change, increasing demands for independence, potential dangers (e.g. drugs, pregnancy, sexually transmitted disease), and declining ability to exercise control over their children.

Relationships Problems

Being a parent is difficult in isolation. Active and long-term support from others is required so as to help meet the needs of parents themselves (e.g. for friendship and self-esteem) and hence the needs of their children. However, there are frequently problems in the relationships that might provide effective support for parents.

Of particular importance is the relationship between the parents. When this is warm and respectful, it is the source of enormous support, practically, socially and emotionally. However, it is frequently problematic, as indicated, for example, by statistics on divorce, which has increased in the UK with more than two in five marriages ending in divorce and doing so earlier (e.g. Clarke & Berrington, 1999). It is currently estimated that this means that nearly 30% of children experience the breakdown of their parents' marriage.

Since family break-up is a process that may occur over a considerable time, these figures signify not only an absence of support for large numbers of parents over extended periods, but also high stress levels and serious threats to their self-esteem. It also means a reduction in the capacity of parents to interact effectively with their children, who as a consequence will experience increased distress and emotional disturbance, as well as the associated economic, practical and social consequences. It is clear, therefore, that when working with parents, many are likely to be experiencing relationship problems, varying from coldness and neglect on the one hand, to conflict, hostility and even violence on the other. They will also be concerned about the effects of this upon their children, with many having to deal with their consequent emotional and behavioural problems.

Parents also need support from others in their wider social network to sustain them personally and in their parenting role. If the marital/partnership relationship is problematic or a parent is looking after children on her/his own, then the importance of this increases. Such support is necessary for a variety of reasons, including practical child care issues of taking and collecting children from school, or shopping with a sick child at home. Just as important, however, is the need for social stimulation, enjoyment and the emotional support provided by being valued by others or sharing problems with them, so as to derive both personal support and solutions.

However, many families have problems with their support networks. At the extreme is the absence of any effective support and this is not uncommon in inner city areas, where as many as 20% of parents are lacking support (Davis et al, 2000). This might arise for many reasons, but social mobility has led to families being more dispersed geographically, and local communities may not be as supportive as they could, particularly in deprived inner city areas, where the environment can be highly threatening, because of burglary, street crime, and racism. In such circumstances disputes with neighbours may be common (experienced by 26% of parents in the survey by Davis et al (2000), and housing structures (e.g. tower blocks) segregate families from other people and from the resources needed for children to play safely (e.g. parks). All such factors are likely to disrupt the development of social support, but are also very debilitating stresses in their own right.

Even in circumstances where there is a social network or an extended family nearby, these can also be the source of problems and increased stress. As with neighbour disputes, family relationship problems are common. There are also many potential demands that can arise in terms of having to care for others, such as elderly and ailing relatives.

In conclusion, there are many parents who might need help with problems in the nuclear and extended family. They may also frequently need help in finding sources of friendship and general support outside the family, to enable them to maintain a personal equilibrium, to be able to share problems with others, to have peers for their children, and in finding practical sources of support for all aspects of parenting. They may also have needs in terms of dealing with active problems within their own extended families and their general environment, all of which may affect their children adversely. Although managing such problems involves many different possible ideas and strategies, it is interesting to speculate about the extent to which what is required is the development of the social skills of relating to people more effectively under difficult circumstances.

Other Problems

There are any number of other problems that could be mentioned, in relation to the paid work parents do, for example, and the stresses this might invoke. Financial problems and debt can be enormously stressful, as can problems in all other aspects of life. We will not try to cover them all, largely because we hope we have already illustrated the effects of a variety of stresses on parents, on their other problems, on their interaction with their children and therefore on their children. Further exploration of the mechanisms of these influences will be taken up in chapter 11, when we will look at parent–child interaction in more detail. However, this quick review of problems and needs would not be complete without reference to the plethora of difficulties that arise as a result of poverty and the deprivation one might see in many urban, but also some rural areas.

Having children is demanding economically, and yet the number of children living in poverty has increased significantly over recent years, in spite of the general increase in wealth enjoyed by many Western societies. As many as 25% of children in the USA, perhaps the richest country in the world, are subject to quite extreme poverty (Coleman & Karraker, 1997). This obvious disparity in wealth, displayed via mass media, can be seen as being a significant problem in itself, increasing dissatisfaction, for example, and emphasising inferiority. However, the more immediate concern is that there is an increase in the frequencies of all the other problems we have listed above with decreasing wealth. Children have more psychosocial problems, poorer diets, poorer health, higher mortality rates, and experience higher levels of abuse. Parents are more likely to have mental and physical health problems, to be isolated, to have less social support and lower self-esteem. Families are more likely to be living in poorer housing, in more threatening environments, with poorer facilities in relation to child care, health, and education.

In such circumstances, the needs can be extensive and of course very difficult to meet without enormous resources. There are not the overall resources available to meet the needs, which is why we are so concerned to elaborate the roles of people working in the community and to coordinate the different potential sources of support. However, although individual helpers may not be able to increase the wealth of a family very easily, there may be much to do in facilitating their belief in themselves and their self-efficacy, which in the longer term may be highly significant.

The Aims of Helping

We have attempted to illustrate the problems that commonly crop up when listening to parents, and to demonstrate the needs that exist for parents, no matter what the helping context (e.g. health, education, child care, social or voluntary services). We will now go on to consider the potential aims of helpers, operating in the system of care as we view it.

One person cannot meet all the possible needs of another, nor should they. Our overall intention, however, is to enable all helpers to make the best use of their own expertise in meeting some of the need, while at the same time doing everything they can to value and strengthen parents, so that they can begin to feel good about themselves, feel effective, and hence begin to meet their own needs themselves. This means having concern for the problems and needs already described, but also attempting to provide help of a general nature, regardless of the helper's specific role. Such help needs to be broad-based and to take account of the people involved, not only their problems. It has to look beyond the immediate situation with a view to preventing further problems and facilitating parents' future resources, problem solving abilities and general adaptation. It needs to be founded on the quality of the interpersonal relationship between the parent and helper, and this is the essential vehicle for such change.

DO NO HARM

Whatever else we do when attempting to help, we should try not to make the situation worse, precipitate further problems or increase the distress already experienced by the family unnecessarily. In one sense this means providing the best help and advice possible, closely tailored to the requirements of the family. It should be relevant, appropriate, of known effectiveness if possible, and without excessive costs or side-effects. To what extent this is possible depends to a large extent upon the evaluative research surrounding our strategies and techniques, and it is clear that the evidence base for much of what people do is currently lacking.

However, what it also means is that we should not make the experience of being with us aversive, unpleasant or distressing. Indeed, we should try to provide a highly respectful situation, in which we listen to what is of concern, involve parents completely in the process of helping, and wherever possible give them the control they need. Under these conditions, harm of any kind will be minimised, since the help provided will be as closely attuned to the needs of the family as possible, taking account of their views, and with them in control.

IDENTIFY, CLARIFY AND MANAGE PROBLEMS

The next general aim is to help parents identify and be clear about the specific problems they are facing, and begin to manage them. The processes involved in doing this are discussed in the next chapter, but this aim implies a comprehensive exploration of all the issues and problems that the parents see as relevant to them and bear upon their presenting problem. This includes problems related to the child, themselves, or other people, on the grounds that they are likely to be closely interrelated.

An obvious implication of this is that problems beyond the helper's expertise will be discussed, putting what might be considered inappropriate pressure on the helper, and raising unrealistic expectation in the parents. The point here, however, is not that helpers can or should find solutions to all the problems. What we are suggesting is that these problems are there anyway, whether or not the helper knows about them. What the helper can do, therefore, is to acknowledge them, and help parents to be aware of and clearer about them and any relevant issues. By understanding the situation more generally and particularly the relationships between different problem areas, the helper may enable them to decide priorities, and, where necessary, to determine and seek out the most appropriate sources of expertise.

FACILITATE THE WELL-BEING OF CHILDREN

An obvious aim in working with parents will be to deal with problems of parenting and problems in children. Although the initial focus may often be on meeting specific needs, such as behavioural problems, the helper should always also keep in mind the general well-being and development of the child. However, even if the focus of the helping process is not on the children, it is important for the helper to do whatever he/she can to help parents relate appropriately to their children, so as to understand and be able to the meet their needs more effectively. This relates to all aspects of parenting, including the understanding of children and their development, the qualities and skills of parenting, and the interaction with their children. Whatever the specific issues in particular episodes of help, the aims should include minimising the effects of other problems on the children and maximising their developmental potential.

ENABLE PARENTS

Clearly parents have needs of their own, as described earlier, which affect their lives generally and their ability to meet the needs of their children. It is important, therefore, that these be addressed whenever possible. Helping parents to tackle specific personal problems has been covered by an earlier aim, but here we are referring to a more general aim of enabling them to take power and control, to face life with confidence, and to be more effective at meeting both their own and hence their children's needs.

This can be seen as a process of both reducing their vulnerabilities, as well as increasing their own abilities and resources generally. It may be achieved in many ways, but can be understood in terms of strengthening or improving general and central aspects of themselves as people, including self-esteem, self-efficacy, social skills, and skills in analysing and finding solutions to problems. Although there may be many different ways of doing this, the most potent influence is the helper her/himself, the general ways in which she/he interacts with the parents, and the relationship established. The ways parents think about or construe themselves can be powerfully influenced by the nature and subtleties of the ways in which the helper relates to them and communicates.

PROMOTE SOCIAL SUPPORT

Very few people can function in isolation, especially when children are involved, yet relationship difficulties are frequent. A major aim, therefore, should always be to enable parents to build, strengthen or use existing social support networks more effectively. Clearly establishing a working relationship with parents may go a little way to meeting this need, but this will not make up for the lack of relationships or problems in their own social networks, nor meet all the needs that are potentially fulfilled from social sources. It is important, whenever necessary and in agreement with them, to help parents consider and work on relationships, both inside and outside the family. Obviously, the relationship between the parents themselves might be an important focus for this, but this should not mean a neglect of all the other potentially supportive relationships with extended family members, friends and neighbours.

Enable Service Support

As described earlier, there will be a need for multiple service support for some families at particular points or over time. In consequence, an important aim is to enable parents to obtain information about services relevant to them and to facilitate their access and use of these as necessary. Since this is likely to include services for parents themselves and their children across all agencies, detailed knowledge of local facilities is crucial, and may be helped, for example, by the development of an appropriate resource index.

Predicting Future Difficulties

Although this has been implied earlier in relation to empowering and enabling parents, we should like to make a specific point of the need to look to the future whenever possible. This involves both helping them foresee potential problems, to prepare for these as much as possible and hopefully, therefore, to prevent or ameliorate difficulties when they do occur. This is obviously a specific concern of promotional and preventive programmes, but should always be in mind, whatever particular current problem is being addressed. This is so important, since change is an integral feature of children's development, and enabling parents to look ahead to transition points, for example, can be empowering, allowing them to anticipate events more realistically than would otherwise be the case.

Compensate Where Necessary

In describing these aims, we have assumed that it is preferable to work with and through parents, attempting to foster their ability and motivation to manage themselves and their lives and in so doing to facilitate the well-being of their children. There will of course always be the need for people to work directly with children (e.g. child care and teaching staff), but this still requires close cooperation with the parents. However, there are situations in which it is ineffective or unsafe to work solely through parents. There are situations, including those that are abusive, where parents are unable to care for and protect their children appropriately. It may take time for this to become clear to the helper, but if parents are unable to provide for the child's needs, because of addiction, for example, or mental health problems, then the aims must include the provision of alternative high quality support in order to compensate.

In Conclusion

Although we are concentrating on working with parents, it is clear that this does not mean focusing only upon problems specifically to do with children and parents' interactions with them. Parenting is demanding as a task in its own right, but there are many possible problems that potentially interfere with the ability of parents to care for their children effectively and provide them with the appropriate circumstances in which to develop. Over time parents may be confronted with a whole range of problems individually or in combination. These include an array of child problems from the physical to the academic and psychosocial. However, parents may have to deal with their own physical and mental health problems, relationship difficulties within and outside the family, as well as a host of other life stresses, all of which interact, possibly distract parents, and potentially disturb their relationship with their children.

Parents' reactions to problems depend upon many factors, not the least of which is their own developmental experiences and their current circumstances, including the support available to them. Every parent is different, as is each child and each family, and their whole situation needs to be taken into account when providing help, which we would argue should be broad-based. We have, therefore, described a set of aims as relevant to every situation in which people are called upon to provide support. These take account of the range of problems and needs that are commonly found, and are set within a general context of caring for parents as people, facilitating them to manage current problems, as well as empowering them to develop and use their resources more effectively in the future.

These comprehensive aims might seem impractical under the conditions in which most people in the public services work, given the constraints on their time; we are aware, for example, of excessive health visitor caseloads and the pressures on teachers. We realise that it will take more time to relate to families in the ways that these more general aims imply, with their remit to include the psychosocial. However, we suspect that many of these issues already arise implicitly, if not explicitly, in the current work of health visitors, teachers, child care staff and others, whose effectiveness will be significantly influenced by them, even if ignored. We would argue that unless these issues are considered, outcomes will be compromised and little will be achieved in addressing the psychosocial problems that should be a major concern of us all.

We are advocating that changes are needed in how we work individually and how we coordinate. There is a need for all of us to work together as a coordinated community of helpers with shared aims that acknowledge parents as people and their importance in the development and well-being of their children. Doing this will increase the resources available, but will also enable and facilitate parents' own resources and hence the overall outcomes, once given the opportunity of working in partnership. Although more time consuming initially, by understanding the psychosocial nature of the helping process and by developing the associated skills, this will be offset by the benefits to be gained in the long term by helpers, parents, children, families and the community as a whole. We will begin, therefore, in the next chapter by outlining a model or framework of the helping process as the beginning of an exploration of effective communication.

CHAPTER 3
THE HELPING PROCESS

Having discussed the general aims of helping in the context of the needs of parents, we should now like to explore the helping process. Supporting others is a complex activity and it is, therefore, important to have a clear model or framework of the process in order to simplify the situation and guide potential helpers. We will describe the process as a set of steps or stages, as shown in Figure 3.1. Each stage represents an important general task, which can stand alone, but is highly related to the other tasks sequentially. Each stage depends upon the completion of the task before it and is also a prerequisite of the next. The degree to which each subsequent step is successful, will be determined to a large extent by the effectiveness of the preceding stages, with each building on the foundations of those before it.

The process can be seen as a simple series of eight steps, one following directly from the other, and taking only a few minutes to complete in the easiest situations, but potentially many hours when the problems in the family are multiple and complex. It begins with the development of a relationship between the parent and helper, while exploring the problems of concern in order to gain a clear understanding or model of them. On this basis goals can be set and strategies planned. The next steps are to implement the strategies, review the outcomes, and then at an appropriate point to bring the process to an end.

In practice, the process is often more complex, and the arrows in the flow diagram give some indication of this. Firstly, each step can have effects upon the preceding tasks. For example, the parent–helper relationship will change and develop as a function of what happens in each of the following stages, and will certainly initially develop rapidly in parallel to the task of exploration. Secondly, some of the stages may be irrelevant for specific parents. They might, for example, only need to explore and gain a clearer understanding of their situation in order to continue on their own without the need for further help. Thirdly, for any given problem one might need to backtrack through previous stages when subsequent events cast doubts upon conclusions drawn in previous stages. Finally, when there are multiple problems, one might circle through the whole process a number of times, although earlier stages are likely to be more easily navigated as the relationship between the parents and helper develops.

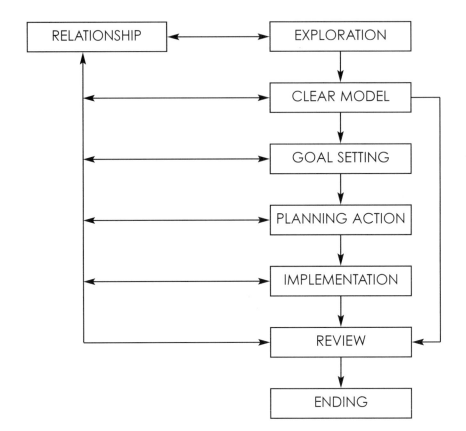

Before going on to describe each of the stages in detail, we should like to acknowledge the fact that preparation is almost always required as a prelude to the process and may have considerable influence upon the tasks. How the family is referred, the practical arrangements of the first meeting, and the process of making contact with the parents by whatever means are all likely to have effects upon the parents' expectations and hence potentially influence the relationship.

Relationship Building

The process begins with the development of a relationship between the parent and helper. This is a vital task, which may be enormously helpful to parents in itself, but certainly an important prerequisite of all the stages to follow. Without an effective relationship, communication will fail and the helping process will become ineffective. Support is impossible, for example, if the helper is disliked or distrusted.

The development of the relationship is a mutual process in which the people involved get to know each other and come to an agreement about whether and how to work together. This can occur very quickly or take considerable time, but will evolve and develop like any relationship. It involves absorbing a great deal of information about each other from their name, how they look and communicate, to what they are like as a person. It is a very basic process of attunement, and includes the forming of essential impressions of each other, and for parents, almost certainly tentative decisions about whether they can relate to and work with the helper, in terms of whether she/he is or will be caring, understanding, trustworthy, helpful or useful.

Much of this goes on automatically; it is implicit and not necessarily in full consciousness. However, the process will be facilitated by an explicit discussion and agreement at some point about whether it is appropriate to work together and how this should occur. Although this may not be done (e.g. in a GP consultation), there are clear benefits to the helper eliciting the parents' expectations, making sure they understand the helper's role, and agreeing a contract, so that each knows what to expect.

Parents require help for many reasons, and it is important to know their expectations or run the risk of failing to meet them without knowing it. If parents have unrealistic expectations of quick solutions for complex problems, then they will be easily disappointed, and hence likely to reject the helper as unhelpful or incompetent. Parents' understanding of the helper's role, including its limitations, need to be checked, because they might also come with a variety of negative expectations, derived from prejudices (e.g. about social workers removing their children) or previous unsatisfactory experiences with professionals. Explicit discussion will enable, where necessary, clear information to be provided, and misconceptions corrected, so that a realistic agreement about working together might be reached.

The process of helping is dependent upon good communication, which influences and is influenced by the nature and quality of the parent–helper relationship, especially if one includes psychosocial issues in the aims. This requires an accurate knowledge of what parents are really thinking and feeling, this can only occur if they trust the helper and are prepared to be open and frank. When seeking help, parents are likely to feel vulnerable. They may have problems that are in themselves distressing. They will be uncertain about the future and what they should do. They may be unsure of themselves and the helper. Asking for help may be novel to them, and they may not be used to disclosing and discussing intimate aspects of their lives with a stranger. They may also be embarrassed to admit psychosocial difficulties.

Before parents can be open and express what is really important to them, they need to trust the helper not to judge them (e.g. as stupid). They need to know that what they say will be respected and confidential and that they will be shown care and consideration. That professionals may be seen as authority figures, who are powerful and even superior to them may make this more difficult.

Although for some parents the relationship might develop quickly and include trust and open communication, for others it will take a long time and perhaps even longer than the helper is prepared to invest. This might be particularly true of people who have been abused at some time in their lives, and as a result will see other people as not to be trusted and themselves negatively as unworthy or low in self-esteem. The lower a person's self-esteem, the more trust will be required in the relationship to enable openness and depth of exploration. Without this, parents are likely to edit their stories because of guilt, shame or embarrassment, or even because they are unable to face issues that are personally difficult.

A strong and trusting relationship is also required because the process of helping can be threatening in itself. If there are issues that parents are unable to discuss, these may have to be raised by the helper. At times the helper may need to challenge parents in order to change their ways of looking at situations. Since this almost always involves a degree of conflict, there is a risk of alienating them, if they were to feel attacked, threatened or defensive. It is important therefore that they know the helper sufficiently well and to have a sufficiently strong relationship, that they can accept the intervention as positive, and trust the helper's intention as constructive, for example, and not attacking.

Parents may also have to challenge their helper. They may want to disagree, or express a contradictory opinion. They need to be able to make their feelings plain, even when they think the helper might be upset or offended. Not expressing such views would make communication one-sided and would distort the helper's view of the situation, when there needs to be an open and mutual dialogue for them both to be clear about the problems. If the parent is unable to give the helper honest feedback on his/her reactions to the helper, communication will be severely restricted. Being able to communicate openly and constructively in these ways is not necessarily easy, but again requires faith in the helper and an awareness that the relationship is of a nature and strength to allow this to happen.

The final reason for stressing the importance of the helper–parent relationship is because of its potential significance in empowering and not disempowering parents when used appropriately. Close relationships are extremely supportive in their own right, and since this is a major aim of the help we are trying to provide, it is important to use the parent–helper relationship to full effect. Almost by definition, helpers are in a powerful position by way of their expertise, qualifications and titles, and parents in a relatively weak and vulnerable position, because of their help-seeking status, and because of problems of self-esteem, for example, mentioned earlier. However, if parents are made to feel secure and personally valued in a strong relationship with someone they respect and value (i.e. the helper), then they may value themselves more and have greater self-esteem.

To conclude, the task of establishing the parent–helper relationship is crucial to the process of helping, influencing to a large extent the subsequent tasks, the outcomes and the achievement of the overall aims. Although it is shown in the Figure 3.1 as the first step in the process, it takes time, overlaps considerably with the other stages, and is constantly affected by them as the helper and parents interact.

Exploration

The next task, which begins almost from the point of meeting, contributes significantly to the development of the relationship, as it determines many of the parents' initial judgements of the helper. It involves a careful exploration of the problems presented by the parents in the unique context of their lives. It begins with a basic statement about the issues as perceived by the parents, or at least as far as they are prepared to disclose them at this stage. Once the broad outline is clear, then the problems can be explored in detail, considering them from all angles. Although this can be done quickly, it may also take some time, depending upon the complexity of the situation, the severity and number of problems, and the motivation of the parents. Some issues may require a detailed exploration of many aspects of parents' lives.

Exploration requires the skills of careful and active listening, questioning and discussion, with the intention of deriving a clear view of the parents' picture of the problems, trying to see the situation through their eyes. The process involves the helper attempting to build an undistorted picture of the parents' views, while at the same time allowing her/his own pictures to arise from the exploration, as possible alternatives for subsequent comparison (see next stage).

The task is more than a diagnostic or assessment process in which an attempt is simply made to discover what is wrong from the point of view of the expert, or to categorise the problems. It can encompass this, in that one might realise that the child has a disorder (e.g. Asperger's syndrome or conduct disorder) and want to explore this further. Nevertheless, what we are attempting to describe here is a mutual social activity in which the participants work together in the first place to derive a clear image of what the parents think has happened, and its context, with as much concern for discovering strengths and resources, as for determining what is wrong.

The importance of this stage lies in its contribution to the development of the relationship between the parent and helper, in that it demonstrates a clear concern for and interest in the parents and their views. Secondly, it contributes to the next stages in that it forms the basis for all the next tasks, including firstly the derivation of a mutual and clear understanding of the problems and eventually to the development of solutions, where this is necessary. One frequently sees helpers attempting to short-cut the process, jumping within moments from a partial description of the problem to ready made solutions, even though this is unlikely to be successful, unless there is a clear picture of the problem and the issues involved.

Clarification and Development of Clear Models

The aim of exploration in the previous stage is to derive a clear model of the parents' problems, as we have said. Where possible this means an explicit picture of the problem in its context, including a useful explanation of how the problems arose. This is particularly important as it can give indications of what needs to be done to improve the situation, and is therefore the point at which problem management begins. Although one might think of exploration and the current stage as one, we find it useful to separate them, both to emphasise the need to reach the end point of clarity, but also because developing a useful model of the problem may require more than exploration.

For some parents, this may be achieved simply by being able to think about the problem systematically and in detail, and this is why we have stressed the mutuality of the process/dialogue. Although it is important that the helper tries to understand, it is vital that the parents are clear, since they have to manage the situation. Simply telling their story to an effective listener can be illuminating for them. Simply talking can in itself relieve the parents, but may also provide new insights that enable them to change and improve their situation, even when the helper is not yet clear. For example, the sudden realisation that her son's outbursts were the result of grief made worse by not being allowed to attend his grandfather's funeral, enabled a mother to put aside her own sorrow and to help her son to deal with his anger more appropriately. Another father talked non-stop for 30 minutes to the health visitor, who had no idea why his son had been showing highly disturbed sleep patterns for many years. When she returned for a second meeting, he greeted her with the news that he had done what she had said (even though she had not suggested any solutions whatsoever) and that the problem was solved!

On the other hand, for many parents the development of a useful and usable understanding may not be so easy, and the helper may have to work hard to bring this about. This requires the parents to change and may include the helper using a variety of techniques and the skills to challenge the parents' views (see Chapter 9). This involves the helper in looking at the parents' story from all angles, and developing alternative views. This may be understood in terms of the helper accepting what the parent presents, but assuming these are hypotheses, which need to be tested. The helper's role is to work with the parents and to help them test their model for its clarity and validity. This involves an active dialogue in which the parents' model is challenged by comparison with alternative hypotheses with the intention of changing their views and deriving a more useful explanation.

As an example, in exploring her concerns, a woman explained her daughter's constant defiance in terms of the mother's own inadequacies as a parent. In listening, the helper accepted the mother's view as one possible hypothesis, but also developed an alternative explanation that the defiance was the result of the daughter's own dissatisfaction with herself. Armed with both pictures, the helper challenged the mother by presenting the alternative view, without implying its superiority, and by suggesting that they should find ways of testing which was the most accurate. This led to the mother engaging her daughter in a calm conversation in which the two possibilities were explored. The result was a further, more elaborate explanation involving the daughter's poor self-esteem, associated with criticism of her by her estranged father.

Reaching a clear understanding of problematic situations is an aim of the helping process in itself. It may reduce parental anxiety and can be a relief, even when little else can be done to change a situation. It might, for example, eliminate unnecessary and inappropriate shame or guilt. It may lead people to realise they are not incompetent, that they are able to think for themselves. It may illuminate previous misperceptions and provide new and different perspectives for them. This may be useful for parents in reaching acceptance of traumatic situations, where there are no solutions in themselves (e.g. bereavement), or may be a direct impetus for them finding immediate and effective solutions themselves. Through discussion, a father who was concerned about his relationship with his daughter, changed from seeing her as deliberately excluding him, to seeing that she was experimenting with a developing sense of independence related to her waking sexuality. As a result he felt less anxious and personally threatened, and was able to deal with the situation much more effectively without further help.

Setting Goals

As discussed above, a clear model is important in itself and may be the ultimate aim of helping. However, when appropriate, it is also a prerequisite of this next step in the helping process. A clear description and explanation of the problem situation provides the basis for finding solutions, and the first task in doing this is to help parents decide their aims or goals. Aims can be seen as more general outcomes, whereas goals are much more concrete and specific. However, both are essentially statements about what one is attempting to achieve; they are the end points, and not the means or strategies by which they might be achieved.

Goals and aims are dependent upon the prior exploration, so that the clearer parents are about the problem and its explanation, the easier it is to set goals. For example, a father who realised his son's disobedience was related to his own behaviour was able to set an initial aim of being more consistent in handling him. However, although the general aim is to help parents manage their particular problems, it may not be obvious what they need or would like to achieve, and this needs to be discussed explicitly and agreed with them.

This discussion is frequently omitted, but is crucial if one is to work effectively with parents, because there are always alternative goals from which to choose in any situation. If there are multiple problems, priorities need to be set, since it is impossible to tackle them all at the same time and the parents' views have to be taken into account. For example, a couple who were having rather general difficulties in controlling their son's behaviour decided to focus initially upon his tendency to hit out at others when he was annoyed as opposed to trying to change his untidiness or his swearing. However, even with this focus, they then had to set specific goals where alternatives included, for example, reducing the number of times he became annoyed, reducing the frequency with which he lashed out, stopping his aggression entirely, or finding, more acceptable ways of expressing his feelings.

As this example shows, there are almost always multiple options. Since each option is likely to have very different implications in the search for strategies, which is the next stage of the process, it is crucial to select carefully, to be explicit and to involve the parents. Discussion is important, since parents might not be clear about what they want, for example, or they might be unrealistic in what can be achieved. There may also be disagreement between members of the family about possible goals or even between the parent and helper.

Just as exploration and clarity are vital in understanding problems, so they are with goal-setting. The choice, nature and clarity of goals and the way they are expressed are highly likely to influence the selection of appropriate strategies and therefore the eventual success of the process of problem management. This should involve the parents directly beginning with a discussion to elicit what they think they would like to achieve. These ideas should then be explored to enable them to be very clear about the goals, negotiating and agreeing them where necessary. This includes decisions about priorities (e.g. what problem to tackle first), choosing between and deciding the order of multiple goals, and thinking about small steps or subgoals on the way to a longer term outcome.

For example, in dealing with her teenage son's constant complaints of ill health and refusal to go to school, a mother's overall goal was to have him attend school as normal. However, in discussion with the helper it was decided that the first goal should be to involve the son fully in the decision making process, in order that he might take at least partial responsibility for attending school. Nevertheless, when they began to think about strategies for doing this, it became obvious that a prior goal would have to involve obtaining the agreement of her husband, whom she predicted would disagree with their son taking any responsibility because of strong authoritarian views about parenting.

As we have said, the importance of this stage clearly relates to the development of strategies, which we will now go on to discuss as the next stage. However, explicit discussion of goals has a number of other benefits, which include the direct involvement of the parents in the process, taking into account their wishes, knowledge and expertise. This is also likely to enhance the parent–helper relationship, as well as giving clear signals of respect for them. This in turn may strengthen the parents through increased self-esteem, but it also gives the opportunity for them to learn and enhance their own problem-solving skills for the future, by sharing the process with them explicitly and modelling the process with them.

Planning Strategies

Once appropriate goals are set, it is then possible to consider strategies or solutions. The task of this stage is to decide upon the best ways of enabling the goals to be achieved as quickly and as effectively as possible. If one has a clear understanding of the problem and has formulated appropriate goals, then the creative process of finding solutions is likely to be easier. The exercise is essentially one in which all possible options are made explicit, and considered carefully, so that the most effective plan possible can be implemented. This should include a careful evaluation of each of the options for likely success, and detailed consideration of the possible obstacles to each suggestion, so that they can be anticipated and overcome in advance. This might involve careful preparation of the parents for implementing the plans in terms of the knowledge and skills they might need to carry them out.

The process of finding solutions is likely to be most successful if the parent and helper work together sharing and combining their ideas. Putting the onus solely on the helper at this stage (as is frequently the case in the health service, for example) not only makes the task unnecessarily stressful for the helper, particularly where issues are psychosocial and beyond their direct expertise, but also neglects the obvious investment and expertise of the parents.

This does not prohibit helpers from making suggestions about what parents might do, and this is always an option to be considered. However, it is likely to be much more effective and efficient if parents are intimately involved in the process of creating, evaluating, and deciding what strategies to use. Solutions simply provided by helpers may be impressive and may work, but the benefits of working together far outweigh this. Involving parents directly and engaging them in the planning process does not detract from the helper's expertise, but increases it by bringing to bear the parents' own resources and knowledge on the task of creating and evaluating all the options, as well as foreseeing and overcoming possible difficulties. Additionally, if ideas are generated directly by parents, then: 1) their confidence and self-efficacy will also be increased; 2) their understanding of both the strategies and the process will be enhanced; 3) they are more likely to accept the strategies, carry them out effectively and persevere; and 4) they will derive a much greater sense of control, effort and achievement.

The role for the helper in this model is to try to elicit suggestions from parents and to explore and develop these together, adding possibilities of his/her own as they occur. Once all possible options have been pooled, whatever their source, they can then each be considered carefully and evaluated for their feasibility and likely outcome, so that the most effective individual method or combination may be chosen. The aim here is to decide exactly what should be done, when, where, by whom and how, trying, as mentioned earlier, to predict likely obstacles and difficulties and how these can be overcome.

Implementation

Once careful plans have been agreed, the next step is of course to carry them out. This can involve the helper in intervening directly with the child (e.g. with a teaching programme or drug prescription), seeking information from other professionals on behalf of the parents, or referring them on to more specialist help. However, it will always involve actions and responsibility on the parents' part. This will sometimes include relatively simple actions like monitoring the child, or attending further appointments, but more often will involve major responsibility for the actual strategies. These will depend upon the nature of the problem, but may frequently include, for example, changes in their behaviour towards the child, carrying out intervention programmes, both physical or psychosocial, or attempting to change the ways they interact with their partner or other members of the social network.

If implementation does involve the parents directly in the strategy, it is important to ensure that they are well prepared to do what has been decided, particularly if this requires them to act in different ways or to use new skills. This might, therefore, include an element of training, where the actions they are to carry out are discussed in detail and the skills practised beforehand. This is illustrated by a distraught mother who could not bring herself to tell her 14 year old son that his estranged father, who had a long history of violent and criminal activities, had been murdered. After careful discussion with the school nurse, the mother came to the decision that he had to be told and that it would be best if she did it herself. Detailed preparation included reading a book she discovered on breaking bad news and role playing with the nurse specific sentences that she might use in actually talking to her son.

If the planning has been adequate, including clear information about roles and responsibilities, careful consideration of possible obstacles, and coaching in specific approaches or skills for the parents, then there is every chance that the implementation will proceed smoothly. However, whatever the helper's direct role in the plans, she/he has a continuing responsibility to support the parents emotionally and practically. Although this will vary from case to case, it will include generally monitoring the situation to see whether the strategies are carried out as planned, discussing unforeseen difficulties and helping the parents to adjust their strategies to compensate where needed. In addition, the role of valuing the parents and their efforts with encouragement and praise cannot be underestimated.

Evaluation

The next stage of the helping process is the important task of evaluating the outcomes of the implemented strategies. This involves the helper and parents in exploring the extent to which the strategies were successful in achieving their goals, and deciding the next steps in their interaction. In general this requires a careful analysis of what happened and consideration of the implications of the outcomes, which could range from complete success to complete failure.

It is valuable to consider with the parents the reasons for successful outcomes and the process involved in producing the changes. This can shed light on the reasons for the difficulties arising in the first place, but can also give indications of how such problems might be avoided or managed in future. In the discussion the helper can also ensure that the parents take appropriate credit for the success by acknowledging and valuing their contribution. This is important, because parents are inclined to attribute successes to the helper, but also because it is an effective way of enhancing their self-efficacy and therefore their ability to cope independently in future.

The situation is similar, but even more important, if the strategies have been unsuccessful. The need to encourage the parents to continue is obvious, and this can be achieved by communicating positive expectations of learning from negative outcomes. This should, therefore, involve the parents and helper in a detailed analysis of the outcomes, searching for what there is to be learnt and particularly the reasons for the lack of success. This is likely to include backtracking through the different stages of the helping process, beginning with an evaluation of the ways in which the strategies were implemented.

Reasons for the lack of success can lie anywhere in the different stages of the process. For example, unforeseen problems in the strategies themselves or their implementation might suggest a return to the stage of strategy planning, before implementing an appropriately revised means of reaching the goals. One might return to the stage of goal setting and then further strategy planning, if it were concluded that the original goals were unrealistic in retrospect. It might even be necessary to return to further exploration of the problem, since the failed strategy might still have provided further insights into the nature and explanation of the problems, with implications for the development of a clearer model, different aims and revised strategies. In essence, evaluation is the final step in a process of experimentation, where the model of the problem is the hypothesis and the strategies are the methods by which is it tested.

Whatever else occurs in this stage, one outcome is to reach a decision about what the parent and helper will do next. This might involve revision of one's strategies in the case of a previous plan being unsuccessful, or a decision to move on to tackle other problems or goals where success has been already met. In each case this means continuing to work together and looping back to a different stage of the helping process and pursuing the various tasks again. At some point, however, the question of ending the intervention will arise and we will move to consider this as the final stage in the helping process.

Ending

Ending the intervention is the final stage or task in the helping process and is important for a number of reasons. Although it needs to be considered as carefully as any of the other stages, in many cases it is taken out of the helper's hands. For whatever reason, many people terminate prematurely and decide of their own volition simply not to attend the next appointment.

Although this unilateral decision may arise because the intervention has been successful or unsuccessful, the unfortunate aspect of ending in this way, is the uncertainty and dissatisfaction likely to be engendered in the helper. It also potentially leaves the family on their own, without easy subsequent access to the helper, if it were necessary.

If at all possible endings should be planned, mutually agreed and arise naturally from the evaluation determining to what extent the aims and goals of the intervention have been met. Just as the length of a single session should be agreed at its onset, so ideally should the number of sessions be agreed early in the intervention, with a review scheduled at the end in order to decide whether to continue and for how long. This has all the advantages of explicitly agreeing all aspects of the work together in terms of the development of the parent–helper relationship, but it also means that the parents should know exactly what to expect, and when the helper is likely to withdraw.

Endings are not necessarily easy, since people may become attached, outcomes are never perfect and people rarely if ever attain a point of being absolutely problem free. It is valuable, therefore, if there is time to discuss the ending explicitly, especially when the relationship has existed for some time. This enables the parent and helper to review what has happened, and to consider the implications of ending, practically and emotionally. Together they can look back, summarise the outcomes, draw appropriate conclusions, and provide each other with useful feedback, from which they might learn general lessons for the future. Such discussion also provides an opportunity to consider how to maintain the changes achieved, what further support might be needed, and whether and how the helper can be contacted in the future, should this be necessary. Where a close relationship has been developed, there may need to be time to talk about how the parents feel about the ending of an important relationship and how they are likely to feel without the support. There may be the need to consider questions of dependency in long-term relationships, although it is hoped that this is minimised by the present model, where the emphasis is constantly upon developing the strength, independence and self-efficacy of the parents.

In Conclusion

In this chapter we have attempted to describe the helping situation as a general process involving a series of interrelated stages or tasks, equally applicable to short or long-term interventions. Our hope is that this provides a relatively simple model, that enables people to think more clearly about their work with others, guides them when they are stuck, and improves the effectiveness of their intervention through a greater understanding of the process.

This model underpins much of what we have to say about helping and we will return to it again throughout the rest of the book. We have made much of the importance of the parent–helper relationship for the process and therefore will take this up in the next chapter and consider the specific nature of this relationship in more depth.

CHAPTER 4
THE PARENT–HELPER RELATIONSHIP

In the previous chapters we have described a broad set of needs and problems facing parents and formulated a number of general aims of helping that encompass not only the management of specific and immediate problems, but also the overall well-being of children and the general support for parents in their adaptation to the role of raising children. We have also elaborated a model of the helping process as a series of stages or tasks in order to provide simple guidance and direction for the helper in achieving these aims and in meeting the needs of families effectively.

The first, and perhaps the most important task in the process is the development of the parent–helper relationship, and it is this that we should like to explore in the present chapter. Since there could be any number of different types of relationship, it is vital to have a clear understanding of the nature of the relationship that is most likely to facilitate the process of helping. By way of contrast, we will begin by exploring the most widespread relationship model seen in practice, the expert model. We will briefly describe this and look at the difficulties in it, as an introduction to what we consider to be the much more useful and effective alternative of the Partnership model. We will therefore go on to define and describe this more collaborative model, which we propose as an ideal to which helpers and parents should strive, and we will finish specifically with an exploration of its benefits.

The Expert Model

If one closely observes helpers of all kinds (e.g. doctors, nurses, social workers or teachers) interacting with parents, one might notice that the nature of the relationship between them varies considerably. It differs according to the profession and personality of the helper, the characteristics of the parents and the nature of their problems. One can see relationships modelled on notions of friendship, particularly in befriending services such as Home Start, Friends United Network, or Newpin, or those in which there is a more managerial relationship, as in certain social work practices. However, what is common to many of the relationships one sees is an implicit or explicit set of assumptions about the expertise of the helper being superior to that of the parent, with relative power accorded to the helper for control of their interaction and decision making. We will call this the Expert model.

Parents, like everyone else, tend to approach potential helpers with pre-conceived notions about what to expect, based upon the problems they are facing and their past experiences of the variety of helpers they have already encountered. For obvious reasons, they are likely to meet the helper with at least a hope, if not an expectation, that he/she will have a solution (prefer-ably simple) to the problem and that this will be immediately and complete-ly effective. Whether it is realistic or not, parents are naturally looking for an expert, who can solve their problems for them, with an expectation that sig-nificantly superior expertise exists, if only they can find it.

Similarly, professionals, who have been trained in relation to a particular body of knowledge for long periods and have considerable experience of helping, are likely to see themselves as experts, and to value their superior expertise. They will tend to assume that they will be able to make sense of people's problems, and will have the expertise to formulate solutions to them, so that the problem can be removed entirely, or at least ameliorated considerably. Indeed, they are likely to define their role in relation to prob-lem solving within a specific area and to derive most of their job satisfaction from the speed and efficiency with which they are able to do this.

As a result of the pressures of parents' expectations and the self-expecta-tions of professionals, relationships tend to occur that are almost entirely characterised in terms of the superior expertise of one of the participants, the helper. Implicitly or explicitly, both parties assume the importance or power of the helper, whose expertise is the most significant defining characteristic of the relationship. As such, helpers tend to control what happens, generally leading the interaction in terms of their own agenda, without eliciting or pur-suing the aims of the parents. These helpers tend to decide what information is required and they then look for it, as opposed to any other information, which is considered irrelevant. On this basis, they formulate a diagnosis or explanation, and then give advice on what should happen by way of solution or treatment. They may even then take responsibility for carrying it out, in terms of medical procedures, for example, or specialist therapy or teaching. This may be done with varying degrees of care, warmth or respect, but the implication is almost always that the helper is in the most powerful position, is superior in expertise and is the leader.

SHORTCOMINGS OF THE EXPERT MODEL
In reality, although widespread, this model of the relationship, has consider-able shortcomings. It may initially feel supportive in relieving parents of the burden of understanding and finding solutions, and it may feed the self-esteem of the helper. However, it does not take account of the centrality and extent of the parents' role, particularly in relation to problems of a psychoso-cial nature or where one is attempting to meet aims with a broader remit than

simply solving immediate problems. Firstly, most problems require careful exploration to be understood sufficiently well to formulate solutions, and this is impossible without the knowledge, expertise and full cooperation of the parents. Understanding can only occur on the basis of their information, and they are only likely to pursue aims and goals, with which they agree. Secondly, there may not be obvious and immediately available solutions, whatever the problems. However, even if there are, not all helpers may know or feel confident in using them, especially if they relate to psychosocial issues. Thirdly, it is usually the parents and not the helpers, that have to implement problem management strategies, again indicating the importance of their agreement, cooperation, time, energy and expertise. It is not necessarily easy to change the way parents behave towards others, including their children, and compliance with advice cannot be taken for granted.

By defining the relationship in terms of the helper's expertise, other equally important aspects of the situation are neglected or ignored. The expert model does not allow predictions about the importance and nature of the psychosocial processes involved in helping, and the considerable demands upon the communication skills of the professional. It does nothing to specify the circumstances required for the most effective parent–helper communication, nor the importance of the parents' contribution to it in terms of questioning the helper and providing feedback. The considerable evidence of poor communication and parental dissatisfaction with health care communication attests to this (e.g. Davis & Fallowfield, 1991).

The expert model does not make explicit the importance of the mutuality of the helping process, and the crucial part played by parents. Such a relationship may not, therefore, be effective in empowering them. In fact, since credit for success is often attributed exclusively to the professional, it may well have the effect of enhancing the parents' vulnerability and feelings of inadequacy, and even encouraging dependency. Such a relationship does not put the parents at the centre of the helping process; it does not predict the need to share an understanding of the process of helping with them explicitly. It fails to place the parents in the lead role in controlling the process, and certainly most clearly denies their obvious expertise. Without their knowledge of their child, themselves, their history and current situation, no helper will be able to understand nor formulate possible solutions. Without the parents' efforts and skills, no problem management strategies could possibly be implemented.

THE TRANSPLANT MODEL

A variant of the expert model has been described by Cunningham and Davis (1985) and called the transplant model. This adds a quality of sharing to the expert model in that it recognises the advantages of parents working with their children, and assumes that they can be provided with the expertise to conduct specified education programmes with their children themselves. The name, coined as both a surgical and a horticultural analogy, is intended to indicate the idea of taking professional expertise and sharing it with parents, where the skills and knowledge will take (root) and grow effectively to the benefit of the parents and hence their children.

The advantages of this relationship model are considerable and certainly superior to the expert model. For example, communication is likely to improve, as an important process of communication between the helper and parents is assumed, since this will be the only way in which expertise can be shared. The role of parents is acknowledged explicitly, with the likelihood of them feeling more powerful and having a measure of control. They are also more likely to derive self-efficacy and self-esteem from their contribution to the effort for the child, especially if successful. However, the model still assumes the professional as leading the process, deciding what is relevant information to elicit from the parents, what goals are appropriate, and what strategies are likely to be of value. This also means that other relevant psychosocial issues may be neglected, problems may still not be seen in the total ecological context of family life, and parents will not be seen as the ultimate decision-maker.

The Partnership Model

In reality it is the parents who lead all interactions with professionals, whether this is understood by the participants or not. Parents do not always seek help, whatever their problems, nor continue the process once started. They control what information is given to the helper, editing it according to their own reasons. They certainly do not have to do what the helper advises and frequently do not, as is indicated by the literature on treatment compliance (e.g. Ley, 1988). If they do comply, the decision is highly related to their relationship with the professional and especially to their satisfaction with their communication.

As a consequence, it makes sense to acknowledge the importance of the role of the parents in the helping process and to try to specify a relationship model that takes this into account. This has led to the elaboration in the last two decades of models that assume the need for the development of a partnership between helper and parent as the essence of the relationship. This has produced changes in a number of areas, including legislation such as the 1989 Children Act in the UK, but has been particularly prominent in the areas of childhood disability and special education. For a very detailed exploration of the concept see Dale (1996).

The Parent Adviser model and associated training has taken this on and is based upon an explicit assumption that the most effective relationship to which one should strive in working with parents is a partnership. It is acknowledged, however, that all relationships are different, and that what we are talking about is a general model that has to encompass very broad variation. The word 'strive' is used deliberately to suggest that this type of relationship is not likely to occur automatically, but requires time, negotiation and qualities and skills in the helper to enable it to develop. It is also intended to signify a broad ideal for guidance through comparison. Developing this more collaborative model is not intended to deny the expertise of the helper, only to acknowledge that parents also have expertise and that successful outcomes are dependent upon the complementary knowledge and skills of both being combined appropriately.

According to the Oxford Dictionary, a partner is 'a person who shares or takes part with another or others, especially in a business firm with shared risks and profits'; 'a companion in dancing'; 'a player on the same side in a game'; or a 'member of a married or established unmarried couple'. All these have features in common with the notion of partnership as applied to the helping relationship, which assumes that if parents and helper can work together as partners, combining both sets of expertise, then there will be increased benefits for the parents, their children, their families, and for the helpers.

THE INGREDIENTS OF PARTNERSHIP

Because of its importance, we will elaborate the specific characteristics of partnership in some detail.

WORKING TOGETHER: The first implication of the notion of partnership is that the partners, as in business, games, dancing or marriage, must be working closely together. It is not possible for one of the partners, the parent or helper, to carry out the work alone and complete the process from exploration to evaluation and ending. Successful outcomes require the efforts of both. Partners require a commitment to work hard and to the best of their ability, with their efforts closely coordinated.

The partners should not, however, be so close that their roles merge. There needs to be some distance to enable separate resources to be brought to the situation as a strength of the relationship. As Gibran (1926) said about the partnership of marriage, 'And stand together yet not too near together: for the pillars of the temple stand apart, and the oak tree and the cypress grow not in each other's shadow.'

POWER SHARING: Partnership as envisaged here involves a strong notion of sharing, including the sharing of power. To redress the balance from the expert model, we assume that neither partner is in overall control, that they both have power, that they share decision making, and that they attempt to work by consensus wherever possible. This does not mean that they have equal power necessarily, and the balance is likely to shift over time, and will vary in different areas (e.g. in terms of their positions, their personal power, and their control of resources). However, it is assumed within our model that parents are in reality the senior partners under almost all circumstances (unless this is changed by the court), since the helper is supposedly there to provide them with a service.

COMMON AIM: Whatever the power balance, an essential ingredient of this model of partnership is agreement about every step of their journey together. At its base there needs to be an agreement to work together, and this requires them to be travelling in approximately the same direction, pursuing common aims and goals. If the parent and helper are to work together effectively, there must at the very least be implicit agreement about what they are trying to achieve. However, there should preferably be explicit agreement, specifically negotiated, as this is likely to prevent misconception arising on the basis of false or untested assumptions.

COMPLEMENTARY EXPERTISE: The model of partnership counters the notion of professionals as the experts with an alternative assumption that parents and helpers are both experts. They each have expertise, for which they should both be respected. This is not to assume, however, that their expertise is the same or that one is superior to the other. What is proposed here is that their knowledge and skills are complementary. It is only by them being combined appropriately that the desired outcomes can be optimal. One person cannot work without the other. The helper cannot assess or understand the situation without exact information from the parent, and cannot enable anything to change unless the parent is able and prepared to do what is agreed. Just as the paediatrician will find it extremely difficult to diagnose a problem without a history from the parent of a very young child, so a social worker concerned to alter the environment of a distressed child will find it extremely difficult to effect change without the effort and skills of the parent.

Parents and helpers are likely to differ in every way possible, in role, personality, values, concerns and training. The professional is most likely to have superior knowledge in areas related to his/her specific profession (health care, child development or education). Parents will not have such levels of expertise initially, even though they may come to match or occasionally surpass that of the professional in situations where the problem is chronic (e.g. dyslexia, diabetes). They nevertheless do have knowledge and skills that are crucial to the problem, whatever it is.

They know their child better than the helper; they know his/her problems; and they are more likely to be effective in communicating with him/her. They will of course be much more knowledgeable about themselves, their strengths, weaknesses and difficulties. They are, in fact, the only people who can decide what they want for their child and family. This is expertise, and it is as essential for the process of helping as the professional's knowledge. Kelly (1991) used the analogy of the research student and supervisor, where the latter has a general expertise which complements that of the student, whose expertise of the specific research question/problem may far exceed that of the supervisor.

MUTUAL RESPECT: To be successful, a partnership requires mutual respect, which may not be present initially. Although professionals tend to command respect simply by their titles and positions, they must also attempt to earn it with every parent. This is likely to be facilitated by the helper coming to the relationship with the intention of showing complete respect for parents, as will be discussed in the next chapter. We find this easy to do in most situations; firstly because we have seen parents coping with the most horrific circumstances and yet still able to care for and protect their children. They also tend to protect the professional from the full extent of the pain and suffering. Secondly, however, we believe strongly that without respect for parents, the broader aims of helping will not be met. Without the helper acknowledging the parents' value, expertise and differences, the parents' respect for the helper will be diminished, but more important it will do nothing to build their own respect for themselves and hence their ability to relate effectively to others.

OPEN COMMUNICATION: A partnership can only be established if communication is good. This requires effective two-way transmission of clear information, so that both partners simultaneously understand and are understood. Misunderstanding needs to be minimised. This must be led by the helper, who has to do more than say things clearly. He/she has to set up the circumstances in which the parent feels willing to communicate and able to give clear and appropriate information, even if (or rather especially if) this contains feedback about the helper that is negative or contradictory. Only then can an effective dialogue be initiated. It also means listening to and interpreting this information as accurately as possible, and responding appropriately, without offence or defensiveness.

What is required here is not only accuracy, but honesty. Each partner needs to feel that they can be as open and honest as possible with the other and that this will be accepted as having positive or beneficial intentions for their mutual activity. The importance of this underlies the ability of the helper to challenge the ideas and actions of parents when seen as unhelpful, but also the ability of the parents to challenge and question the helper, when they feel the need.

NEGOTIATION: Although the notion of partnership engenders working together with openness, honesty, and respect, it is unrealistic to expect there to be complete agreement and no conflict. Disagreement is always possible and must be managed. Our impression is that conflict is more likely to occur in the more expert relationships, but is not acknowledged or even identified. For example, parents who are prescribed a treatment with which they disagree, tend not to comply, rather than object. There is also evidence that they are less likely to question the expertise of the professional for fear of causing offence.

In contrast, a partnership implies a relationship in which negotiation is the norm, where a deliberate attempt is made to identify sources of conflict and to work at resolving these. Agreement is not assumed but sought. An approach which indicates respect for parental views is hopefully likely to identify differences of views and potential conflicts at an early stage. Handling these with respect should indicate acceptance and a willingness to explore all views, with the aim of negotiating an appropriate way forward. The probability of serious conflict or disagreement will be reduced, if everything the helper does is invitational, and presented for the parents' consideration, as opposed to a command or assumed wisdom. This in itself is likely to enable open communication, but will always require sensitive negotiation skills in the helper and very high levels of flexibility.

THE BENEFITS OF PARTNERSHIP
The advantages of this type of relationship in comparison with that of the expert model are numerous. Parents are much more likely to be engaged appropriately in the process, to provide more information of a higher quality, and to be clear about what they want. The helper is therefore more likely to be clear about their problems and the aims of the intervention, and more able to judge the requirements for intervention, and to use his/her expertise more effectively. Under these circumstances, the outcomes for the parents will be more positive, since their resources will be pooled and their joint expertise brought fully to bear on the problems involved.

Specific problems will be better understood, enabling them to be managed or even resolved more effectively. There will also be benefits in terms of the broader aims of helping. In the short term, being genuinely respected by a valued helper in a relatively powerful position will offset the vulnerability and anxiety parents experience in the situation of having problems. In the longer term, it is also likely to enable them to feel valued and hence to value themselves and increase their self-esteem. This is likely to be further enhanced by being a part of a successful enterprise in which they contributed to the outcomes. This has consequences for their self-efficacy, and hence their ability to adapt to and deal with other problems immediately and in the future.

The overall experience of being respected, involved and listened to can be used by parents to good effect. Some use the experience as a model of how to interact with and relate to others in their daily lives with general improvements in their relationships and the support they derive from these. For some parents this includes their children, who are given respect as people, so that their views are to be elicited, valued and negotiated. By being so closely involved in the exploration of problems, and the development and implementation of management strategies, parents may also be strengthened by acquiring general problem solving strategies and even specific techniques for future situations, as well as through increased belief in themselves as being capable of achieving what they intend.

For helpers, the situation is likely to have increased rewards in terms of using knowledge and skills successfully and improved outcomes. One might also expect them to find the process less stressful, as a result of being closer to the parents and understanding them better, but also because they are joined by the parents in the activity of finding solutions as opposed to being solely responsible for them.

POSSIBLE DISADVANTAGES OF PARTNERSHIP
There are some possible disadvantages of working in partnership, although we believe these are far outweighed by the advantages of this approach. For example, a partnership approach is likely to require more time, and this is an important concern when many services are already overstretched. It makes more demands upon helpers in terms of a range of qualities and skills. It is potentially more tiring to listen to people properly and more demanding emotionally. It may decrease the ability of helpers to distance themselves from parents as people and to avoid hearing their real problems. In addition, the process of helping cannot be automatic. This is firstly because parents are all different, but secondly because the outcomes are not in the hands of the helper alone, but just as dependent upon the parents, and this changes the responsibility of the helper. Working in this way also increases the demands upon the skills of helpers. It puts clear pressures upon them to communicate effectively and therefore demands appropriate qualities and skills.

These potential difficulties are important, but can be overcome by a variety of service changes. Firstly, there is an implication for increased resources, of having more people working in support of families generally. This needs to be matched by changes in service aims and policies and the application of these in effective management. Secondly, there are important implications for the selection of personnel, both for basic training and local appointment, since there needs to be some attention to the emotional strength of helpers and their personal qualities and communication skills. Thirdly, there are considerable implications for training, which has to meet the needs of parents by ensuring that helpers acquire the appropriate understanding of helping processes, develop the personal qualities required and become highly skilled in communicating appropriately. Finally, the demands of this way of working require formal personal support for helpers by way of skilled and effective supervision, which mirrors the processes and skills of helping.

In Conclusion

We have attempted to outline as clearly as possible the partnership model, which underlies the overall Parent Adviser framework. We have done this in some detail, contrasting it with the more usual expert model, because of its important implications for all aspects of the helping process. It significantly influences the engagement and involvement of parents, the directions taken and the outcomes in specific problem management terms, as well as in the broader aims of helping taking the psychosocial context fully into account. The basic assumption is of two separate and different people agreeing to work respectfully together, attempting to achieve benefit for the parents via the pooling of their different but equally important knowledge and skills. We do not expect that partnership can be achieved immediately and in every case, but it is presented as a model for close consideration and to which to aim in effective helping. Although it is thought to have significant advantages over the more usual expert relationship, it does put considerable demand upon the psychosocial qualities of the helper and his/her communication skills, and these will therefore be addressed in the following chapter.

CHAPTER 5
QUALITIES AND SKILLS OF THE HELPER

Having considered the process of helping overall and the nature of the relationship involved, we will now go on to introduce and elaborate the qualities needed by helpers to develop a partnership with parents and to begin the process. Six general qualities will be presented including: respect, genuineness, humility, empathy, quiet enthusiasm, and personal integrity. Each will be described and explained in detail and their implications elaborated. This will be followed by a description of some of the most basic communication skills needed to demonstrate these qualities, including the skills of attending and active listening.

These qualities and associated skills should not be taken to deny the need for the technical knowledge and expertise of the helper. They are described as a complement to the existing expertise of the paediatrician, nurse, social worker or teacher. The assumption is that these qualities will enhance the helper's ability to use specialist expertise more effectively. If one is concerned with the psychosocial aspects of children and their carers, then one should have, for example, an understanding of child development, the nature of families, and particularly knowledge of parenting, including a detailed understanding of parent–child interaction (see Chapters 11 to 14). One would also need a detailed knowledge of available services before one can be effective, and such knowledge should grow with experience, service developments and research.

Fundamental Attitudes

If one talks to professionals or parents and enquires about the characteristics of a good helper, the list that can be derived is extensive. Many different qualities are mentioned, and usually with feeling and conviction. We have tried to synthesise these into a small group of general human qualities that can be considered fundamental to the process of helping. These ideas have been heavily influenced by the pioneering work of Carl Rogers (e.g. 1959). Like him, we will refer to these qualities as attitudes to indicate a general and pervasive stance taken by skilled helpers towards the people with whom they work and themselves. How these characteristics influence the process is complex and no doubt differs in every case, but Rogers proposed an 'If...., then....' model. He argued that IF certain conditions are met, including the helper being congruent, showing unconditional positive regard and empathy, and the person seeking help is aware of them, THEN the person will change beneficially.

We have elaborated these ideas somewhat, and assume that these qualities are central to supportive work with parents and may have significant effects, in themselves, regardless of the specific advice or techniques that might also be used when helping. We assume that they will have general and important effects both on the process of helping and the eventual outcomes. We will describe each of these qualities in turn, on the grounds that doing this will provide the reader with direct practical guidance on how to act in the helping context. We have included the qualities described by Rogers, but have extended the list in order to highlight and draw out further ideas. Although discussed separately here, these qualities are, in practice, all highly interrelated.

RESPECT

Respect is perhaps the foremost attitude, and relates closely to what Rogers called *unconditional positive regard*. It is a complex notion that refers to the helper trying to suspend judgemental thinking; valuing parents as individuals; thinking positively about them without imposing conditions, and regardless of their problems, status, nationality, values or other personal characteristics. Respect means treating parents as important, and according them honour or esteem, assuming it is a privilege to be trusted by parents and allowed to share in their lives briefly. It means being available to them psychologically and working for their benefit principally. Above all it reflects a very positive belief in their capacity to adapt and change.

The implications of this attitude for the behaviour of helpers are numerous. It means treating parents with courtesy, being interested in them fundamentally, and making them the complete focus of our attention for the time we are with them. Respect implies allowing them to speak freely, listening to what they say and valuing it, even if we disagree. It involves willingly using our knowledge and skills to do whatever we can to help, but it does not mean taking over from them or denying their role in the process of change.

This last point is crucial. It is of little value to look down on people for having problems. They do not necessarily become less valuable or capable as a result of the problem, and their responsibility for adapting to and managing difficulties is not lost. Parents generally cope, no matter what the problem; they are stronger and more capable than we think. For example, although Mrs N. lived in poverty, without a partner, with a child who was blind and another with cancer, she not only managed well, she provided support for other people, even those who were more fortunate than herself. According respect to this woman and all others in similar situations is a precious and powerful gift.

Respect includes being constructive, warm and positive towards parents, provided it is balanced, genuine and appropriate to the circumstances. For example, in a short, ten minute conversation, a project worker genuinely praised or thanked a mother and father for: 1) the care bestowed on their house; 2) the father's handling of a problem with their son's teacher (he did not get angry); 3) their attempts to understand their son; and 4) their positiveness towards each other.

This quality is also intended to imply that the helper acknowledges and accepts the problems parents present, no matter how serious. It is not appropriate to deny, minimise or avoid their problems for any reason. This may happen, for example, when we have a different view (e.g. the problem is trivial) or do not know what to do. However, it is likely to be of little value to give false reassurance or to imply that everything will be all right, when it will not. Saying, 'Never mind', 'Don't worry', 'It will be all right' or presenting immediate solutions can all imply an attempt to diminish the problem. Accepting the problem is much more likely to be reassuring in that it suggests one is prepared to look at it no matter what anxiety it provokes. Doing otherwise can even imply that the parent should not have the problem, or that there is something wrong with them for having it. In fact, there are situations (e.g. bereavement, relationship breakdown, terminal illness) in which acceptance is the only effective help, and simply being prepared to be with the person physically and psychologically in spite of one's own helplessness may give a very powerful message of support.

The importance we give to respect here does not simply derive from humanitarian values, but from the belief that it has a number of important functions, in facilitating the process of helping. Firstly, it is likely to help parents overcome the humiliation, vulnerability or stigma often experienced by those who require help. The more parents feel respected, the more likely they are to engage in the helping process initially and to be open in sharing their problems. Secondly, respect is therapeutic in itself. If the helper, as a respected individual in a position of power, sincerely demonstrates that the parents are important, valuable, and capable, they are likely to come to believe this of themselves, and their self-esteem and self-efficacy will be enhanced. Thirdly, respect is perhaps the most important facilitating factor in the development of an effective working relationship between helper and parents. As a consequence, it will have considerable influence on the whole process of helping and, most important, on the eventual outcomes.

According respect as suggested here is not necessarily easy, and may be extremely difficult, for example, when parents have harmed or failed to protect their children. However, without it the helping process is likely to fail. Seeing a police officer treating a young offender and his family with complete disdain achieved nothing, except to endorse the negative views they already had about themselves. It did nothing to engage them, to initiate a relationship, or to enable change. Showing respect might have at least made the officer stand out as different from others, as worthy of their attention. The assumption that parents are somehow bad, incapable, or helpless, not only makes it impossible to engage in a meaningful partnership, it can make the situation worse. It is likely to alienate the parents, increase antagonism, reinforce their deviant status, reduce their self-esteem, and therefore inhibit their ability to help themselves.

In contrast, the project worker's praise for the mother and father mentioned earlier visibly lightened their mood, counteracted their vulnerability and increased their self-esteem. It was clearly attractive and endeared her to the parents, and therefore enhanced the helping relationship immediately in ways that increased its effectiveness. If a helper is known to be warm and trusted to look for and comment upon the positives, then if there is ever a need to address negatives, the parents are less likely to be threatened, more likely to allow themselves to be challenged and work with it, without it damaging the relationship.

GENUINENESS

The second fundamental attitude to be discussed is genuineness. This is a complex quality or set of characteristics, which we use in a way closely related to Rogers' notion of congruence. This involves being open to experience, perceiving it accurately, and not distorting it with defences, personal prejudices and one's own problems. People who are genuine are not acting a part or pretending, deliberately or otherwise. They are real in appearing to be what they are, and are flexible and prepared change.

Genuineness involves honesty and sincerity, and implies valuing the truth, not deliberately misleading others, and reliability. Such helpers do everything they say they will, or provide prompt and clear explanations for why they have not. They will be prepared to admit ignorance or mistakes. This quality also implies being with the parents for their purposes, without the helper's own motives intruding (e.g. need for self-esteem). It involves a clear belief in and demonstration of the fact that the parent–helper interactions are confidential, and that communication with a third party would only occur after explicit negotiation with the parents. Apart from demonstrating genuineness, this has the added benefit of putting the parents firmly in control of the helping process, and demonstrating it clearly to them.

Two final aspects of genuineness worth mentioning are spontaneity and consistency. Spontaneity is important, and refers to the helper being able to respond to the parents openly, naturally and freely at all times. It means being oneself in the helper role, not hiding behind it. As a way of helping, one needs to communicate naturally and fluidly, and not in a laboured, mechanical or artificially deliberate way, or it will lose effect. Consistency refers to the helper not presenting extremely different pictures of him/herself on different occasions. Although we all have changes in mood, dramatic changes are minimised if we are open and unpretentious. This means that factors that might create inconsistency (e.g. illness, distress or fatigue in the helper), if not otherwise avoidable, should be shared with the parents so that they are not misunderstood. One mother, for example, became distressed because she thought she had upset her health visitor, whereas in reality this usually gifted helper was preoccupied with family troubles of her own.

The attitude of genuineness has very important implications for helping. It is firstly crucial for the development of the relationship with parents. We are all very sensitive to other people in terms of whether they are real, whether they are what they appear to be. If parents detect any indications that helpers are not genuine, then they will not trust them and will certainly not open up to them in ways that facilitate the helping process. If helpers are not seen as genuine, then the potential effects of all other helper qualities (e.g. respect) will be eliminated. For the relationship to be effective, the parents must trust the helper completely. They must come to believe that the sole reason for the helper's involvement is for the benefit and service of the family, even when there is a need to challenge unhelpful views or address issues that are distressing or hurtful to the family.

Secondly, genuineness is important in terms of the helper enabling parents to explore their situation, be as clear as possible about the problems facing them, and therefore to manage them effectively. This by definition requires being very open to what the parents say and accurate in understanding them. If, however, the helper is not genuine in the sense of congruent, then he/she will not be open, will distort meaning, will not understand accurately, and will be unable to help parents to develop clarity as the basis for adapting to and managing their problems. The helper's role is to perceive the picture intended by parents and not distort it with unfounded assumptions that are more related to his/her own constructions, prejudices and biases, than those of the parents. Being genuine involves seeing all their problems clearly, not denying or minimising them, no matter how remote from one's own experience they appear to be.

HUMILITY

The third quality or attitude, closely related to both respect and genuineness, is humility. This was not specified by Rogers as a separate helper characteristic, but can be seen as an aspect of genuineness, because it derives from congruence and an accurate awareness of oneself. Since we see it as crucial to work with parents, we have chosen to highlight it specifically.

Although it might be considered to carry negative connotations, we use it to indicate the helper not having an inflated sense of his/her own importance in relation to parents. It involves an acknowledgement of differences between ourselves and others, but not an assumption about inferiority either way. In this sense it is not a weakness, involving self-denigration, low self-esteem or false modesty. We regard it as a strength, in that it requires being open and realistic about oneself, seeing and accepting both one's positive characteristics and strengths, as well as the weaknesses.

People with genuine humility can be effective helpers, because they are realistic about what they have to offer, aware of their limitations and accepting of the contributions of others, whether parents, children or other professionals in multidisciplinary teams. It enables respect for others and, in so doing, facilitates the development of effective relationships and hence the helping process. It prevents the helper's self-importance detracting from the value of the parents' own contribution to the outcomes of the helping process.

Humility has a clear function in preventing false expectations. Parents may have unrealistic beliefs, arising more from understandable wish fulfilment than from reality, about the knowledge and competence of professionals. In practice, the knowledge of chronic illness, disability, and psychosocial problems is limited and intervention outcomes are never as good as would be liked. Unrealistic expectations are likely to lead to disappointment sooner or later, with damage to the parent–professional relationship. However, helpers that are open to the parents and have humility are much more likely to identify such expectations and naturally to deal with them appropriately before they are harmful.

Finally, humility prevents professional pretentiousness and defensiveness. Helpers with unrealistic expectations of themselves are likely to have difficulties in communicating openly with parents, are likely to fail to achieve what they expect, and are likely to be easily threatened. For communication to be open and effective, helpers must facilitate a dialogue, allowing parents to question them as necessary, and even to express criticism or negative comment. Humility enables this to occur, through diminishing the likely threat to their expertise. Without it, a model of partnership becomes impossible, and there will be a tendency for helpers to hide behind the expert model criticised in the last chapter. In addition, without humility, helpers are likely to need higher levels of validation of their own competence. As a result they are more likely to withdraw earlier from potentially difficult situations, and therefore fail to provide the human support of being with parents in real need, when there is nothing concrete to do.

EMPATHY

Empathy is another of Roger's major qualities, referring to a general attempt by the helper to understand the world from the viewpoint of the parents. At all stages of the helping process, the helper must try to see the situation through their eyes, acknowledging that it is their constructions that are the basic concern of the relationship, and that it is changes in the parents, their situation and relationships that are the outcomes to be expected, whatever the views of the helper. Helpers must think and feel themselves into the inner life of the parents, and work with the model that this generates.

We stress the word 'attempt' here, because in reality it is not possible to understand in any absolute sense the inner world of others no matter how well we know them. Nevertheless, by discussion we can derive an approximation of the picture or model they use. What is particularly important, however, is that helpers demonstrate their understanding to parents. It is of little value if this all occurs in the helper's head without indication. We will describe the skills of doing this later in the chapter, but empathy can be communicated in all aspects of helpers' behaviour, from the ways they sit, look and move, to the way they speak and what is said. It is demonstrated by the way in which their actions are synchronised (in tempo and relevance) to the behaviour, meaning and feelings of the parent.

Learning about the parent's picture does not prevent helpers from attempting to evaluate its adequacy once it is available to them. This is not a simple decision about how good it is, but involves exploring its validity; does it fit the parents' situation, for example, and how useful is it in adapting to their circumstances? This requires an acceptance of the parents' model, which is then explored and tested with them against other ways of thinking, including the helper's. Being empathic does not necessarily imply that the helper should agree with the parent, nor does it mean that either the parent or the helper is right or wrong. They might both be right or wrong, but more important, their views may be different and these differences are avenues for exploration, clarification, and change.

To illustrate this, one mother had a picture of her son as generally naughty and difficult to handle. She saw him as easily upset, single minded and determined not to conform, either at school or at home. In exploring this picture in detail, the school nurse discovered that he was particularly upset and difficult in situations where he was required to read or write. As a result of this and other observations, the nurse formulated the hypothesis that the boy was having severe literacy difficulties, which were upsetting him and motivating anger and avoidance behaviour. She shared this alternative picture with the mother, who initially found it difficult to accept, but agreed to try to test it. By carefully watching him and listening to what he said when he became upset, she confirmed that this was indeed a better hypothesis, which led to a formal assessment and subsequent improvements.

Being able to demonstrate empathy is vital to the helping process. Like the other qualities already discussed, it has the important function of enhancing the parent–helper relationship. Being empathic is likely to indicate to parents that the helper understands them and this will increase the parent's inclination to trust the helper and motivate them to open up further. This is likely to have powerful effects at least partly because demonstrating such understanding is a direct indication of both respect for the parents' views and genuineness. However, it is also the vehicle by which the problems facing the family are explored and tested, as demonstrated above. The helper's understanding of the parent's picture is what guides the exploration in terms of what questions are asked and what directions are pursued. It is also a significant factor in enabling them to clarify and even change their models.

PERSONAL INTEGRITY

This is the fifth helper quality considered particularly important in the Parent Adviser model. It is again a complex characteristics, but is used to refer to the capacity of the helper to be strong enough to support those who are vulnerable, to tolerate the anxieties of the helping situation, and to take a reasonably independent viewpoint. It relates closely to Roger's notion of genuineness, but is again presented separately to endorse its importance.

Listening to the problems of others can be distressing and, therefore, requires someone who can cope with the suffering of others and not be overwhelmed by it. Considerable strength is required to listen to difficulties, to accept and acknowledge the issues presented, without diminishing them by jumping straight to solutions or immediately attempting to take over and rescue the people involved. Helpers also need strength not to be drawn into the problems with parents and not to become so emotionally involved that they are unable to think clearly and independently about the difficulties. They need the independence or objectivity to be able to help parents derive alternative, more useful ways of thinking and possible solutions at the appropriate time.

To do this helpers need to be reasonably secure in themselves, and not emotionally vulnerable. They have to be able to leave their own problems outside the helping situation so that they do not interfere with it. This is important in terms of the relationship, which is unlikely to occur or develop, if the helper is seen as weak; parents are unlikely to talk about their own problems or to trust someone who is vulnerable. If helpers are preoccupied with their own problems, they are unlikely to be able to listen to others sufficiently well for an adequate relationship to occur. They will certainly be unable to retain the degree of objectivity necessary to develop the helping process from exploration and clarification through to goal setting and strategy development.

What is more, a helper's own distress may also confound the situation in a number of ways. It might, for example, inadvertently imply to the parents that their situation is worse than they had assumed, or that they are incapable of dealing with it. The implication of this is that they might be made to feel worse. At the very least they may be distracted from their own task, by having to consider the feelings of the helper, or even to think that they have to look after or help her/him.

By using the notion of integrity, we are also assuming that helpers must retain a measure of independence at all times. They need to be able to think constructively without feeling pressured to accept explanations or to conform. In a sense, this requires the strength to be able to stand alone without feeling alienated, forced to accept a particular view as correct, or pressured to persuade others of the correctness of their own views. This is particularly important given the need to understand the parent's picture or story, but to evaluate it with them and possibly help them change, if it is of benefit to them.

Personal strength or integrity is required to enable helpers to challenge parents and not just to provide passive support. Although it is important to elicit and respect the constructions of the parent, helpers also need to try to formulate their own picture of the parents' situation, so that comparisons may be made and change facilitated by appropriate challenges when necessary. In essence, the task of helping requires exploration, testing and appropriate development of the parents' construct system as a way of making changes. Without the integrity of the helper, there is no point of comparison, and one reduces the chances of the occurrence of change.

QUIET ENTHUSIASM

The final characteristic we wish to emphasise is enthusiasm, and is related to Roger's notion of respect and to integrity. Anyone who does a good job has enthusiasm for what they do, whether teacher, mechanic or shopkeeper, and the same is true of the helper. We have deliberately said 'quiet' here, because it is inappropriate to be loud and flamboyant when dealing with people's troubles. Although it is sad that they have problems, it is inappropriate if the helper were to feel this in a general way. There needs to be a positive aspect to this, and this can come from taking pride in what one does and enjoying the attempt to do it well to the benefit of the parents.

It is possible, for example, to feel good even about giving bad news (about an illness or a disability) in the sense that one can be aware of doing an unpleasant job with the care and skill it deserves for the benefit of the person receiving the news. Although the helper's own needs should not overshadow those of the parents, helpers must derive reward from their work, or they will not want to continue and will eventually stop, or suffer 'burn out' as the modern jargon puts it, and deteriorate in their function as a helper. People who are unsure of their role, preoccupied with personal worries, defensive, pressurised or not absorbed by what is happening here and now in the helping situation, are diluting their effectiveness as supporters.

Enthusiasm is therefore important in terms of the motivation of the helper, but is also likely to be attractive and infectious for parents. It is easily transmitted to parents and their children, and again has the function of enhancing the helper–parent relationship.

Core Communication Skills

These fundamental qualities have to be demonstrated and this happens by way of a set of communication skills, that we will now describe. These are the essential skills needed for helping and are predictable to a large extent from a knowledge of the fundamental attitudes we have been exploring in the first part of the chapter. The skills to be described here are pertinent to the first and most important stage of helping, the formation of the parent–helper relationship, and are central to all further stages. Additional skills arise as one moves into these further stages, and they will be covered in relevant sections as we proceed through the next chapters.

ATTENDING

Perhaps the most significant skill of all is the ability to attend completely to the parents, to indicate this to them and to exclude all other distractions, including personal worries. It involves deep concentration on the parents. It is only by focusing your whole attention upon them that you can be most receptive to them and what they are saying or implying. Close attention also indicates to the parents that you are listening carefully and it will, therefore, facilitate your relationship with them. Giving someone your full attention is like a gift and is highly respectful. It provides the best encouragement for parents to begin talking and to continue doing so, in order to explore the issues confronting them.

All aspects of our behaviour, especially the non-verbal, indicate to parents that we are attending. Although it is the total picture we present that is seen by parents, it is worth looking briefly at specific cues, which should be carefully regulated by the helper.

GAZE: The most important cue is the direction of our gaze. To be seen to be attending, we must look at the other person somewhere in the region of their face. We do not have to stare without movement, but we do have to indicate that we are looking at the person almost all the time, when listening. In fact, there is a distinct pattern of looking when people interact, and this has the function of not only providing information, but also of regulating the interaction. The person listening, looks at the person who is talking most of the time, whereas the speaker shows a variable pattern: looking to get the other's attention, then alternating looking with looking away in a manner depending upon the content of the conversation. If it is simple, the speaker looks more; if complex, he/she looks away more, glancing briefly now and then to check the attention and reaction of the other person.

FACIAL EXPRESSION: The ever-moving pattern of the face tells us an enormous amount about a person, including the direction of their attention. The different ways in which people smile or frown, lift the eyebrows or wrinkle the eyes or nose, provide information about their thoughts, feelings, interests and reactions. We can detect momentary uncertainty, a question, surprise, happiness/sadness, anxiety, interest or anger. People who are interacting monitor each other's face continually for such information. If you are really attending, therefore, your face is likely to show this by being dynamic and reflecting in an unobtrusive way what the person is saying, thinking and feeling.

BODY ORIENTATION AND POSTURE: The general orientation of our body and posture also gives varied information about us. To indicate attention, we must orientate our body in the general direction of the other person. This might be directly face to face, but when observing people talking, one most often finds them standing or sitting at an angle of about 45 to 90 degrees to each other. The advantages of this are largely to do with comfort in that such a position allows people to sit closer without invading their personal space (which is smaller at their side) and entangling one's legs. Secondly, it allows the person who is talking at any moment to look away without having to make a deliberate effort to do so, in order to think about what they are saying, free from the distractions of the information being provided by the listener's face.

The picture we present is further complemented by our posture, which again should be relaxed and comfortable. Attention is thought to be particularly indicated by an open posture, without arms and legs tightly crossed, with the upper part of the body inclined slightly towards the other person. Although one may be able to attend when slouching back or otherwise contorting one's body, it does not provide a receptive picture for the other person. Leaning forward excessively has connotations of being somewhat assertive or argumentative, but may also be indicative of being too far from the person and not being able to hear effectively. By sitting slightly to the side at an angle to each other allows an optimal distance of about a metre to a metre and a half between the heads and about a third of a metre between the knees.

Relative height is also important to consider in this respect. Although it does not indicate attention directly, it can detract from the interaction if people are not at about the same level. For example, it can have status connotations, with the higher person being superior, and it does explain the observation of good listeners who are tall tending to stoop conspicuously so as attain the same level of the person with whom they are interacting.

MOVEMENT: Movement of all kinds indicates one's level of attention. Attentiveness is not indicated by absolute stillness. It is natural to move slightly all the time and, if we are attending carefully, these slight movements of the head and body tend to be in rhythm with the movements, tempo and conversation of the other person. This is called interactional synchrony, and may be a highly significant, if unconscious, indicator of attention and interest. Movements of the head (nodding or shaking) for example, clearly indicate attention. Mannerisms, however, rattling coins, fiddling with a paperclip, swinging one's legs, or drumming one's fingers are all likely to indicate inattention, boredom or impatience. They are also distracting to the person talking and contribute little positive to the interaction.

Appropriate movements serve to facilitate the interaction and keep the conversation flowing smoothly and encourage the talker to continue, provided they are responsive and unintrusive. Responsiveness and hence attention are, however, indicated by the speed and timing of our reactions. If attending well, we usually nod, reply verbally or otherwise respond within a quarter to half a second at the longest. Delays may indicate the listener is thinking carefully, but frequent and excessive delays can be tedious and laborious for the other person, and are indicative of inattention. Used sparingly and carefully, however, pausing can successfully indicate attention and keep the person talking.

PARALINGUISTIC CUES: A final source of information about a person comes not only from what they say, but also how it is said. The speed, responsiveness, fluency and loudness of speech can all indicate that the person is paying attention. The notion of interactional synchrony also applies here, in that the extent to which speech behaviour matches the behaviour of the other is a clear indication of attention. Extreme sorrow, for example, elicits slow and quiet responses if we are attending. Incongruity or interruption can be interpreted as inattention or even insensitivity.

ACTIVE LISTENING
The skills of attending and active listening are highly related. Giving attention enables you to listen and is the largely the way of indicating that you are

doing so. Unlike attending, listening itself cannot be observed directly, as it is a highly skilled activity that is largely going on in one's head. It involves being receptive to the information that the parents provide, making sense of it, and responding appropriately. Listening is the starting point for effective communication. It is the only way to learn anything about parents, their situation generally and their problems, to develop an active understanding and so facilitate the rest of the helping process.

We have used the word 'active' to indicate that effective listening is not a passive process. It is not used here simply to denote using one's ears to receive verbal information; rather it is intended to imply an energetic search for the underlying meaning, taking into account all available information. The skilled listener is posing the constant question of what the parents really mean; what sense they are really making of the events in their lives. She/he is actively processing whatever information is available, with the intention of deriving a clear model of the parents and their world in all aspects as viewed through their eyes.

This includes hearing and understanding what the parents say, how they say it, what they show through their non-verbal behaviour, as well as noticing what it not said or shown. The helper tries to register the parent's thoughts, feelings and behaviour in their whole context, whilst at the same time being aware of his/her own reactions. Egan (1990) described this as having a second ear lightly tuned to yourself, so that you are aware of what you are doing and feeling in response to the parent; noticing that the parent is making you anxious, angry, sad or irritable, is important, because it is relevant to them and their problems.

For example, a mother, with a PhD in physiology, complained that hospital staff were being rather curt and avoiding her, when she was on the ward with her son for investigations of constant vomiting. She was obviously anxious about the likely results, but while she talked, the helper became aware of feeling irritated by her abrupt rather forceful manner, and felt threatened by her use of technical terms and knowledge of the very latest research. Guessing that this was also the staffs' reaction to her, these feeling were carefully shared with her. Although initially rather threatened herself, she was able to change the way she approached the staff, and this led to a much better rapport and more effective communication with them.

As this suggests, although the process of listening involves building an unbiased picture of the model presented by the parent, it also involves, as a second stage, a comparison of this with the helper's own model, derived from the whole of his/her experience. These two pictures or models need to be as clear as possible and held separately. If they are treated as alternative theories or hypotheses, they can then be compared and evaluated against each other in order to enable the development of the most useful and clear understanding possible. We gave an example of this in the section on empathy, but a further example may help.

A woman was upset about her daughter, who had recently become very argumentative and seemingly angry with her specifically. With all other people, including the rest of the family, she remained calm and considerate, never angry, always compliant. The mother construed this as a rejection of her, and was looking for something that she had done wrong. The teacher, who the mother had approached for help, listened carefully and saw a slightly different picture. She had a tentative hypothesis that the child was not rejecting her mother, but taking out all her frustrations on her, as the person to whom she was the closest emotionally, and whom she trusted sufficiently to show her anger. Although the teacher could have shared the comparison of the two hypotheses with the mother, she came to the same conclusion on her own as a result of their detailed exploration of the situation.

To listen in this way requires intense concentration. Distraction needs to be minimised, and since these can come from the surrounding environment, the ideal is to meet in a comfortable, quiet and private place if possible. However, it is also important to avoid or control distractions that are related to the helper's internal environment. It is difficult to listen when you are sitting in an uncomfortable position, with a full bladder, for example, or when you are tired or unwell. If personal worries or anxieties, thoughts about what you are doing next or other pressing matters come into your head while you are with someone, they will distract from the ability to listen effectively. Such obstacles are to be avoided if possible, but require the helper to be very focused and disciplined in clearing the mind of all irrelevant matters for the duration of the meeting.

Egan's (1990) analysis of such barriers to listening is useful in this context. These include the avoidance of evaluative listening, where one is judging what the person is saying as opposed to understanding it first and then evaluating it with them once the picture has been shared. He talks of being aware of filtered listening, where our prejudices and biases in relation to class, race or gender, for example, prevent us from hearing people, or where professional concepts such as diagnostic categories inhibit our thinking; diagnosing a child as conduct disordered, for example, should not prevent us from thinking of the person. He warns of the dangers of trying to obtain all the facts of situations, but in so doing missing the person, their characteristics and styles of processing information. Rehearsing what you are going to say next or worrying about solutions when you are still not clear about the problems are further obstacles, as is sympathetic listening where our own pain can distort what the parent is saying.

In Conclusion

We have described a set of helper qualities or general attitudes which we propose as fundamental to helping. These include respect, genuineness, humility, empathy, personal integrity and quiet enthusiasm. Each is a complex set of characteristics or general ways of viewing the world that if demonstrated to parents adequately are likely to enhance the relationship with them, to enable the establishment of a partnership and hence set the scene for the whole process of helping in terms of achieving the general aims of supporting and empowering families. Since such qualities are of no value unless perceived by the parents, the chapter continued with an outline of the fundamental skills of attending and listening, by which these attitudes are communicated and hence the helping process facilitated. There are further skills associated with the demonstration of listening in the sense of showing the helper's understanding of the parents and their situation, including empathic responding and summarising, for example, but we will return to these in the chapter on exploration of problems.

CHAPTER 6
THE FIRST MEETING

In the last two chapters we have discussed the notion of partnership and the qualities and skills for developing this kind of relationship with parents. We should now like to bring these ideas together and to consider them further by exploring in some detail the situation of the first meeting between the helper and parents. This is a crucial time, since it is the point at which the relationship is initiated and work of helping is begun.

We will focus only on the initial part of the helping process here, of establishing the relationship and beginning to explore problems. We will cover the skills of exploration and subsequent steps in the next chapters. We are not necessarily assuming that there will ever be more than one session, since in practice with low resources and high caseloads it may be difficult to envisage long episodes of care. Nevertheless, the process we have outlined and the skills discussed so far still apply, whatever the length, although the more constrained the time, the more demand there is on the understanding and skills of the helper to cover the process effectively.

Interventions with severe time limits may work if the nature of the problem and potential solutions are obvious, and the personnel are highly skilled. They are unlikely to have significant effects when dealing with psychosocial issues, including supporting parents and enabling them to provide for the well-being and effective development of their children. Help from GPs, for example, is seriously compromised if sessions are 6 to 10 minutes in length, even if the relationship may have been developing over many years. Thirty minutes with a health visitor may allow one to achieve much more, but again the effects will be limited in terms of the broader aims outlined earlier in the book. We will say more about this in the final chapter, but ideally if one is to meet the needs of families and prevent the level of difficulties currently being seen, there needs to be an overall system of care. We envisage this to include screening for risk factors, options for longer term support where appropriate and the coordination of all services to provide consistency.

We will explore the tasks to be undertaken in the first meeting with parents, including greetings, introductions, explanations, establishing the problem, contracting and ending. We will begin, however, with some thoughts about preparation.

Preparation

At a broad level, services can be organised in many different ways, but careful thought needs to be given to these system arrangements, to ensure the needs of parents are identified and met effectively. Whatever the organisation, parents should feel as though the service is there for them and that they are important and respected. For example, it is crucial that services and helpers are accessible, and thought needs to be given to how the first contacts are made, either directly or via a referral system. Parents should find it easy to contact the service, which has to be well advertised in all appropriate places. All interactions should be respectful, warm, and personalised if at all possible. Receptionists, for example, need to be trained to welcome people appropriately in face-to-face situations, since it is easy for them to appear unwelcoming when they are busy. All communications from parents should be acknowledged promptly, and they should not have to wait excessively to be seen without an appropriate explanation.

The first meetings with parents can be arranged in a number of ways, depending upon how a particular service is set up. Although one might always need to provide appointments by letter, the use of the telephone should be exploited to its maximum, because of the opportunity for initiating an appropriate relationship. One should certainly try to supply information on the service as early as possible. If in writing, it needs to be presented clearly and concisely in language that can be read even by people with limited literacy skills, taking into account the language requirements of people from diverse ethnic and cultural groups. Full use is yet to be made of electronic communications to provide this, including email and websites, which allow for spoken as well as written information.

For individual helpers, preparation for the first meeting is crucial. They will have made an appointment time and place (see below), but it is essential that they have a few moments to orientate themselves to the parents they are about to meet and to clear their thoughts of what else has been going on. They will need to think about the purpose of the meeting and to go over what they know about the parents already. For the parents it may have been useful to have made personal contact already (e.g. by telephone), and if this has occurred then the helper will have begun to form initial impressions. Some helpers like to have as much information as they can about parents they are about to see (e.g. from referrers or case notes), while others prefer a fresh approach. Since case notes can be extremely limited and the impressions of others can be misleading, there is a strong argument for finding out about families directly from them, and then supplementing this with further information from other sources with their permission.

Location

Thought needs to be given to the location of all meetings including the first. Our preference is for home visiting, if this is possible and acceptable to parents. The advantage is that the parents are in their own environment and may, therefore, be less anxious, more in control, and have less to do in adapting to the novelty of all aspects of a relatively unknown institution (e.g. a health centre). It is also likely to be easier for them in terms of travelling, especially with children, and particularly if the child has a long-term problem requiring appointments with multiple professionals. The disadvantage is that the helper has less control over the physical layout (e.g. seating arrangements), the degree of privacy, interruptions from the telephone and visitors, and other distractions such as the television. It also means that helpers spend more time travelling and may have to carry relevant equipment with them.

An essential requirement of the location is privacy. The likelihood of parents being able to talk about their real feelings and difficulties is remote, to say the least, if they are confronted with, for example, a large clinic room full of a variety of professionals and their students. Ideally, if the parents come to see the helper, the room should be quiet, sound-proof, with no interruptions, either from people walking in or from other sources such as the telephone. The aim is to be able to give your full attention to parents, and to indicate to them that you are entirely at their disposal for the duration of the meeting. Interruptions of any kind are clearly disrespectful, as they deny the importance of parents and indicate that they are of secondary concern to the professional role. Talking in public places (in the corridor of a school) is inappropriate, as confidentiality is immediately destroyed, complete attention to the parents may be difficult, and the parents may be distracted or inhibited in expressing their feelings and ideas.

If possible, rooms for working with parents should be pleasantly decorated and inviting. They should be reasonably spacious, and appropriately lit and heated. Most important is that the seating arrangement should be conducive to the interaction. The chairs should be comfortable, of the same height and arranged as naturally as possible. For two people, the positioning of the chairs should reflect the arrangement that tends to happen naturally. As indicated earlier, this is not with people directly face to face, but more side-by-side at an angle somewhere in the region of 90 degrees with their knees relatively close and their heads about a metre apart. If there are several people with the helper (e.g. two parents), their positioning might best approximate a circle. Having a desk between the helper and parent contributes little, and may act as a barrier to open communication. If writing is required, then a desk could be situated to the side of the helper away from the parent.

These general points about privacy, lack of distraction and comfortable positioning apply equally to the situation of home visiting, since the object is to enable the conditions for parents to communicate effectively and for the helper to concentrate fully on what they are discussing. However, these are not entirely in the helper's control when in the parents' home. There may be interruptions from the telephone or from other visitors. There may be a variety of distractions including the television left on and pets wandering around (a three metre python in one case). The seating arrangements may not be convenient for conversation, and in extreme cases there may be little by way of furniture and there are times where comfort is difficult because of hygiene.

Clearly the helper must make the best of the particular situation, which will vary from home to home. For example, one can still orientate oneself appropriately even when sitting next to each other on a couch. One can be explicit in acknowledging distractions, and a gentle request for the television to be turned down or switched off is likely to be effective if accompanied by an appropriate explanation. For regular visiting it is highly likely that once a working relationship has been established, many of these context problems will be resolved by explicit and respectful negotiation, allowing protected time without interruptions.

Given the need for privacy and a non-distracting environment, the presence of young children in the meeting will frequently be an issue when working with parents. Often it is absolutely necessary for them to be in the meeting, and they should be directly involved in the interaction, and may be the joint focus of the work when thinking about their development. This provides the opportunity for both implicit and explicit modelling of interaction with them. For the helper to spend time focusing on the children directly is an important compliment to the parents and has enormous value for the parent–helper relationship. However, there are times when their presence will be distracting, when there needs to be a complete focus on the parents or when it is inappropriate for children to hear the adult conversation. In such circumstances a variety of strategies might be useful, including timing meetings to coincide with the child's sleep patterns, or nursery/playgroup sessions, or making temporary child-minding arrangements. Certainly there are likely to be times when a home visitor requires the skills and strategies of helping parents engage and occupy children in order to enable the parent and helper to talk. Some health visitors, for example, carry mobile play facilities to help with this!

Greeting

The very first part of the session is the point at which the helper and parents physically meet and greet each other. This is where the parents are acknowledged or welcomed and is important, both in terms of first impressions and in diffusing initial anxieties and uncertainties that are invariably present when people meet for the first time.

This usually involves the helper in a traditional greeting such as 'Hello', which is likely to be followed by an inquiry about the identity of the parent ('Are you Mrs Jones?') and an initial specification of the helper's name ('I'm Jane Smith, the health visitor.'). For home visiting in a climate of high crime rates, this almost certainly needs to involve the deliberate presentation of formal identification. To show respect visitors should be punctual, but to make an appropriate impression and initiate the relationship, they need to be deliberately warm, considerate and deferential. This might involve smiling gently, standing back a little and not being overly assertive. It certainly includes carefully attending to the cues (e.g. of recognition) given by parents, responding sensitively to these, and deliberately putting them in control of the interaction. One might, for example, respond to doubt on the parent's face by asking, 'Were you expecting me?' or 'Have I come at an inconvenient time?'

In addressing people by name, it is probably most courteous and respectful at this stage to be formal and to use a title such as 'Mrs' or 'Mr'. Other indications of respect are to stand up, if meeting someone when they come into your room or even in a public place, and making other appropriate gestures, such as shaking hands, if this is culturally appropriate. If there are several people present, then each of them should be acknowledged individually. Children should always be addressed directly, preferably bending down to their level, but being aware that they might be anxious of strangers and, therefore, being careful not to appear threatening or intrusive. They should never be ignored, both because of respect for them, but also because of concern for the development of the relationship with parents; 'Who takes a child by the hand, takes the parent by the heart.'

Where the greeting is on the helper's territory, as in a health centre, for example, a mark of respect is for the helper to leave her/his office and to personally fetch the parents, greeting them as we have described wherever they are waiting. There are a variety of other methods ranging from the use of receptionists to buzzers and tannoy systems, which may fit the requirements of a busy clinic. However, none of them begin to match the impression of care and respect given by the helper going to the parents and addressing them personally.

Orientation

The next task after the greeting is likely to involve the helper and parents in moving to the place of the meeting, settling down in the physical context and orienting to each other. In visiting the home, this will include being invited into the house, taken to the appropriate room and being shown where to sit. The parents should lead this, with the helper again being very sensitive to them, allowing them to go first, being very courteous, and being responsive to them and their feelings. On the helper's own territory, she/he has to lead to some extent, so that the parents know where to go. They should be given very clear guidance, for example about seating arrangements, so that unnecessary uncertainty or awkwardness is avoided. She/he should nevertheless remain highly responsive to them, treating them with care and allowing them to have as much control as possible. One might open doors for them if necessary, and allow them to sit down first before doing so oneself.

Something by way of neutral conversation at this stage is a very good way of orienting to each other, in terms of the very first steps of getting to know each other. The topic is irrelevant, provided it is natural, spontaneous and genuine. Commenting upon the weather, talking about the journey, or commenting positively on the garden or house are examples. It does not have to take a long time, but it is important in allowing the participants to form the very first impressions of each other, about how they look and speak, and to adapt to these. It allows the first anxieties about meeting a stranger with all the uncertainty involved to dissipate. It provides time to relax into the situation a little, and enables the parents and helper to gather baseline information about their non-verbal behaviour against which to judge subsequent interaction. Offering and discussing whether to have refreshments, for example, has a similar function as well as being an act of courtesy.

Introduction

It is then practical and respectful for the helper to introduce her/himself again properly, giving her/his name and an indication of her/his role as soon as possible. It is wise not to assume that the parents are familiar with what the helper does, even if the role title is common (e.g. school nurse or teacher). One way of doing this which indicates a real concern for parents is to ask them to say what they understand of the helper's role or what they expect to happen. This is much better than the helper simply giving a pre-arranged speech, because it takes account of the parent's existing knowledge, allows any misconceptions to be corrected and clearly signals that you are expecting to work closely with the parents. The helper may simply be able to endorse what the parents have just said, or add to it as necessary, so that the parents are clear about the helper's role and the nature of the service being offered. Although the helper is likely to be taking some control of the interview at this point, nothing should be done or said in a dogmatic or controlling manner. The style needs to be tentative and invitational, (e.g. 'I wonder if it would help to …') consulting with the parents and negotiating how to proceed.

It is equally important to make sure that the parents and the children have the opportunity to re-introduce themselves, or to explain things about themselves that they feel is relevant before continuing. One should attend carefully throughout, listening to what is said and trying to pick up the feelings being expressed. Since it is a common event to immediately forget names when we first hear them, it helps to be unhurried and relaxed and to focus on each name, rehearsing it, either by repeating what the person says out loud (for example 'So, you are Paul Jones') or quietly to oneself. Depending upon the circumstances, formality in the use of names might be relaxed at this stage, but it indicates respect and offers control to the parents, if first names are only used after they give explicit permission to do so. Asking children, in particular, how they would like to be addressed clearly values them, and may enhance the development of the relationship with them and the family generally.

Preliminary Exploration

If at any point the parents launch into a description of the issues or problems confronting them, because of excessive concern or worry, then one should as usual follow their lead and listen to them without going through the whole process above. It is always possible to backtrack if necessary at a later point. However, if they do not bring up the reasons for the meeting following the introductions, the helper should initiate this as the next step.

This is usually done by asking an open-ended question such as, 'Well now, what is it you wanted to discuss?' or 'So, how can I help you?' By being open-ended, the question does not prejudice the parents' response, and allows them to tell their story as they please, in any order. Encouragement may be necessary, if they hesitate, have difficulty in starting or minimise their problems (e.g. 'It's silly really'). Otherwise, the helper's role is to attend closely and to listen carefully to what they have to say.

Once they begin to talk, it is best not to interrupt, but to let them speak for as long as they need, which might vary from a few sentences to a long and involved description. The temptation may be to interrupt or to try to structure the story-telling differently, but this should be resisted at this stage, so as to hear in their own words what it is that really concerns the parents. One might intervene occasionally, but only if you cannot follow what is being said or it is essential to clarify something with them on the way. However, you are trying to hear their story with all its nuances, and any interruptions run the risk of interfering with this and imposing your own picture. If they have very little to say or difficulty in communicating, further open questions may be used to help them talk. Whatever happens, however, it is important to concentrate upon the story and the way it is being told. Absolute attention and the skills of active listening, as described earlier, are vital, as these in themselves will prompt the parents to continue.

At this point you are trying to indicate profound interest in what the parents have to say, indicating that their story is important and valuable. However, the first telling is only the beginning of the exploration process, since it is almost always the case that the helper will need further detail and together they will need to analyse the situation in depth, so as to understand it. Because of the importance of this stage for the helping process as a whole, the skills of exploring will be covered specifically in the next chapter.

An Initial Contract

It is impossible to completely characterise what occurs next. The helper must simply be responsive to the parents, following what they require. As we have just said, one is most likely to continue for example with a more detailed exploration of the issues they raise. Nevertheless, working in partnership necessitates the helper and parents agreeing how they should proceed. This is initiated somewhere in the first session. This task is sometimes referred to as formulating a contract and is particularly important where the work together will last more than a few minutes. Where the parents have initiated contact with the helper, this might occur once the helper has an idea of the problem, and they can then discuss the likely process and agree a way forward. In the case where it is the helper who has initiated the meeting, as in routine surveillance or universal promotional work, this discussion might even precede the preliminary exploration of the parents' concerns, beginning and incorporated into the task of introductions.

Contracting implies an initial negotiation in which the helper and parents reach an explicit agreement about what they are to do together and how. This might include, for example, the practical details (e.g. place, time and frequency) of meetings. The helping process might be reviewed with the parents, and this might involve explicitly sharing the model with them, including the notion of partnership. One might make clear the responsibilities of the helper and parents within the process, and of course the aims. The issue of confidentiality may also be acknowledged here generally, including the practical and legal limits to this, and their implications (e.g. permission seeking or informing).

There is no set way of negotiating, but as stated earlier, it is useful to try to begin by asking the parents for their views and expectations, as opposed to pre-empting these, by giving the helper's views first with the danger of imposing. Beginning with the parents' views is likely to signal that the parents have power within the relationship and that their views matter. It allows the helper to be sure the parents are fully informed and will enable her/him to correct any misconceptions. Without this, the helper is in danger of failing to meet unknown and even unrealistic expectations. For example, one might have to counter expectations that professionals are all-knowing and all-powerful, and that parents are inferior and have a passive role. This can take time and care as in the case of a woman whose child had diabetes and severe behaviour problems. When asked by the psychologist what she was expecting, it quickly became clear that she thought that the problems would be resolved with the prescription of medicine. In fact, subsequent discussion indicated that her unrealistic beliefs about professionals and negative views of her own competence were significant causes of the problems in the child, so that the negotiation of the process became a crucial part of handling the whole problem.

It is important to note that we are talking about initial contracting, with the implication that it is an on-going process. By definition, partnership requires agreement, so that the participants can work together, and clearly know what is likely to happen. However, such agreement must be reconsidered and revised as necessary as the situation unfolds. Doing this ensures that the parents are aware of and involved in the process as it unfolds.

Ending

A first meeting might also involve subsequent stages of the helping process, from exploration onward. For example, one might in a single meeting be able to clarify the situation sufficiently for the parents to continue without further help. One might be able to help them set aims, plan strategies, and implement these on their own, without the helper needing to be involved again. Ideally this is how it should be and these tasks are described in the next chapters. However, if the major aims of the helper's service are to provide broader support, or the problems are multiple and severe, one might expect little more of a first meeting than to establish the helper-parent relationship, explore at least initially the problems presented by the parents and negotiate a preliminary contract.

If these have been achieved, then a great deal has been done to lay the foundations of a supportive long-term relationship. However, the final task of the session is to bring the meeting to a close, which is not necessarily easy in the context of severe problems, where emotions are heightened. The duration of meetings may vary, but should not be much longer than 50 to 60 minutes. Longer sessions may be impractical to fit in for both parties, but what is more relevant is that active listening and the discussion of emotional topics are very tiring, and sustaining concentration will be difficult for much longer than this.

The task of ending is made easier if an effective contract has been negotiated, but also if the length of the session has been agreed clearly at the outset. We again tend to begin this with a question, asking the parents how much time they have, as this indicates power to the parents and contradicts the more usual assumption of professionals' time being more precious. This does not mean that you have to have long periods of time available, since the outcome must result from a negotiation. Asking the question, however, does mean that you are likely to find out if the parents have to be elsewhere in the near future (e.g. to pick up the children from school). It indicates that you regard their time as equally important, and furthermore shows a willingness to be open, to negotiate and to work in partnership.

Whatever goes on in the session after this negotiation, it is important to monitor the time, so that one can finish when agreed, but also give a warning of the ending five to ten minutes in advance. Keeping track of the time should be unobtrusive, since overt glances at one's watch can seem rude and have negative effects upon the people you are with. A warning that the session is about to end, enables the parents and helpers to orientate themselves to finishing. They can summarise what has been discussed, draw together what has happened, and agree what to do next, including the time of their next meeting where relevant.

Signalling the end of the meeting in advance enables parents to compose themselves if they have been upset. One should take care not to finish when parents are distressed, but to allow them to recover their equilibrium emotionally, explicitly checking with them that they are able to cope with their journey home, or to be left if the meeting is at home. Finishing with instructions about what they might do in the period before the next meeting (e.g. to make explicit observations on the problem) can help to introduce a more upbeat feeling, to continue the process in the intervening period, and prepare the parents for the next session.

Having decided to end, leave should be taken quite quickly with fully consideration for the courtesy of the situation. However, parents occasionally introduce a new and even urgent problem towards the very end of the session, and sometimes literally as one is leaving. This is a difficult situation, because it is likely to make caring helpers feel as though they should stop where they are and deal with it immediately. On the other hand, it is unlikely that one could explore the new situation and find instant solutions without spending significant time doing so, when you probably have other imminent appointments. It is also worth pondering why, if it is really such a pressing issue, it was not mentioned earlier.

It can be difficult if this happens, and there are no clear rules of how to deal with it. The problem should of course be acknowledged by the helper, but it is preferable to delay the discussion of it until the next session, even if this has to be scheduled specially. This might require appropriate explanation, including the fact that there is not time to do justice to the issue under the present time constraints. Although this can make the helper feel as though he/she is failing the parents, it is important to keep in mind that parents also have a responsibility for the process of managing their problems. Throwing out significant problems at a last moment is not an effective way of doing this, and they may come to realise how important it is to prioritise issues in future sessions.

Having taken leave of the parents, it is important for the helper to have a little time to relax before going on to the next task. A short period is necessary to let what has happened in the session settle, before making preparation for whatever one has to do next. This ought to include making short notes of the session as a reminder and preparation for the next meeting; this might include impressions and general conclusions from the present session, as well as points about the aims and intentions for the following session with the same parents. Making such notes gives a chance to think through the session and its implications, but also reduces the need to be writing during the session with the parents. This should be avoided in general, as it is impossible to both write and relate to people in the responsive and skilled way advocated here. Writing puts the focus upon the professional's role with implications of expert assessment; it prevents you from listening effectively while thinking of what to put down, and it makes it difficult for the parents to speak while you are writing and not looking at them. If there is a need to remember specific information by writing at the time, this can be explained at the time, and by seeking the parent's permission for it, one can also foster the partnership.

In Conclusion

Although episodes of care can be completed in one session, we are assuming that longer term intervention is generally necessary to achieve the wider aims of psychosocial support, particularly when the concerns are promotional and preventive. Within this context, therefore, we have explored in some detail the tasks of the first meeting. These include appropriate preparation on the part of the helper and consideration for the place of the meeting. Significant tasks include the initial greeting, orientation and settling into the session, introductions, preliminary exploration of the problem, agreement of an initial contract and ending the session with negotiation of subsequent arrangements. Since these are all crucial to the appropriate development of the helper-parent relationship and the helping process, demonstration of the qualities described in the last chapter need to be of concern throughout. A major intention is to enable a partnership through being with the parents, focusing entirely on them, being genuinely interested in their views, accurately understanding what they have to say, indicating this to them, and negotiating explicitly each step, beginning with a consideration of their views. The second important aim is the mutual exploration of the problems confronting parents in the context of their lives, and since this is such a skilled activity we will go on to cover this in some detail in the following chapter.

CHAPTER 7
EXPLORING THE PROBLEM

This chapter is specifically concerned with the processes and skills of exploring the problems and issues confronting parents when they seek help. We have previously designated this as the second major stage in the overall helping process (see Chapter 3). It begins in the first session, as discussed in the last chapter, and may continue thereafter depending upon the complexity and number of problems. We will begin by considering what is meant by exploration, and look at some of the general issues involved in helping parents think carefully about what is troubling them, so that they might be able to develop a clear picture before initiating more specific problem management. This will include a list of the areas to be explored in relation to any particular problem to ensure systematic and thorough investigation. We will finally describe and explain the various specific skills involved in exploring and consider their implications.

Exploring
WHAT WE MEAN BY EXPLORING
In using terms like exploring or exploration, we are referring to a process of investigation, where the helper works with parents and tries to: 1) motivate them to paint the picture or tell the story of their problems; 2) focus upon the important aspects of them; 3) identify everything that is relevant; and 4) enable them to make sense of the problems in the context of their lives generally. This might encompass the notion of assessment, which has connotations of an expert model in which the professional leads an investigation (by interview or testing procedures) so as to make a diagnosis, assess academic skills or formulate an explanation of a problem. However, although there are very good reasons for such investigations to occur, our intention is to use the notion of exploring to indicate a mutual process, in which both helper and parents engage, with a view to reaching a clear picture and understanding of the problems together.

It cannot be assumed that parents are necessarily clear about their problems, when they first seek help, or that they understand them sufficiently to begin to do something about them. The helper's aim, therefore, is to enable them to look carefully at their situation in all its aspects and to begin to make sense of it in ways that will eventually help them to adapt to or manage it. There is a deliberate emphasis on the parents here and facilitating changes that increase their own resources and ability to cope without further help.

This can happen without the helper necessarily having a clear view of what is going on. By being requested to explore, parents may spontaneously realise something or develop insights not previously available and possibly not shared with the helper. Nevertheless her/his task is to try to understand the parents' picture, and to do this without making unfounded assumptions. A subsequent step is then to evaluate it against other possible pictures that might apply to the situation and might have more potential for change. We gave examples of this in Chapter 5, and we will look at this process specifically in Chapter 9, where we will consider ways of deliberately challenging parents to change. It should be acknowledged here, however, that the skills of exploring outlined in the present chapter may also have the effect of producing change, whether intended or not. These skills and techniques are by definition challenging, because they make parents think about issues they might otherwise have avoided, and go into more specific detail in the process.

EXPLORING AND RELATIONSHIP BUILDING

It should be remembered that the stages of exploring and the development of the parent–helper relationship, are occurring almost simultaneously. Clearly therefore the process of exploring will influence the relationship, but the relationship will also affect the quality of the exploration. Whatever one does in exploring problems will be influential in determining the nature and quality of the relationship; this is the time at which the parent is getting to know the helper. However, if the exploration is done well and facilitates the relationship, then the depth, quality and effectiveness of the exploration will increase as the relationship develops and as the helper is trusted more and more.

SUSPEND THE SEARCH FOR SOLUTIONS

It is important at this stage to suspend one's urge to solve parents' problems. The task here is to be interested and to learn all one can about the problems in the context of the family and their lives more generally. There is always, however, a very strong tendency in us all to try to solve people's problems immediately, whether we are professionals or not. These pressures are increased, if we are professionals and have an implicit expert model (see Chapter 3). When one observes people naturally in situations where they are listening to someone with a problem, they frequently make suggestions about how to solve it within minutes of hearing it for the first time.

Although this is probably quite natural, because most people care and want to help, it is unlikely to be successful either in terms of managing specific problems or in terms of the general aims of helping presented earlier in the book.

The reasons that immediate solution suggestions are unlikely to be effective are firstly that the so called helper will not know all the relevant circumstances surrounding the problem or even what the real problem is at this stage. Secondly, the helper is unlikely to know anything about what the parent would like to achieve. Thirdly, the possible solutions that are given so quickly are unlikely to have been adequately evaluated for their effectiveness. Finally, such suggestions do little to respect the person with the problem and their part in the problem management process. If it were so easy to solve the problem within a few minutes of hearing about it, surely the person would have done so already without help. It should also be remembered that we are trying to take account of the gamut of psychosocial problems facing parents, and these are not subject to simple solutions. They are not in the same realm as providing a simple method for remembering a particular spelling or providing a drug to stop pain, and they almost invariably require the person's own involvement.

EXPLORING CAN HELP

Listening without attempting solutions is valuable and supportive in its own right; people are often relieved and feel better by having had the chance to talk and tell their story. There may be many reasons for this, including the realisation that they are not 'stupid', 'mad' or 'bad'. If someone listens as we are suggesting, parents may discover that they are still valued even though they have problems. Enabling them to feel important and good about themselves is an aim of the process. In addition, allowing parents to talk about their situation is also likely to clarify and simplify it for them. This is helpful in increasing their understanding and decreasing anxieties, but it also puts them in a better position to know what needs to be done about it.

By trying to resolve problems for parents prematurely, we are not respecting their competence and not working in partnership. By implication, we are also in danger of giving them a negative message, suggesting, for example, that they are incapable of generating solutions themselves or not able to cope. In contrast to this, we believe that it is more productive to indicate that life is about having problems and that the task facing us all is that of adapting to and managing them. In reality, pain and impotence may not be removed easily. For example, one cannot and should not try to remove the pain of bereavement or the distress of watching children undergo painful treatments over long periods. Although extreme examples perhaps, these do demonstrate the importance of respecting people and their problems, allowing them to have, express and explore their problems, and not always being quite so desperate to take them away. Although, if we care, we will always want to find solutions, we have to keep this in check and not feel incompetent when solutions are not immediately forthcoming. We should certainly not give up on parents, because we cannot do anything by way of finding solutions, particularly as this is often the means by which helpers obtain their gratification. What is more, this can also serve as a model, indicating that parents do not have to fear such feelings in others, including their children, and that respect and acceptance may be helpful.

WORK IN PARTNERSHIP

It helps to keep in mind the self-esteem and self-efficacy of parents throughout the process of exploration. Influencing these self-beliefs is a major achievement, and this is unlikely to occur by taking over from them. Such positive effects can only arise by working with parents, who must be totally involved in the process, discovering insights and finding solutions for themselves, or at least being part of a team that does this. The more parents achieve themselves in this way, the more competent and capable they will feel, and the better able to adapt subsequently and meet inevitable new challenges.

This re-emphasises the mutuality of the process of exploration and the importance of working together in partnership, with both exerting some control over the process and neither leading it throughout. This contrasts with the expert model, where the helper asks a set series of questions, so as to cover all the issues he/she considers important. Although this is possibly effective in relatively simple diagnostic or assessment situations, in circumstances where the helper does not know the nature of the specific issues, it is vital to follow the parents' lead; for example, where the child behavioural problem becomes confounded with an issue of a parent's depression or a marital problem.

Partnership therefore implies that the exploration should be commenced in as open a way as possible and be highly responsive to the parents. Although the helper must be able to provide the opportunity and motivate them to talk, the parents must be free to pursue the issues and problems they consider important in the order they determine and at a pace appropriate to them.

Partnership also implies that in raising particular areas, the helper should explain and negotiate what she/he is doing. It is not appropriate to launch into a particular topic without saying why, and without the parent's agreement. This is specifically illustrated later in describing the skills of questioning.

AREAS TO EXPLORE

Helpers who lack the skills of exploration are often content to elicit minimal information about a problem, take this at face value, and assume an understanding of what parents have said, even though the parents may not have been clear in their own minds about what has happened. Instead of attending to what the parent has just said and questioning, clarifying and elaborating it, they move on to different aspects of the problem, aspects which are more determined by their own assumptions and hypotheses about the problem than those of the parents.

What can be particularly worrying for some helpers is that the parent's story is complex and difficult to follow, or they will not be able to remember it all. In fact, this is likely to be true in most cases, since our ability to retain new information is far from complete. Anxiety about this can further prevent helpers from listening with full attention. However, once the parents have outlined their problem initially, no matter how fully, one can then go through it systematically as many times as necessary to obtain as clear a picture as possible. The opportunity to explore the problem in depth by going over the situation several times, for example, is precisely what is necessary for the parents to derive a clearer understanding irrespective of the helper's grasp of the situation.

Our experience is that if the helper is skilled in exploring, prompts the parents appropriately and is sensitive and responsive to what they say, all the necessary information is likely to be provided in their own way and at their own time. However, since it is important to be thorough in exploring the issues raised, and to be systematic in considering all possible aspects of their problems, we have provided as a guide a list of possible areas to be explored. This is not intended to imply that these are the only relevant areas, since problems vary enormously in content. The list should also not be used as the way of eliciting all the necessary information in a pre-set order (like taking a medical history). Parents should be prompted to explore as we have suggested, and if particular areas are not mentioned spontaneously by parents, they might be tentatively questioned by the helper without forcing the parents either to discuss issues that are clearly not relevant to them, or that they find particularly difficult or traumatic.

- What is the general nature of the problem?
- How is it manifested specifically?
- When did it begin?
- What were the circumstances surrounding the onset?
- How frequently does the problem arise?
- When does it occur and when not?
- Where or in what context does it occur and not occur?
- Does anything specific trigger the problem?
- What are the consequences?

- Who is involved in the problem?
- How do those involved react?
- What do they each think and feel about it?
- How do they feel about themselves?
- How do they feel about each other?
- What are their hypotheses about the reasons for the problem?
- What have they tried to do about it?
- How successful have their attempts been?
- Why?

It is important to remember that whatever else you do while exploring, you are looking for clarity and for an explanation that might be of value in directing what should be done about the problems.

DURATION

Although exploring particular problems can be completed very quickly indeed (e.g. in a matter of minutes) it does take time, and can, when there are multiple complex problems, last for several sessions. However, if the major aim of help is to provide support, then the time taken is not necessarily relevant, except in terms of the practical constraints of the overall time available to the helper and parent. In terms of meeting the needs of parents, the important issue is whether the parents derive something from the exploration in terms of the relationship, understanding of the issues facing them and the basis from which to develop strategies for managing the situation. What is important, however, like everything in the relationship, is to negotiate explicitly and come to an agreement about what you do at all stages and for how long.

The Skills

We will now go on to consider the specific skills involved in helping people to explore. These are the skills of: 1) giving people the opportunity or getting people to talk in the first place and to continue to do so as necessary; 2) guiding them, so as to cover all relevant areas; and 3) probing so as to explore specific areas in depth. Although focusing upon exploration as a specific stage of the overall helping process (see Chapter 3), the skills to be discussed are relevant to the other stages or tasks. For example, when working on goals or ways for achieving them, the helper and parent are actually engaged in further explorations, not of the problem this time, but of possible pictures of the future (aims/goals) and potential strategies.

For most parents, exploration will be unproblematic. Having decided to seek help or to meet the helper, they will be willing to talk, given the opportunity, and will work with the helper in covering the appropriate ground. Some will be naturally talkative, open and friendly; for others their difficulties will be so pressing that they will be happy to unburden themselves. For many, it will be a real relief to talk at length about their difficulties within the context of a situation in which someone is willing to focus solely on them and to listen.

For a few parents there may be difficulties. This includes, for example, situations where parents talk endlessly and seemingly aimlessly. The helper may have trouble in stopping them and certainly in guiding them into particular directions. The skills to be described below should enable this to be managed, although they may need to be applied quite assertively at times. However, in extremes, it might be appropriate to focus upon their talkativeness as a problem in itself, with implications for many aspects of their relationships, not the least of which is a failure to listen to other people. This requires respect, tact and skill, because such an issue is potentially very threatening. On the other hand, the parent may be well aware of the difficulty, but never been able to do anything about it, or may never previously have had anyone courageous enough to raise it as a problem.

A more common situation is where the person is extremely hesitant or reluctant to talk. This may arise for a number of different reasons, including anxieties or uncertainty about the helper situation, because of low self-esteem or because of the novelty of talking about intimate issues. If the helper is aware of the skills to be discussed here, it should help, but again there may be a need at some point to raise the issue with the parents as a particular problem to be addressed. Significant distress is a frequent cause of hesitation, and may be handled by the helper by recognising the depth of feeling and using the skills of empathy to help the parents to share it if they can.

Perhaps the most difficult, although relatively rare, situation is where the parent is literally unable to talk because of extreme distress, depression or confusion. There are no simple answers to this, and it may be that the person needs more specialist help. Although the skills below are relevant and may have some effect, it is difficult to stop oneself from completely taking over or from allowing the conversation to degenerate into a helper led inquisition with monosyllabic interjections from the parent. In such a situation there is the risk of simply adding to the parent's problems by indicating that their reticence is unacceptable, for example, and hence further endorsing their own negative self-image.

Under certain circumstances (e.g. as in bereavement) one option, requiring patience and a longer term view, is to sit quietly with the person and to respond as invited. Being with parents like this when they are in crisis can in retrospect be viewed by them as a powerful and positive experience, like a valued gift. Such experiences have endorsed for us an important principle of helping: that skills are not everything and that you do not always have to be active or think you are in control.

Before considering other skills specific to exploring, it is important to say that the skills of attending and listening are basic to what we are discussing; without them the skills listed below will be ineffective. Attending and listening provide the backdrop for them; they are themselves major prompts to facilitate parents to talk and explore, and they are the means by which what they say is heard and understood.

People attending fully indicate they are doing so in a number of ways and these act as essential prompts for people to talk. These include all the non-verbal cues discussed in Chapter 5 (e.g. eye contact, body orientation) as well as the variations in facial expression, nods of the head, and responsive comments like 'Yes', 'mh-mh', or 'I see'. These have been called minimal encouragers for obvious reasons. When clearly and genuinely present, they prompt the person to talk; without them, she/he would falter and stop very quickly. In interactions, although people talking spend time looking at the listener, they also look away for much of the time. This is particularly so when they are preoccupied with strong feelings or are having to think carefully about what they are saying. Since it is difficult to formulate one's ideas and at the same time process information about the listener's reactions, what the talker does is to repeatedly look at the listener briefly every few seconds before looking away again. This enables the talker to check the listener's reactions, including whether he/she is attending and is interested.

Clearly attending to someone is a major ingredient of the fundamental qualities of helpers, and it is worth just making the point here that the parents' awareness of these attitudes in the helper will be important prompts in themselves. Valuing the person, being genuinely interested in what they have to say, being quietly enthusiastic are all strong factors in motivating people to talk, and indicating how the general context of the overall model we are attempting to describe is in itself a significant impetus, prompting and guiding the process.

This includes the concept of partnership, with similarly strong effects likely to be derived from the parents' perceptions of the developing relationship. Perceiving the helper as attempting to work with them in partnership, whether expressed overtly or not by this stage, will be a strong prompt to engage and communicate. Soliciting and accepting their views, overtly sharing the helping process with parents, explaining the need for careful exploration and how it links to the other stages, and being prepared to negotiate are all part of the process. Not being hurried, working at the parent's pace, allowing them control, acknowledging their difficulties in talking, for example, and not putting undue pressure on them are all important aspects of this.

QUESTIONING

Using questions is perhaps the most obvious skill specifically concerned with exploration. As mentioned in the last chapter, the process of exploration is commonly initiated with a question, such as 'Why have you come to see me?', 'What prompted you to want to see me? or 'What has been troubling you?' These are called open-ended questions, because they do not limit the response; parents can answer them in many different ways and may talk for as long as they like without being constrained unduly by the question. A series of such questions, therefore, on their own may be all that is necessary to enable parents to explore their problems comprehensively. The question 'How have you been getting on?' is a prompt or invitation to provide a vast array of responses from 'Very well' to 'Well, I thought I was getting on very well yesterday, until my ex-boy friend came round, and ....' On the other hand, the very similar, but closed question, 'Have you been well?' tends to limit the reply to 'Yes' or 'No'. Given that the aim of exploration is to discover the parents' own picture of their world, the more one is able to pose open-ended questions, the more likely parents are to tell their story with minimal interference from the helper.

It is impossible to do this with closed questions, and you might like to try to explore a particular issue like this with a friend. The difficulties are illustrated by the existence of a variety of games that allow only closed questions and/or 'Yes/no' answers for the discovery of an undisclosed piece of information (e.g. an actor's name). Although closed questions have a place in acquiring specific information, their value is limited. Extensive use of questioning of this kind can make the parent feel as though they are being interrogated; it gives a much more authoritarian impression that is more associated with an expert approach to helping than a partnership. Perhaps the most important point here, however, is that such questioning imposes the helper's view of the situation, since each question is determined by what the helper expects, and not by what the parent wants to convey.

Although open questions are effective, they should not be overused. People tend to ask questions when they are not sure what else to say. As suggested by Egan (1990) a question should only be asked if it serves a purpose for or is useful to the parents, helping them move from the abstract and general to the specific and particular, and enabling them to focus. Even so, a series of open questions can feel like an assault under certain circumstances.

One can observe professionals, for example, asking questions without responding significantly to the answers. It is as though the parents' answer was not very interesting or meaningful, and they move on to ask a further question about another area entirely. It is much more effective if one responds to the answer, acknowledging it, valuing it and even exploring it further, preferably incorporating other ways of probing. Skilled exploration, therefore, can be seen as a synchronised interaction in which the helper prompts the parent to talk, takes up the points made by the parent, and prompts further elaboration based upon the what the parents have just said. This cycle may be repeated in long sequences and may be all that is needed to understand the problem

A final point to make here, and it applies to other ways of exploring, is that one can enhance the effect of questions by explaining them. Instead of saying 'How have you been feeling recently?', one might say, 'Sometimes children become difficult when their parents are stressed. So, I wonder how you have been feeling?' This not only prompts the parent, it gives the reason for asking and therefore provides the context for a more effective reply. What is more, it is a way of indicating a willingness to work closely and in partnership, since it is the means by which the specifics of the process can be shared.

STATEMENTS

There are many other ways of prompting, and these include the use of simple statements, as opposed to questions. 'You are looking much better today' is as likely as a question to initiate an open response, whose content and length will again be determined by the parents. Similarly, 'I don't quite understand what you mean by saying ......' is likely to focus parents and to help them explore further and to elaborate and clarify what they have just been saying.

REFLECTIONS

These are prompts or probes that again involve the helper in making a statement, but this time they are direct reflections of what the parent has just said. 'So you think he feels angry with you' or 'He's getting angry' in response to a mother's description of her child's angry behaviour, will indicate clear interest in what she is saying. Assuming that you have picked up an important point, this is likely to focus her upon this issue specifically and to prompt her to continue, elaborating what she has been talking about. A similar effect may be obtained by repeating what the person has just said with a questioning intonation. For example, following a parent's statement, such as 'He keeps getting upset', with 'Upset?' will immediately prompt a more specific exploration of what has just been said and probe it further.

Such methods of interjecting may involve the exact words used by the parent or a close paraphrase. In either case they are likely to have the effect of indicating that the helper is listening closely and is actively trying to understand, and they will have a big impetus on the conversation continuing appropriately. Again, however, as with questions, these methods should not be overused, as it can become intrusive and irritating to have everything you say repeated.

DIRECTIVES

Another method of probing or prompting includes the use of gentle commands. One might say, for example, 'Tell me more about that', 'Tell me how you felt' or 'Go on.' Although linguistically these are orders to the person, they are likely to be most effective if presented in an invitational manner, with a tone that is more indicative of a statement such as, 'I should be very interested to hear more about that.'

PAUSES

Another method of prompting further exploration is the use of silence. Pausing or not responding directly to something parents have said allows them to continue talking if they wish, but also pushes them to do so, as silences are not necessarily easy to tolerate. One notices, however, that these pauses are often accompanied by non-verbal prompts, such as a slight forward body movement, a questioning facial expression, or a gesture signalling interest and expectation of continuing. This can, therefore, be a very effective and non-directive form of prompting. However, again if overused or used badly, pausing becomes counterproductive, making parents feel awkward. It can also appear rather manipulative, particularly where the situation is novel to the parents and some guidance is required.

DEMONSTRATING EMPATHY

Earlier we said that empathy was a fundamental attribute of helping. It is, in fact, crucial to the process of exploring the parents' model or picture of their situation. The essential requirement of this process is for the helper to try to grasp the way the parents see the world. It is the demonstration of this understanding that serves to guide the exploration and to motivate it.

Empathy may be shown in a pervasive way by the whole presence of the helper, in attending, listening and enabling parents to talk. If she/he understands, then everything the helper does, verbally in terms of the content of questions and other prompts, and non-verbally in terms of posture, facial expression and tempo, will be in tune with the parent. This has been called interpersonal synchrony, and indicates an attunement that is clearly empathic.

However, there are more specific and direct ways of demonstrating empathy and very good reasons for using them. These are usually verbal statements attempting to encapsulate what the parent means. Although one frequently hears potential helpers saying, 'I understand', this does not demonstrate one's understanding, it simply states that this is the case, even though it might not be true. Empathy is demonstrated by specific statements attempting to describe the parents' experiences, thoughts and feelings. Reflections, as described above, may be empathic, whether using exactly the same words as the parent has just used or paraphrases of them, provided they are attempts to portray what the person is experiencing. For example, in response to a mother's emotional description of her daughter being bullied, the teacher said, 'So you are feeling very angry that she is being hurt and no one is stopping it.' A health visitor exactly demonstrated her understanding of a mother's feelings in saying, 'You seem to have lost trust in your son, because he lied to you that time.'

Such statements do not necessarily have to reflect what the person says, of course, but what they mean, taking full account of all aspects of communication, including the non-verbal. 'You look as though you weren't expecting me' was the gentle response of a home visitor to the expression on a father's face, or 'You seemed to have tears in your eyes when you were talking about your mother.' The skill is to make a short, concise statement that accurately and completely captures what the person is saying, thinking and/or feeling, but doing so in a tentative way, that allows the person to deny it, if she/he wishes, for whatever reason (see below). Such statements should not be rushed, and should also reflect the tone, manner, tempo and language of the parent at that time.

Demonstrating empathy like this can be very powerful and, if not over-used, serve a number of purposes. They are the clearest indicator that the helper is listening carefully. They, therefore, signal the fundamental qualities of respect, genuineness and, of course, empathy. They also show that the helper is someone who can be trusted to understand and be helpful, and they therefore enhance the parent–helper relationship. This in turn improves the communication between them, so that the helping process is facilitated as a whole. More specifically, empathic statements are effective probes. They tend to motivate people to talk more, but particularly to begin to go into more depth about what are hopefully the more important aspects of the issues facing the parents.

Empathy depends upon very careful listening, but, even so, it is not necessarily easy to be completely accurate, and one can be wrong. An analogy is with the game of darts. As long as the dart hits the board it will gain some points, but the most effective is the one that hits the bull's eye. The more accurate the statement, the more effective it is in indicating that you are listening, that you understand and that you care. Hitting the bull's eye can have dramatic effects on parents, including them spontaneously showing genuine emotion (e.g. crying or pleasure) and opening up further.

We remarked earlier on the need to be tentative, and this is because empathic statements can be threatening and upsetting. You may light upon a very significant and emotional point, that the person might not want to talk about or even think about, and might even be inclined to deny under certain circumstances. You might not have read the situation properly and may, therefore, be inaccurate or even totally wrong. However, by being tentative, attempts at empathy still have a vital function, in that they provide the means by which the you can put your understanding of the other person to the test. People are complex; their words and behaviour may be unclear or confused; their non-verbal behaviour may be at odds with what is being said; or the helper may simply not understand. In all such cases, a tentative attempt at empathy allows the parent to comment and to provide feedback. This prompts a deeper exploration, but also provides further information for the helper in validating, partially confirming or even completely contradicting the picture he/she has been developing. One mother replied to an attempt at empathy by saying: 'Yes, you're right. I was devastated when my husband said he was going to leave me, but what really angered me was his complete indifference to my feelings; he didn't care about me!' Always making empathic statements tentative and questioning enables parents to reply freely, agreeing or not to some degree, denying, ignoring, enlarging or correcting what the helper has said.

SUMMARISING
This is another skill of value in exploring. It involves the helper in drawing together and expressing the main points of the conversation as a whole or of the current part of it. Summaries should not be long monologues, as they would lose meaning and purpose; they would become boring and would exceed the information capacity of the listener. They should be as brief as possible, but also clear, accurate, and specific. To illustrate, after a ten minute conversation with a mother of a five year old, a health visitor said, 'So you think there are a number of reasons why Ian (the son) gets so angry. It's possibly because he's tired and run down, or frightened of what is going to happen at the hospital, or because you're tense and somehow transmit your feelings, making him less secure'.

Like all such skills, summarising should not be over-used. However, it can be a particularly useful way of: beginning new sessions; stimulating the conversation when it is flagging or going round in circles; drawing together scattered thoughts and feelings; prompting further exploration; and even closing a particular issue. The function of summaries is to clarify and simplify information; they highlight what seem to be the most important issues and provide repetition to help ensure the points are remembered. They show the helper is listening carefully, and may of course be empathic, showing the helper's understanding, or checking the accuracy of what has been understood. This is illustrated by the mother's response to the summary in the last paragraph. She hesitated, as though thinking, then said with some excitement, 'Well…That's right…but it's probably more to do with me than him. I get so tense before we go (to hospital)… In fact, exactly the same happens before John (the estranged father) comes round. Ian always plays up, because I get so snappy.' This not only reflected the mother's developing realisation of her role in the child's problem, but it was also the first time that she had brought her ex-husband into the conversation.

Specific Methods

Although we have largely been talking about skills in this chapter, there are a number of specific techniques that can be used to further the process of exploration. These may be used in the sessions themselves, but more usefully can be used between meetings and the findings discussed subsequently. Parents do not stop thinking at the end of a session. If it has been productive, they will continue to address important issues afterwards, and this might be encouraged by negotiating with them to carry out a variety of exploratory tasks between the sessions.

One might, for example, depending upon the problems being considered, ask parents to make specific observations of themselves, the behaviour of their child, or their interactions with others. They might count the number of times their child has a tantrum or they have an argument with their partner. More detail can be gathered by getting them to observe when these happen, what starts them, and what happens subsequently. Such observations can be made very systematic and specific of more open and general by asking parents to keep a diary about whatever it is that concerns them. It can be useful, for example, to ask them to keep a record of how they are feeling or their child's mood, and to try to note patterns and associations. An additional option here is for them to use basic rating scales as a way of quantifying their observations and making them comparable (e.g. rating their child's anxiety on a 1–10 scale). Further discussion of these methods is provided by Edwards and Davis (1997).

We often ask parents, where appropriate, to think about particular issues and to write notes on their conclusions. For example, where relevant it can be useful to ask parents to do what Kelly (1991) called a self-characterisation sketch. This requires them to write a description of themselves in the third person as though through the eyes of a sympathetic friend. Similarly, they can be asked to write such a sketch about their child as described by Cunningham and Davis (1985) and Davis, Stroud and Green (1989), or even their partner or any other relevant person. These are all useful ways of making parents think carefully and are frequent sources of useful insights both for the parents and the helper.

For example, a mother was asked by a specialist nurse to write down how she thought her son was feeling about his regular dialysis and his wait for a kidney transplant. She took the task very seriously, and her notes were discussed at length in their following session. She found both the process of writing and the subsequent discussion informative. It made her question several assumptions, so much so that she wanted to test her own conclusions against those of her son, whom she then asked to write down how he felt. She had construed him as downcast by the experiences and diminished by the situation, whereas by soliciting his views directly (they had never talked about it before) she realised that he was not negative, but was positive about being alive. The treatment was therefore not a chore, and the possibility of surgery was very much welcomed by him for its likely benefits. This in itself relieved her, but it also enabled them to communicate more effectively. Although the mother learnt (to her initial dismay) that her own sadness had made his adjustment more difficult than it needed to be, she was put into a much better position to help him thereafter.

In Conclusion

In this chapter we have attempted to analyse the processes involved in exploring problems and to describe the basic skills in sufficient detail to enable the reader to use them. These skills facilitate the process of exploration in themselves, but they have to be seen in the context of the whole process of helping and particularly the development of the parent–helper relationship or partnership. Exploration requires the helper to be keenly interested in the parents and their situation and to suspend, at least temporarily, the search for solutions. It can be extremely helpful in its own right in a number of ways. Its main purpose however, it to help parents be clear about their situation, as a precursor to them managing their problems more effectively.

Exploration is mediated via the helper's understanding and by its very nature the process may challenge the parents to change. Under certain circumstances, where the parents' views are inaccurate or unhelpful, a further set of skills may be required to deliberately help parents to change. These will be described in Chapter 9. Before this, however, we should like to present another major model underpinning the Parent Adviser framework. This is based upon the work of George Kelly (1991) and provides a way of thinking about how individuals function psychologically and adapt. It will enable us to be clearer about what is involved in both exploring and helping people to change when necessary.

CHAPTER 8
HOW PARENTS ADAPT:
CONSTRUCTING MODELS

So far we have presented models of the helping process and the relationship and we have looked at the general qualities of helpers and some of the basic helping skills. However, if we are to be effective in our attempts to help, we also need to understand how people function psychologically and socially. We need a relatively simple model of how they adapt to their environment and life situation, and to consider the implications of this for the helping process.

There are many possible models from which to choose, as can be seen from any general textbook in the areas of psychology, personality, counselling or psychotherapy (e.g. Patterson, 1986). These range from the notion of people as a set of general characteristics or traits (e.g. Cattell, 1965), to Freud's ideas on the unconscious and the need to fulfil fundamental drives (Kline, 1984). There are behavioural theories that view the person as a set of conditioned responses (e.g. Yates, 1970), and more recent developments seeing people as conscious information processors, capable of thinking and intentionally striving for goals (e.g. Beck, 1976; Ellis & Dryden, 1987).

In this chapter we will set out a general model of the person as trying to make sense of the world, as has been implied in much of what we have already written. We have talked, for example, about parents presenting their picture of the world, telling their story, or exploring their model. We are assuming that just as we are trying to build a model to make sense of the particular events of helping, so parents are building a more general model of all aspects of their lives. We will elaborate this below before looking at how this might help us to help. The focus will be on parents, but it should soon become clear that the same model can apply to all people, including the helper and, of course, children. We will begin the discussion with a demonstration to help orientate the reader and illustrate the general points we should like to make.

Demonstration

Recently we showed a videotape to four child health nurses as a means of beginning some training in observational methods. The tape lasted only two minutes and was of a young woman interacting in a playroom with two children, a girl of about 18 months and a boy of three. They were asked to watch the tape carefully and write down what they observed. They were then shown the tape twice, once to familiarise themselves with it, and a second time to look carefully at the content.

The results were extremely interesting in that the observations of each of the nurses could not have been more different on every level. For example, one mostly reported what she understood of the conversation between the young woman and the children, whereas the other three largely attended to their actions (e.g. playing with a toy). Of these three, one focused predominantly on the children, whereas the others mainly recorded what the young woman was doing. However, even the two reporting the woman's behaviour were very different in what they saw; one reported specific and concrete actions (e.g. 'She picked up the car and gave it to the boy') and the other presumed intentions behind the actions (e.g. 'She was trying to please him, because she thought he was getting upset').

We then asked the observers a series of questions to try to ensure the same focus. When asked how the little girl was feeling at a particular point, one nurse said she was 'annoyed', another said she was 'enjoying herself', a third said she was 'distracted and not feeling anything particularly', the fourth said she did not know, 'She could be feeling lots of things.' One volunteered the information that the children were perfectly normal, whereas another thought that they were acting abnormally. When asked about the characteristics of the young woman, one described her as 'lovely and very gentle with the children', a second said she was being 'rather intrusive', a third thought she was 'bored, and not interested in the children', whereas the last said, 'she adores them.' This instituted a discussion in which they not only continued to disagree with each other, but expressed considerable disbelief that the others could have reached such conclusions. They did agree, however, that the children were siblings and the woman was their mother, even though there was no explicit evidence to support this!

Although they were shown exactly the same sequence of videotape, the four people saw extremely different situations. It was as though they were seeing different films. However, since the film was the same, the explanation for the difference has to be in the nurses themselves; they were seeing the film through very different eyes. They were not simply absorbing a set of events; they were obviously thinking about what they saw. They were actually processing the information, making sense of it, and finding different meanings in it.

One can argue convincingly that they each constructed different meanings as a result of having very different pre-existing models or ways of looking at their lives and their world already built into their heads. Interestingly, even though they agreed completely about the relationships between the children and woman, they were nevertheless still imposing an interpretation or a meaning rather than it being suggested by the events themselves. Presumably they saw a picture of a mother and children, because this is usually the case when one sees children and an adult playing together. One could, of course, argue that there were non-verbal cues to the relationship in the film and that they had all picked these up without realising it. However, when their assumptions were questioned overtly, two of the nurses still thought the woman was the mother of the children, whereas the other two were convinced that they were not related, and that it was a research assistant playing with the children. Even this last conclusion came not from the film, but from the nurses' thoughts of being in a research facility for their training.

Now what do we make of this? What are the implications and what has this got to do with helping? It might seem as though we are being negative about the people watching the videotape, and criticising their ability to think rationally and logically. However, we are not being critical at all, but using these observations to illustrate the fact that we are all making assumptions all the time. We cannot experience something and not find meaning in it. By being human we interpret, and desperately try to make sense of our world in all aspects all of the time; we cannot stop it. By being alive we are sense making machines, whether we consciously know it or not. This is not just for the sake of it, but because it is vitally important in enabling us to adapt to the world; without it, we would fail. In fact, in situations where we find it difficult to make sense of what is happening we tend to become very anxious.

The Theory of Personal Constructs
To elaborate these observations, and to enable us to look at the implications for helping, we will try to understand and explore them further by considering the theory of personal constructs, devised by George Kelly (1991). The theory is detailed and complex, and was originally presented as a single Fundamental Postulate and a set of 11 corollaries, which elaborate the basic notion. These are worthy of study and reference should be made to chapter two of Kelly's book or to an elaborate description and discussion of the theory in a book aptly named 'Inquiring Man' by Bannister and Fransella (1986). Much simpler accounts can be found in Cunningham and Davis (1985) or Davis and Fallowfield (1991).

A detailed description of the theory is beyond the scope of the current chapter and is not entirely necessary in order to use it successfully in thinking about the helping processes. We will present the basic ideas as simply as possible and limit what we have to say to the points that have direct implications for us here.

The Person as Scientist

Kelly's basic model uses an analogy with science, and presents a picture of the person as a scientist. This appeals to us for a number of reasons, but it is the respect for people implied in this that is particularly attractive, given the status of science within society. Scientists are concerned to invent and subsequently develop useful theories in order to understand the world better, and this in practice means being able to predict accurately what will happen. Theory is supposed to enable the formulation of specific hypotheses, which are simple predictions about what is likely to happen in the particular realm with which the theory is concerned. These hypotheses form the basis for an experiment, where the scientist carries out certain procedures in order to test the validity of the hypothesis and hence the theory. If the hypothesis is refuted by the experiment, the theory from which the prediction was derived may need to be modified significantly, so that the new version might be more accurate.

People Anticipate Events

Scientists are humans, of course, and it makes some sense to try out this model as the basis for understanding all our behaviour, even if people are not necessarily conscious of inventing theories, deriving hypotheses and experimenting with them. Kelly, therefore, took the view that we can only adapt to events in our world, if we are able to anticipate them. It would be impossible to adapt successfully if we had to rely on split second last minute timing in order to react. It is much better to be able to know what is likely to happen so as to be prepared for it, whether this be a catastrophe, an attack from a predator, the weather, public transport, or reactions of our spouses, children or neighbours. Adaptation can therefore be assumed to be a question of anticipating circumstances and events, so that one can respond appropriately as a result, and continue to live, have protective shelter, food or the means of getting it (via money), and relationships to fulfil a variety of biological and personal needs.

Constructing a Model from Experience

In order to enable us to anticipate, Kelly assumed that we all build in our heads a model of our world, which he called a construct system to emphasise the notion that the model is built up or constructed by the individual. The idea is that our past experiences (or more accurately the meaning we have put on these) are the basis of the model from birth onward (or perhaps even before). Its function is to allow us to anticipate the future, under the assumption that future events will generally be replications of the past. If someone deceives us, for example, then we will tend to assume that he/she will do so again in the future. If we meet someone who interests us, then similarly we will assume that he/she will be interesting when we meet them again.

One might think of it as painting in one's mind a complex picture of the world as it impinges on us as individuals. The picture includes the physical objects and events we encounter, as well as an image of ourselves and all the other significant people with whom we have contact. It is basically composed of the discriminations we are able to make (e.g. male vs. female; human vs. object). If we experience school as hard and ourselves as failing in this system, we are discriminating between ourselves and others. As a results we may be set up to construe ourselves as inadequate in any subsequent school-like situations or even more generally; some may come to think of themselves negatively (e.g. as stupid) in all situations. If people hurt us, physically or emotionally, we are likely to act cautiously with them thereafter, in effect anticipating or construing them as hurtful, dangerous or the like.

ANTICIPATING BY INDIVIDUAL MEANING

It is important to emphasise, however, that it is not necessarily the actual objective event that determines the construction and hence the future anticipations, but rather the sense people place on the event. As illustrated earlier, it was not the videotape that determined the nurses' views, but their own meanings; what they saw was determined by what it meant to them at the time. One of our children refused to do a second performance in a play, because of how badly she had done it the first time. Although several people had spontaneously congratulated her on her acting skills first time round, her own construction was that it had not been worth the emotional effort she had had to spend and still do badly.

CONSTRUCTIONS MAY NOT BE CONSCIOUS

Another point to make about the model proposed here is that although one might assume that scientists are consciously and deliberately building theories, this is not necessarily the case for people generally. The process of forming and using a construct system occurs naturally, whether or not we are consciously aware of it, and it is likely that we are not particularly aware of doing so much of the time. Going to the station in the morning, buying a ticket, putting it in a particular slot to make a barrier open and walking to the platform may be done automatically (and not even remembered later). Such behaviour, nevertheless, signifies in the person's head a model (or a picture or construct system) which gives meaning to the function of the particular place (i.e. the station), the significance of a particular piece of card (i.e. the ticket), and the expectation or anticipation that a train will arrive. The model, derived from the past enables us to anticipate the future, even though such predictions may be sorely tested in UK underground and rail systems at the beginning of the 21st Century!

Similarly, using a more relevant example from the child development literature (e.g. Bee, 2000) we know that being brought up in a caring home with parents who are loving, responsive and generally predictable is associated with children feeling secure in themselves and able to relate reasonably well to others. This does not necessarily mean that the children are aware of the process, but again it does imply the development of a model about themselves and others that allows them to anticipate being accepted or valued for themselves and trusting other people generally as a result of their past experiences. This contrasts with the low self-esteem and relationship difficulties seen in many children raised by parents who are abusive, neglectful or inconsistent in their care.

CONSTRUCTIONS DETERMINE HOW PEOPLE BEHAVE

Our behaviour is largely determined by our anticipations or constructions, and not necessarily by the objective events themselves. For example, some young children cling to their mothers and hide their faces, not because other people are intrinsically frightening, but because they construe them as strangers, are unable to predict how they will be and hence withdraw (at least temporarily). Others react differently and are much more forthcoming, again because of their constructions, presumably anticipating others to be trusted, for example, or not threatening.

WE DIFFER BECAUSE OF OUR CONSTRUCTIONS

As suggested in the last paragraph, people are individuals and differ considerably one from another. An implication of Kelly's model is that we are different in so far as we construe things differently, not necessarily because we have had different experiences. Whatever our experience, similar or otherwise, it is because we anticipate or construe situations differently that we react differently, just as we saw in the last paragraph and the earlier videotape demonstration. The nurses were looking at a different film, not because of its objective reality, but because of the different models or construct systems that they were bringing to bear on it, whatever their experiences of the world in their lives.

For example, two women were talking and enjoying each other's company, when they suddenly realised that their children, who were playing upstairs in the house, were not making any noise. The event to which they reacted was entirely the same (i.e. silence), but their reactions were totally different as a result of their constructions. One said, 'They're quiet, they're fine', while almost simultaneously the other said, 'They're quiet; they must be up to no good.' A second conversation occurred as two women approached a group of adolescents in the street. The boys were being rowdy, laughing and pushing each other. One of the women said to the other rather worriedly, 'You have to be careful nowadays with these gangs around……' The other replied, 'Oh, they're just having fun and enjoying themselves' and promptly spoke to them with a smile.

This does not mean that we have nothing in common. We might construe the world differently, but there are also likely to be overlaps. Where we share a culture and an environment, there must be similarities in the ways we anticipate, given that we are not entirely out of touch with reality. The point Kelly was making, however, was that similarity is determined by shared meaning and not by having had the same experience or behaving in the same way. One can, for example, behave similarly to someone else, yet be doing so for very different reasons.

Hypothesis Testing and Change

Our constructions are not fixed but are changing and evolving throughout our lives. This process is complex and not necessarily fully understood. However, one might think of constructions as hypotheses, and that each time we anticipate an event, it is a potential test of the construction. If the construction is shown to be wrong in some way, then there is the possibility that we might change. For example, the clinging child above may be more forthcoming if he/she learns the new person is not really a threat. If we construe a person as trustworthy and they let us down, we will change our model, albeit with some pain. If we are using particular constructions, they are potentially open to change all the time as we encounter new events, make predictions about them, and modify our constructions according to whether or not they are validated.

Constructions are Organised

Since we are making predictions constantly, the model we are using must be organised, but might be in very different ways, again influencing how different we all are as individuals. This organisation will include the fact that constructions will have a limited range of application. For example, we might think of a person as empathic but not a road or a tree. Some constructions will be more important than others and probably used more often as a result. For example, people who are generally anxious might well have a construction of 'threatening' as central in importance in their model, hence their fearful behaviour. This would contrast with optimists, who might have constructs such as 'kind' or 'trustworthy' as central predictors, or a general construction of themselves as 'able to manage' or 'effective'.

We will not dwell on the complexity of these ideas in relation to the organisation of construct systems. However, it is worth noting that change as a result of hypothesis testing will generally be determined by a number of constructions working together and not singly. For example, if we construe a person (e.g. a helper) as 'kind' or 'likes me', for example, we are expecting them to demonstrate this in most of what they do. If this does not occur, however, and the person seems 'cold' or 'indifferent to us' we do not necessarily immediately change our construction of them, but test the model against alternative constructions such as he/she is 'preoccupied with problems of her/his own', 'not feeling well', or 'having an off day', for example.

THERE ARE ALWAYS ALTERNATIVE CONSTRUCTIONS
What we mean here is that there is nothing absolute about our constructions; events can always be construed differently and potentially in many different ways. This means that it is not surprising that we might all have very different ways of construing, as demonstrated by the nurses watching the videotape. As a further demonstration, one of us once asked a class of 30 children to think of and write down one word to describe their teacher. This produced over 20 different words with relatively little overlap, spanning the whole range from the extreme positive to the negative on multiple dimensions. People can and are construed differently, as this indicates, but so can objects. A book, for example, might reasonably be construed as something to read. However, it can also be viewed as: a collectors item; an ornament; something to prop up a table leg; taking up space; a mystery (to the non-reader); a source of frustration, even terror (to the child with dyslexia); a weapon; or a way of lighting a fire.

INTERACTION IS ABOUT UNDERSTANDING THE OTHER PERSON'S CONSTRUCTIONS
This is the last point that we should like to make about Kelly's theory and its importance relates to the understanding of how people relate to each other and interact socially. Many of our examples given so far in this section assume that we build a model in order to construe other people and especially those that are close to us. However, Kelly took this a little further and argued that if we are to interact successfully with another person we need to be able to construe not only them (i.e. their actions) but also their constructions.

If people are to interact meaningfully, they must be able to know what each other means, and this implies understanding to some extent how they view their world. We will assume therefore that the more we are able to understand the constructions of another person, the more effective the relationship is likely to be with them, whether this relates to the relationship between helpers and parents or to that between parents and their children.

We will expand on this later, but an example may help for now, and it relates to an observation of a pre-verbal child who kept making blowing movements with his mouth. At first the parents construed it as meaningless behaviour and hardly responded to it. However, being curious, they watched him carefully and came to realise that this action had meaning and was being used as a communication. It seemed to signify a light source for the child (e.g. a lit bulb hanging from the ceiling) and their awareness led to him expressing real pleasure, when the parents responded to his blowing with a knowledge of what he meant, including imitating him and looking at, pointing to or naming the light. This conclusion came from noticing other members of the family blowing the child's mobiles to make them move and then the child imitating it. However, he then began to make the same blowing movements at anything suspended from the ceiling, including the light, street lights, the moon and even side lights in a room. The parents' ability to interact with him was significantly improved by being able to understand his understanding and to share the meaning for him (his construction) of one aspect of his world.

Implications for Helping

We have seen from the earlier demonstration that people seem to have and use different models for making sense of their world. We have elaborated this idea more systematically in presenting ideas from personal construct theory and the model of the person as a scientist. We should now like to consider some of the implications of these ideas for the helping situation.

THEORY BUILDING

Perhaps the first point to make is that this book is itself an explicit attempt to build models or a construct system for enabling us to anticipate the helping situation. We have been presenting constructions about the process (as a series of stages), the parent–helper relationship, and helper qualities in an attempt to enable us to anticipate what is likely to happen and hence be more effective in helping others. However, these constructions are not in anyway absolute or definitive; they are only one way of looking at this situation and are intended to be useful. Our role is to make our constructions as explicit as we can in order to be useful to others. We are aware, however, that the ideas should and will change as they are used and tested. We realise that the interpersonal helping situation is complex and the models being used here may be a poor match.

HELPING IS ABOUT FACILITATING PARENTS TO CHANGE CONSTRUCTIONS

A major implication of what we have been saying is that the process of helping is very much about enabling parents to change. If we look back at the aims of helping as proposed in Chapter 2, it might become clear that these are all fundamentally about facilitating changes in parent's constructions as well as their ways of handling situations. Helping can be seen as the task of freeing people from their current, possibly constraining views, and enabling them to see themselves and their situation differently, to construe their lives more effectively and therefore to be able to react more usefully.

We will not elaborate this in detail here, although the reader might like to return to the aims and consider their implications in this respect. However, to illustrate we can take, for example, the general aim of 'Enabling parents'. This is at least in part to do with the achievement of changes in parents' constructions. Self-esteem and self-efficacy are in effect sets of constructions that parents use to anticipate themselves or their own behaviour. These relate to the extent to which they view themselves as important and effective, and a major aim of helping is to enable these constructions to change positively in the direction of being more valuable and effective.

THE HELPING PROCESS

The process we outlined in Chapter 3 is an attempt to describe how changes in parental constructions are likely to be achieved. The various stages can all be understood in terms of the parents' and helpers' constructions and the production of change. We will try to illustrate this beginning with the development of the relationship.

RELATIONSHIP: The development of the parent–helper relationship is essentially a process of them both developing a picture of the other, or rather putting into place a set of constructions that will enable them to anticipate the other person and what will happen in the relationship. The natural anxiety at the first meeting is actually an awareness of uncertainty, of not being able to anticipate the other. This diminishes quickly as they get to know each other (i.e. form constructions of each other). The role for the helper is to elicit the parents' expectations and negotiate what is realistic. Establishing the relationship will therefore involve trying to determine the parents' pre-existing constructions and then putting them to the test. Of particular significance will be negative views of specific professionals (e.g. social workers, psychologists, psychiatrists) from past experiences and hearsay, and unrealistic views (e.g. that doctors can sort everything out with tablets). Although much of this may be done implicitly, the helper must attempt to make some of these constructions explicit in order to agree a contract or the rules of working.

The notion of partnership is itself a construction, but one that may not be available to parents at the beginning of the relationship. Their previous experiences are likely to lead them initially to construe the situation as gaining the advice of an expert rather than as a collaborative enterprise. The task, therefore, for the helper over time is to facilitate changes in the parents' constructions of the relationship to be more in line with a collaborative partnership, in order to be successful in achieving the general aims of the process. It is perhaps worth just mentioning here that Kelly's model of the helping relationship was related to the notion of a partnership, in that he described it as analogous to that between a research student and his/her supervisor. This explicitly acknowledges the supervisor's general expertise, but also the research student's more detailed knowledge of the very specific issues being researched.

The nature of the relationship is all important, because of the need to foster a situation in which people can communicate sufficiently well to understand (or construe) the constructions of the other. This is crucial for them to play a meaningful and effective role together. Diagrammatically it may be helpful to envisage the interaction between them as a continuous cycle in which they are both listening to each other, making sense of or construing the other (including their constructions), and responding to them according to the sense they made of what they heard (see Figure 8.1). For example, a social worker noticed that a mother's eyes watered while she verbally dismissed an incident and accompanied it with a short laugh. He construed the mother as more moved emotionally than she was prepared to say directly, and, as a result, felt the need to respond with an empathic remark, 'You are laughing, but it seems to have upset you more than you want to admit.' The mother heard this remark quite clearly, and judging from her behaviour, firstly construed it as wrong, and then felt safe enough with the social worker to admit the truth, presumably because she construed him as 'understanding', 'intuitive' or 'caring'. As a result she responded suddenly with real tears, which was observed by the helper and construed as manifesting deep distress, leading to him gently touching the mother's arm, with the cycle continuing second by second over time.

QUALITIES: The important emphasis placed upon helper qualities in Chapter 5 is certainly to do with, at least in part, optimising this process of engagement and relationship building. By clearly demonstrating the qualities (e.g. respect, empathy, genuineness, integrity), the more likelihood there is of parents seeing these in the helper, and therefore construing her/him as worth working with, for example, to be trusted and effective. It is perhaps interesting to note that these qualities are actually general ways in which helpers construe (i.e. superordinate constructions in Kelly's terms) both the people with whom they work and themselves. Respect, for example, is an overriding anticipation that parents are of importance, valuable, and capable of adapting and changing. Genuineness is a general construction about the

FIGURE 8.1 DIAGRAMATIC REPRESENTATION OF PARENT–HELPER INTERACTION

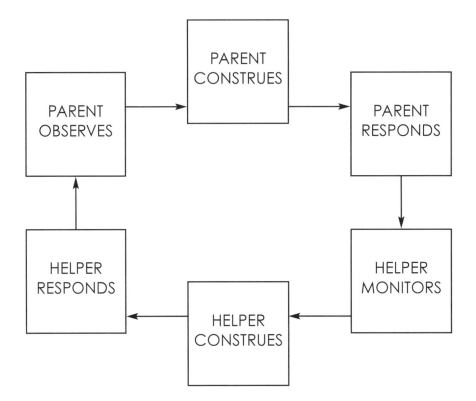

importance of being open to experience and accurate in viewing it. Similarly, empathy is at one level a general construction about the importance of understanding the constructions of parents and at another level the anticipation that parents have their own unique ways of construing and that it is important to understand them. Humility, quiet enthusiasm and personal integrity are somewhat more to do with helper self-constructions, with humility, for example, related to an open and accurate awareness of one's own abilities and limitations.

EXPLORING AND SUBSEQUENT STAGES: As discussed in the last chapter, exploration was described as more than a simple process of discovering the nature of the problem. It is actually an attempt to elicit the ways in which parents construe what is of concern to them, within the context of their constructions about themselves and their lives more generally. Exploring is the process of allowing parents to verbalise their constructions, to identify what is of concern, and to attempt to derive a better or clearer understanding.

What is perhaps striking about the demonstration we presented earlier is that there are always alternative ways of seeing situations, and helping is about enabling parents to develop different and more useful constructions. In the next chapter we will look at challenging skills, which are actually ways of enabling parents to test and change their constructions, at least to some extent via a process of the helper being able to grasp their constructions, while at the same time developing his/her own alternative constructions to be used for comparison and evaluation.

The intention of these stages is to derive a clear and more useful model (i.e. set of constructions) of the problems, on the basis of which aims and goals can to set. Goals are in fact constructions of about the future; the parents are anticipating how they would like the situation to be in contrast to how it is now. The next step of strategy planning is in fact again a process of reconstruction in which one anticipates what a given strategy will achieve, and then tests this in discussion with the helper or in actual practice when the plans are implemented. Again therefore the plan is a set of constructions serving as a hypothesis to be tested by the experiment of implementation. Even the final step of evaluation or review is understandable in construction terms as it is the point at which one looks at the experiment in order to decide what new constructions derive from it; that is to say, what do the outcomes teach us about the situation we did not know before.

In Conclusion

In this chapter we have attempted to present a model of how people function psychologically and socially. It assumes that all people are like scientists and are in the business of anticipating what happens in their lives in order to adapt effectively. Furthermore, it proposes that they do this by constructing a personal model that develops throughout their lives on the basis of their experience. We have explored the nature of the model to some extent and have tried to illustrate it generally. It is applicable to all people and all circumstances, and is certainly useful in terms of understanding how parents function.

For now we hope that this has added to the understanding of how to help parents, in so far as it dovetails with the other models of helping we have been outlining previously. Fitting the models together, the process of helping becomes an attempt to engage parents sufficiently to be able to elicit and explore their individual and particular constructions. The ways each parent sees the world is unique and has to be the starting point from which to allow them to change. The aim of helping is in fact to enable them to look at events differently and to develop an understanding of their world that is much more effective in anticipating events. It is on the basis of changes in their constructions that they will be able to adapt more successfully in terms of the specific problems they present, but also in terms of their more general ability to manage all aspects of their lives effectively, including those relating to their children. This is as true for the situation of a person directly asking for help as for attempts to work with parents in ways that promote their ability as parents and prevent difficulties in the parenting process and their children.

We will pursue these ideas further in Chapter 11, where we will elaborate a model of parenting that can be seen, at least to some extent, as directly parallel to the model of helping that we are proposing in this book. Before doing this we will go on to complete our consideration of the helping process by using the model in the next two chapters to look at ways of helping people to change their constructions and to manage problems more effectively on the basis of their new understandings.

CHAPTER 9
HELPING PARENTS CHANGE: CHALLENGING SKILLS

This chapter is about change. It is about helping parents to change the ways in which they construe events and people, when necessary and appropriate, in order to adapt and to manage problems more effectively. This is particularly relevant to the third stage of the helping process and the attempt to facilitate clear and useful models. However, it is also important in all subsequent stages, where change might be required.

We will begin the chapter by introducing the notion of challenging, or inviting parents to change, putting this into the context of the helping process generally. This will involve a discussion of the style or manner in which parents may be challenged before introducing some of the basic skills. We will finish with a consideration of a number of techniques that might be useful for initiating change. We will discuss these with reference to an explicit process of hypothesis testing consistent with the framework of personal construing.

Challenging

As we made clear in the last chapter, helping is very much a process of enabling people to change, both in the ways they construe their situation and in the ways they act. This may be evident at many points in the various stages of the helping process, but especially at the stages of exploration and clarification. Here the intention is to help parents to develop a clear and more useful model of the issues confronting them in their particular context.

This alone may be of significant benefit to some parents, and it can be achieved simply by gentle exploration (e.g. allowing them to tell their story and prompting them as necessary). This may be enough for them to achieve the various goals set out at the beginning of the book. They may come to terms with or otherwise manage specific problems. They may come to feel more effective in managing their lives. They may see their children differently or learn skills about problem solving and interacting with others. Such changes may result simply from the opportunity to explore the situation with someone who is skilled in communicating and has the qualities described earlier in the book. If parents are aware of being valued, their self-esteem may increase, as well as their ability to cope.

However, for some parents it may not be quite so simple, and they may require the helper to be more active and to use a set of skills and techniques to facilitate change. As we have said before, it involves the helper in seeing the model of the situation as presented by the parents, and then considering this picture in the light of alternatives, including the way the helper construes their situation. The question for the helper is whether the parents' constructions are as useful as they might be, and whether there are better pictures that could be adopted. This is not a judgmental process, but one in which someone who cares for and wants the best outcomes for them takes a look at the picture from the perspective of not being involved in the problematic situation.

It may be that there are gaps in the parents' understanding, they may lack information, they might have constructions that are illogical, without evidence, or simply not useful. Egan (1990) gives examples of needing to challenge: where the person fails to own problems, or feels nothing can be done about them; where their constructions are faulty or distort events; the consequences of their behaviour are not clear; or they are failing to act and manage their difficulties. For example, a mother described her two year old son in very negative terms, as 'naughty all the time', 'trying to get at her', and intent upon 'making life difficult for her'. Having explored this carefully, the helper construed the situation differently. He came to the conclusion that the mother's constructions were over-generalised and did not take account of her own contribution to the difficulties. He saw the child as intelligent and active, busy exploring his world with all the disruption this can mean, but unsupervised by his mother, who was generally preoccupied with other problems.

Another mother of a two month old child with colic was highly distressed. She construed herself as inadequate and failing as a mother, and she blamed herself for the child's disturbed behaviour. The helper, however, had the view of a very committed mother, who firstly had a child who was difficult to manage and a husband who not only failed to support her but undermined her confidence. A final example, is of a father of a child with cerebral palsy. He viewed the local social services so negatively that approaching them for much needed help would have been tantamount to an admission of failure on his part. For the helper this was a distortion of the situation, because: 1) the services were particularly effective locally; and 2) the father was managing well, but denying himself support that would make the situation better for him and the child.

These examples illustrate how existing constructions may get in the way of adapting effectively. Such problems are unlikely to be managed unless the parents' model changes and frequently the task for the helper is to enable this to happen. They may lack information or otherwise need to change their views of any aspect of their situation, before they can move on appropriately, whether this is acknowledged by them or not. The task for the helper is to spot these gaps, inconsistencies or unhelpful views, help the parents to see them too and to enable them to change in order to adopt a more useful or effective model.

The problem, however, is that change in general may not be easy and can be threatening. Making people believe in themselves when they have been put down most of their lives is difficult; as is giving bad news about illness or disability in their children, altering a firm belief in the use of smacking, or getting them to take responsibility for a problem in their child. Asking parents (or anyone) to change is by implication critical; it might imply for example, that there is something wrong with them or that they are inadequate. It may be seen as disrespectful and judgemental. It is worth pondering on the difficulties couples have in managing requests for one or other of them to change; it does not necessarily happen just by asking for it. There is potential inertia in all of us, that makes some change too much of an effort; it has to be worthwhile. It means forming new constructions, and in the short term this is likely to provoke anxiety, since the implications of their views for anticipating events may not be clear. It might involve major and pervasive constructions that have implications for many aspects of the person's world, have been held for a very long time, or may serve purposes for the person that are at odds with what the helper is trying to achieve.

Given that there is good reason for change, then it is important that helpers have the skills of facilitating it. We have chosen to call these challenging skills, following the usage by Egan (1990). It is almost impossible for one person to change another without the latter's involvement. One person cannot force another to change and retain a relationship with them that is helpful. The notion of challenging is therefore used in a very respectful way to acknowledge the parents' active role in changing. They will not change if they are reluctant to do so, and the role of the helper is to find respectful ways that invite or challenge them to do so. It is not a process of informing them of what is correct, but challenging them to think about the situation and potentially to take on the need for change themselves. Challenging is intended to imply a process of presenting parents with, or offering, a new or alternative perspective for their consideration; a hypothesis to be tested. Whatever the helper's view, the parents are at liberty to adopt, discuss or reject the ideas or pictures offered.

PRINCIPLES OF CHALLENGING
We will describe a number of skills and strategies for challenging parents in the next section. However, before we do, it is important to note some common principles about how any attempts at change should be instigated. These are crucial to the likely success of the skills.

WITHIN A PARTNERSHIP: Perhaps the most important point to make is the need for a mutually trusting relationship between the parents and helper. Since challenging can be so threatening, parents may deal with it by discrediting the person making the challenge and ignoring it (e.g. 'He doesn't understand'), arguing against it and finding ways to invalidate it, or even in the extreme ending the relationship. Little is achieved if this happens, and it is one of the main reasons for emphasising the notion of partnership.

If the helper is trusted as respectful and caring, the parents might not like what she/he says, but they will be unable to dismiss it, because there will be a benign and benevolent purpose. They are more likely to hear the challenge, take it seriously and be influenced by it. Telling strangers that it is wrong to smack their child or to throw litter in the street, for example, might embarrass them at the very least, but is also likely to engender hostility. In either case, they are unlikely to continue talking to you or, more important, to change.

FOR THE PARENTS' BENEFIT: If parents' views are to be challenged, then the helper needs to have a good reason for doing so. This does not include simply disagreeing with them, or assumptions about the helper's supposed wisdom. It is important that the helper believes that change will be to their advantage, providing them with different constructions that will enable them to react and adapt more effectively.

EXPLAIN AND BE CLEAR: If you are going to challenge successfully, then it is important to make it clear that you are doing so, and secondly to proceed in words that the parents understand. It may be more effective if helpers can be explicit in telling parents that they are going to question the parents' constructions and give reasons for doing so. The challenge itself needs to be as clear and concise as possible, since parents are likely to lose attention during long monologues and particularly if what you are saying is difficult to follow. 'That's interesting, but there might be a different way of looking at your son's hostility towards you. It may be that he (rebellious adolescent) loves you, but is trying to be independent and to make his own decisions.'

BE CONCRETE AND SPECIFIC: Challenges that are specific and related to concrete objects and events are likely to be more effective than being rather general and abstract. 'I wonder if you have noticed her (newborn baby) looking at you now' might be more effective than 'Did you know that newborn babies can see very well at short distances?'

BE POSITIVE AND CONSTRUCTIVE: Challenges are more likely to be successful, if they are constructive, expressed positively and directed at strengths in the

WORKING IN PARTNERSHIP WITH PARENTS

person as opposed to weaknesses. 'It seems to me you are being disrespectful by talking to him like that' is critical, indicating a possible failing in the parent's behaviour to her son. 'Perhaps he'd feel valued if you asked him for his views' is much more positive. It is constructive in terms of suggesting an alternative way of dealing with the situation, and it is also specific.

INVITE PARENTS TO THINK AND CHANGE: Parents are much less likely to be threatened and more likely to consider change, if challenges are expressed carefully in a tentative or invitational way. By doing so, they are simply asked to consider and explore a view with the helper, as opposed to being dogmatically told by the helper that it is correct. 'I don't think she's trying to get at you at all; I think she wants your attention' states a viewpoint that might well attract active argument. On the other hand, 'She might be trying to make it difficult for you, but I was wondering if what she really wants is your attention' not only accepts the mother's view, but invites her to think of an alternative explanation. It carefully presents a different view for discussion and exploration; it suggests a hypothesis for testing and not an absolute assertion to be automatically accepted. The mother can, of course, and perhaps even should argue, but it is not an argument with the helper, but about different ideas.

Skills

Having discussed the principles of challenging or inviting parents to change, we should now like to look at specific ways of doing so. As we have said, all challenges may be quite threatening, but some less than others. We will begin with the skills of information giving, which is possibly the least challenging, and move through a number of other methods before finishing with direct challenges, which are likely to be the most directly threatening and authoritarian of the skills discussed here.

GIVING INFORMATION

Perhaps the most common way of challenging people to change is by giving them new information. Professionals of all kinds do this constantly in providing a diagnosis, giving a test result, prescribing treatment, or giving the results of a reading test. New information is presented with the assumption that it will be understood, accepted, remembered and will help. However, unless we communicate well, none of these may apply. Since it is such an important method we will outline the steps and ingredients of it:

BEGIN WITH WHAT IS KNOWN: The first step is to determine the parents' existing knowledge, since communication is very difficult without this. Try giving directions, for example, to someone on the telephone without knowing where they are. Discovering what parents know already is actually the equivalent of the exploration stage, and as in all helping, doing it properly makes the process easier. For example, a young doctor was extremely anxious in approaching a couple to inform them of the imminent death of their son on an intensive care unit. Not quite knowing what to say, he began by asking them about their expectations. Their immediate response indicated their realisation that he was going to die, and the conversation quickly moved on to a discussion of their feelings and the implications of his death.

PRESENT THE INFORMATION: After determining what is already known, it is likely to be clearer what information to provide. The next step, therefore, is to present it as effectively as possible. The points made should be as simple as possible in words that the parents can understand. The most important information should be given initially and in small amounts appropriate to the pace of the parents. It should be structured, if possible, into clear categories, beginning with an explicit outline of the structure. For example, information about a disease may be structured in terms of 1) diagnosis; 2) underlying pathology; 3) causes; 4) prognosis; and 5) treatment. Repetition also aids recall, as does indication of the relative importance of particular information.

CHECK THE RESULT: Having presented the information, it is useful to check the effects. This involves determining what the parents now know, whether they are clear, and perhaps how they feel about it. This can be done by inviting the parents to ask questions, but also by asking questions of them and by discussion. If there are problems, then one goes through the process again by presenting the information in a more accessible way and again checking the result. It is certainly clear in our experience that parents need to go over the details of a serious problem in their child (e.g. a disability, illness or learning problem) several times in the early days following disclosure, and only gradually acquire a complete understanding.

ENSURE RETENTION: Providing information in an effective way helps to ensure it is remembered, but this can be facilitated by: writing it down; giving pamphlets; referring to further reading; or recording the conversation on audiotape so that parents can listen to it again at their leisure, and even share it with others.

SUMMARISING
We have already talked about summarising statements in Chapter 7 as one of the ways of facilitating exploration, but they also constitute ways of gently

challenging. They bring together the previous discussion, check the accuracy of the helper's grasp of the parent's picture, indicate careful listening and empathy. In addition, however, they may present a view of the situation that has not previously been available to the parents. This may be in terms of clarity or in terms of putting aspects of the situation together in a different way, but it is likely to make parent think and invite them to consider a changed view.

SELF-DISCLOSURE

It is often assumed that helpers should remain neutral in working with others and not disclose their own views or details of their personal lives. This may partly be to do with protection for the helper, but it can be unnecessarily intrusive, and distract attention from the parents as the focus of the work. It may also have arisen from the psychotherapeutic notion of transference, where there is justifiable concern not to influence the client's perceptions of the therapist, so that these can be understood and used as a means of helping. There are, nevertheless, forms of helping where self-disclosure is a major part, including self-help groups, for example, or where helpers have had similar problems themselves in the past (e.g. drug or alcohol problems).

Although care is needed in personal disclosure, steadfastly refusing to give away any personal information whatsoever will do little to engender a partnership, and is unlikely to be entirely successful, since we are giving information about ourselves in everything we do and say. However, if used judiciously, self-disclosure can be gently challenging, because it potentially enables parents to test their views or actions (as hypotheses) against those of another person. It may be used for example to indicate similarity with parents, and therefore to imply that they are not on their own or strange (e.g. 'Although I would never want it to change, I have never found it easy to be a parent'). Alternatively, it might be used to present a direct contrast to challenge the parent's view. In response to a mother who felt she had to meet the needs of her children perfectly, the helper commented, 'I try to be as good as possible, but my children just laugh at my forgetfulness!'

This statement was intended to present a slightly different way of seeing the situation, although it was done in a way that indicated empathy, humility and genuineness, and no doubt influenced the parent–helper relationship positively. This skill can serve to make the helper human in the parents' eyes, may break down potential communication barriers, and help parents to talk more openly about themselves. However, the general principles listed above must not be forgotten and particularly the need for there to be a very good reason for disclosing; it should be for the benefit of the parent, and not be because of vanity, for example, the need to talk about oneself!

ADVANCED EMPATHY

We have already discussed empathy, both as a general attitude of attempting to understand the worldview of the parents and as a basic skill of reflecting back their meaning, or what they know already. Advanced empathy, on the other hand, takes this a stage further by presenting parents with constructions and implications that derive from them, but that they have neither stated nor perhaps realised previously. When listening carefully, the helper may see different aspects of the parents' picture, putting ideas together slightly differently. Egan (1990) analysed this in terms of four different forms, including: 1) making the implied explicit; 2) identifying themes such as those that are self-defeating; 3) connecting up ideas that are presented separately; and 4) giving more substance to them (e.g. making vague or confused ideas clearer).

For example, although a woman made light of her disorganised home keeping and parenting and laughed at the way her mother-in-law tidied the house on her frequent visits, the health visitor detected and commented upon a deep resentment over the interference (i.e. 'You are laughing about it, but...is there.... do I detect real... uh... resentment about her interference and criticism?'). Although this provoked an initial denial, she almost immediately became angry about many other ways in which her husband's mother tried to make a rift in the marriage. Another example involved a father who was getting angry with his daughter, when the focus of his anger was really her newly diagnosed dyslexia, to which he felt he had contributed genetically. The helper gently commented on the displacement of his feelings by saying, 'You are getting upset with your daughter, although I wonder whether you are really angry about the reading problem, about you causing it and being unable to help.' This produced disbelief at first, but then considerable distress and finally very constructive discussion about how he should stand alongside her and not seem to be against her.

In both examples the helper had been able to see the parents' pictures of the situations, but had then put things together differently and challenged the parents to look again at the situations. The helpers' constructions were tentatively presented to them as alternative hypotheses for their consideration. It enabled the parents to become aware of something that they could not face previously, had not grasped, or had even misinterpreted. The fact that in both cases the parents immediately expressed strong emotion is an indication of the power of this skill. It stimulated open expression of their feelings, and subsequent discussion that was very productive. Nevertheless, such statements are potentially very threatening and were only used when the helper was sure she understood their situations, within a secure relationship where the parents trusted her intentions. Even so the challenges were then made in a very gentle, non-judgmental, invitational way, not as the truth, but as one way of looking at events.

IMMEDIACY

Immediacy, or you–me talk, is an important challenging skill, and refers to the helper expressing her/his feelings about the parent, or talking about what occurs between them in the immediate situation or in their relationship generally. Although this is an important aspect of working in partnership, it is something that occurs less frequently than it perhaps should, except in intimate circumstances or in anger. In most of our interactions with people, we tend not to express our feelings for each other verbally, or attempt to analyse our relationship, even though it is a vital component of effective relationships, and especially partnership. How often do you talk to colleagues about your feelings for them, whether positive or negative, or theirs for you? We seem to have difficulty in complimenting others, and even more problems in talking critically, given the threat to the relationship.

If one is to work closely with others, then the skills of immediacy are essential, both as a means of enhancing the relationship and as a way of helping people with problems. Parents may bring to the relationship with the helper the same difficulties they have in relating to other people in their lives. Immediacy, therefore, may enable them to explore the problems and to change, although it is a powerful and potentially very threatening tool, and should occur with careful consideration of the principles outlined earlier.

As an illustration, a helper worked for several weeks with a mother, whose manner appeared dominant, condescending, and generally negative, and began to irritate and alienate the helper. In thinking about his own feelings, the helper wondered whether this had a bearing on the interpersonal problems she had with her husband, her children, and other people she knew. The helper decided to address the issue, by asking how she felt about the sessions. Predictably this elicited a rather offhand and largely negative response, which then changed to a much more positive view, when she was asked directly about possible benefits. This then allowed an exploration of the inconsistency between her negative comments and her more positive feelings, her behaviour to other people around her and whether this might alienate them and account for some of her difficulties. With care to emphasise the woman's strengths (in effect modelling more effective social behaviour), she was able to realise how she might appear to others and what she should try to change.

DIRECT CHALLENGE

Many people find it difficult to challenge others, because of potential conflict. However, there may be times when helpers need to be courageous and to challenge something explicitly and obviously. This can be seen as a confrontation, and if done badly could be construed as a deliberate attack. Challenging in this way is likely to be the most threatening, in that it involves confronting parents with a completely different model of the problem in contradiction to their own.

This might be used to challenge discrepancies, distortions or self-defeating beliefs. For example, a helper pointed out to a couple, that although they had frequently promised their son to be home early from their business, they rarely did it. Another helper felt compelled to challenge a mother's belief that her daughter's speech was developing normally, when she was clearly falling behind children of her own age. Similarly, having tried in vain to question a mother's decision to move house to an entirely new area, the health visitor was compelled to tell her that she thought it would not change their problems and might even exaggerate them.

One of the most extreme and difficult situations is where issues to do with the protection of the child arise. Here it may be necessary to express one's concerns clearly and to help parents face the idea that their own behaviour may be damaging to their children. Such situations are fraught with difficulties; they are extremely embarrassing to all concerned and highly threatening to the parents, and a great deal hinges on it being done well. The fact that social services have such a poor image in the UK is evidence of the complexity and difficulty of this situation. It has to be done without alienating the parent, persuading them of the validity of the helper's view, and enabling them to change significantly. Such situations make considerable demands on the qualities and skills of helpers, and the principles listed earlier become even more important, and particularly the strength of the relationship, and concern for the good of all family members.

A General Strategy: Construct Theory

We have described some basic skills for enabling change, and there are many other techniques that may be helpful to learn. These can be discovered by reading about many of the different psychotherapy and counselling methods (e.g. Egan, 1990; Dryden, 1999; Nelson-Jones, 2000). We will mention some of these below, but should like to follow up our use of Kelly's theory in the last chapter to think about a more general strategy for facilitating change. The principles and skills we have been describing remain important, but are to be seen within an explicit model of parents and helpers working together as scientists, formulating hypotheses and testing their validity and utility in dealing with problems.

SHARING THE MODEL

In relation to partnership, we have previously mentioned the value of sharing the helping model with parents. This can include any or all aspects of the models described in the book so far (e.g. aims, helping process, relationship) provided there is good reason and that it benefits the parents. Here, however, we are proposing that the ideas about personal constructs be shared with them and the model of science this suggests.

To do this, requires them to grasp some or all of the following:

- People construe the world differently;
- There are always alternate ways of looking at events;
- Any views are like hypotheses derived from a personal theory;
- They are not written in tablets of stone;
- They can and should be tested, in order to check validity and possibly develop more useful ideas.

These ideas can be presented in many different ways, but examples are likely to be helpful, including those given in the previous chapter or preferably from one's own experience. We have found it useful to describe the experience of a father in relation to his adolescent son, who was construed very differently by all the people around him. His father saw him as uncommunicative, rude, incompetent and unmotivated, yet was intrigued to discover that a trusted adult friend construed him as polite, helpful, enthusiastic, and very good company. His teacher saw him as highly competent with a tendency to talk too much, especially in class, whereas his friends described him as funny, creative, and 'cool'. This can be used to demonstrate all the points above and particularly that behaviour may be construed completely differently and the usefulness of testing ideas.

Having understood these ideas, parents may then be helped to work together with the helper to: identify significant constructions; list alternatives; and test them systematically, where necessary. Essentially this is a process of formulating and testing hypotheses.

FORMULATING HYPOTHESES

This is really the stage of exploration as discussed earlier, and may be illustrated by Mrs X, who was concerned about the difficult behaviour of her eight-year-old son, Peter, who had been recently diagnosed as having severe asthma. Her general constructions of him were explored by completing a child characterisation sketch, as described in Chapter 7. Her main constructions appeared to be that he was disobedient, angry, aggressive, difficult to control and unhappy. Each of these was investigated further using an ABC model (see, for example, Herbert, 1988), which involved looking at specific episodes of difficult behaviour, and describing in detail the Antecedents (A) (e.g. the situation, time, people and any triggers), the actual Behaviour (B), and its Consequences (C).

The helper also initiated an exploration of possible causes of the behaviour, which Mrs X felt was somehow to do with his asthma, although she was unclear about how at first. Further discussion led to her formulating a number of possible explanations, without knowing which, if any, were valid. These included: him being born difficult; his diet (e.g. eating vast quantities of tomato sauce); being spoilt by always having everything he wanted; inconsistent expectations of his behaviour from his mother and father; as a direct result of his illness; being resentful of his illness; or because of the parents' anxieties.

Just formulating the list actually made Mrs X feel better. She described a sense of achievement, because although she had half grasped these explanations at different times, she had never explored them systematically, calmly or clearly. In a sense, the exploration had enabled her to change.

TESTING HYPOTHESES

Having made this list, the next step was to try to consider these constructions, to see which, if any, had useful explanatory value. The helper and Mrs X did this together, explicitly looking for ways of testing what were acknowledged as possible hypotheses or different ways of looking at the situation. Hypothesis testing is a creative process, limited only by the imagination of the helper and parents. However, we will illustrate with a number of examples.

DISCUSSION WITH THE HELPER: The simplest way of testing hypotheses is by detailed discussion between the parent and helper. Each construction can be considered in turn to see what evidence they can accumulate for and against, with both parent and helper contributing. For example, the notion that the son was born difficult was eliminated almost immediately, because he had been a 'lovely baby'. Although his mother described him as 'always being a handful', he had only begun to be very difficult when the asthma started. He also cared deeply about his sister, whom he adored. This led them to considering whether his behaviour was simply the result of asthma, and again this was dismissed in its simplest form by evidence that not all children with asthma are difficult, as she knew from experience of two nephews.

Methods of identifying and debating constructions that need to be challenged have been elaborated as part of Rational emotive behavioural counselling, devised by Albert Ellis. These methods are described in some detail by Dryden (1999). The focus is upon identifying irrational beliefs in relation to people's presenting problems, and then disputing these with them. This involves a variety of questioning strategies to enable the person to understand that such beliefs are illogical, lacking in evidence and have unproductive consequences in comparison with rational alternatives.

DISCUSSION WITH OTHERS: Another way of testing constructions or hypotheses is for parents to discuss them with other people in order to seek their views. This might include approaches to other professionals. However, sharing the notion of hypothesis testing with parents in this context has the potential advantage of enabling them to feel in control and effective, because of having thought about the situation, being clearer about what they are doing and having direction. This happened in the example of Mrs X, who took the initiative of approaching a dietician for evidence about the effects of food on behaviour. As a result, following suggested further observations, she was able to deleted from the list her hypothesis about tomato sauce.

The notion of a hypothesis can provide a clear focus for discussion with family and friends in looking for evidence. In discussing her list of hypotheses with her husband, Mrs X discovered that he had found her rather preoccupied and distant since the diagnosis. This distressed her somewhat, but clearly raised the possibility that her mood was at least partly responsible for their son's behaviour. The father admitted, however, that his own upset over the asthma manifest itself in him being much more lenient in his discipline than the mother. He explained this partly in terms of feeling desperately sad for his son, but also to make up for what he saw as his wife's excessive control. Although this was equally motivated by upset over the illness, the combined effect of their behaviour was inconsistency, which gave support for another of the hypotheses.

Motivated by her discussions with both the helper and her husband, as well as the openness of the helper in communicating with her, Mrs X went on to do something quite novel for this family and to involve the children directly in discussing her worries. The hypotheses were shared, and her son told her that he thought she had changed in her feelings towards him, since his asthma began. Although again she found this difficult to hear, it gave further support to the hypothesis that he was responding to changes in her behaviour. In fact, eventually the family finally settled on an explanation combining several hypotheses, including the son needing extra support because of the asthma, not getting this from his mother, and his insecurity being increased by the father and mother's inconsistency. However, the involvement of the children, the newly found openness in family communication and the understanding of what had been happening led to considerable improvement all round.

OBSERVATION: A third way of testing ideas is by direct observation, although this may also be useful in raising or suggesting different hypotheses. We might observe what occurs around us all the time, but we rarely have the time to ponder the events in a detached frame of mind, or to be systematic in our observations. It can, therefore, be helpful for parents to arrange to make more leisurely observation of their own children in situations where they do not necessary need to interact with them.

For example, a mother and father were concerned about their son's lack of friends and described him as being bullied in the nursery school he attended. They construed him as being friendly and sociable, and had some difficulty in understanding these problems. With his teacher's cooperation, they arranged to watch him unobtrusively in the playground at school and at an after school club. It was quite clear that children in general seemed to be avoiding him. When he did manage to engage another child, he appeared to be able to do so for only a short time, before becoming rather frustrated and even aggressive. This allowed them to dismiss the notion of bullying, but did enable them to conclude that he lacked basic communication skills, tolerated frustration in getting his own way very poorly, and responded aggressively. Further observation of their own interaction with him and a little more specialist help by way of social skills training eventually improved the situation considerably.

These observations occurred on two specific occasions and were unfocused. However, one can help parents to make systematic observations over longer periods of more specific events. Parents might count, for example, the number of times a child is disobedient, has a tantrum, cries or wets the bed. A woman, who was extremely negative about her son, was asked to look for occasions when he was behaving positively and was amazed at how frequently he attempted to interact with consideration or affection. She realised she had been so preoccupied with her own worries and her negative view that she had failed to notice the positive events.

Such observations may be recorded systematically over short or long periods, and may be made more detailed and elaborate. This might include attempting to look at the context of particular behaviours and the consequences (see ABC above) each time they happen. One woman, for example, made a record of the times her husband was irritable, and discovered that it was almost always on weekends when he was winding down from the demands of his very stressful job. Another man did something similar in relation to his own feelings. He was generally anxious and found himself almost beginning to panic quite often. By looking at these events over a couple of weeks he noticed that it mainly happened when he was asked to do something by his employer. He further noticed that the surge of anxiety tended to be associated with him saying to himself that he would not be able to do the task well enough for his boss.

These, and other methods, are all potentially useful in helping people to explore their situations and problems, and in terms of them changing their

WORKING IN PARTNERSHIP WITH PARENTS

constructions. Observations may provide information that is not already available to parents, they are a means of testing specific hypotheses systematically, and they can result in improved understanding of situations. Furthermore, such information can provide baseline data against which to compare changes that may result from any attempt at intervention.

EXPERIMENTS: One can begin to make observations in a kind of experimental way by controlling for particular conditions to test specific hypotheses. Again, the possibilities are endless, and determined entirely by the ingenuity of the parents and helper. For example, a mother who thought her daughter's overactivity was due to drinking excessive quantities of a particular fizzy drink arranged to record her behaviour with the drink for a week and to continue her recording during a week without it. Since she noticed no difference whatsoever between the two periods (except an increase in demands for the drink) she eliminated this as a factor.

Another couple decided that their son's poor concentration and disruptive behaviour at breakfast was at least partly due to the high noise levels in the kitchen, where they all ate. Having observed the situation carefully, they focused on the radio, which was always playing rather loudly at this time in the morning. They, therefore, systematically recorded his disruptive behaviour over several days, alternating whether the radio was on or off each morning. Although he remained difficult throughout the period, he was considerably easier to manage on mornings without the radio.

ROLE-PLAY: A more complex method of helping parents to test ideas is by role-play (or enactment as Kelly termed it). Meetings with the helper can potentially provide a relatively safe environment in which parents may be encouraged to set up and act out a variety of scenes. This not only provides a way of testing specific hypotheses, but also a way of learning about situations that are otherwise difficult to face, and practising skills and strategies of potential value in dealing with particular problems.

A mother, for example, was so frightened of the head teacher at her daughter's school that she was unable to tackle her about complaints or concerns she had about how her daughter was being treated. By taking the role of both herself and the head teacher in turn, with the helper playing the other role, she learnt a great deal about the situation and herself in it. They tried the scene several times, stopping and starting as necessary, with the helper trying to give constructive and useful feedback, and even rehearsing the phrasing and intonation of particular questions. As a result she felt much more confident in going to the school and communicating her views.

Kelly (1991) described an interesting technique called *fixed role* therapy, which is somewhat more elaborate, but can be used to help parents experiment with their constructions of themselves, their behaviour and their relationship to other people. This technique consists of carefully setting up a role for the person to play for a few days in their daily lives, with an emphasis upon it being acted. While people may not feel able to change themselves successfully and permanently, they may feel more secure and more capable of change if they feel that it is play or pretend and for a limited period only. Asking someone to act as though they were happy, may help them change more effectively than, for example, telling them just to pull themselves together and get on with it.

A father whose self-esteem was very low indeed had difficulty interacting successfully with others; he was extremely shy and had a number of constructions about himself that were negative, including 'being very boring'. Instead of asking him to pretend to be 'very interesting', which may have been difficult for him, he was asked to spend a week taking on the role of someone who was 'interested in other people'. With preparation from the helper, he managed to carry this out more or less successfully and made a number of interesting discoveries. These included, the idea that interacting was as much about listening as telling stories, that he was a very good listener, and that this was an attractive quality. The technique challenged a variety of constructions about himself, and did enable him to change quite successfully.

In Conclusion

Within this chapter, we have tried to give an indication of the skills and strategies involved in helping parents to change, so that they develop models that are more useful in facilitating their adaptation to events and in resolving difficulties. The importance of respect for parents and challenging, or inviting parents to change, within the context of a supportive relationship must be stressed. There are many possible ways of facilitating change, but we have extended the science model of construct theory as a general way of making sense of the processes and giving coherence to the search for ways within which change can be facilitated.

It should be clear that one cannot make any judgements about what is needed by way of change without very careful listening and a partnership with parents. However, having discussed change, we have now covered the most important aspects of supportive communication. With the ideas discussed in the book so far, the reader is hopefully in a much better position to engage and work closely with parents through skilled listening, detailed exploration and the skills of challenging parents in order to help them develop a more effective understanding of their specific circumstances. What we have described so far is highly likely to be helpful in so far as it will facilitate the achievement of the general aims discussed earlier in the book. As such parents will be in a much better position to be effective in adapting to and managing current and future problems on their own.

However, not all problems will be resolved or managed by the stages and skills we have described so far. There will often be a need to focus upon specific problems and to take the helping process further into the next stages. Our concern, therefore, in the next chapters will turn to the processes of problem solving. The focus for the following chapters will be largely concerned with parenting and problems in children. However, we will begin in the next chapter with a more general overview of problem management, including the tasks of setting goals on the basis of the models parents have formulated, planning and implementing strategies for meeting these goals, and evaluating the outcomes.

CHAPTER 10
PROBLEM MANAGEMENT

So far we have looked at the first three stages of the helping process, including relationship building, exploring and clarifying the constructions parents have about their worlds. In many ways these are vital for the general adaptation of parents to their situation and may enable them to be more effective in managing their lives. However, there are frequently specific problems with which parents will need help, and the remaining chapters are therefore to do with what might be termed problem management. This includes the steps in the helping process of goal setting, strategy planning, implementation and evaluation.

We will consider each of these steps in this chapter, as a prelude to providing frameworks and strategies for dealing with issues to do with parenting generally in the subsequent chapters of the book. Of course, there are many other issues that parents face; like everyone else, they may have problems in all aspects of their lives. However, we do not have the space to deal with all problem areas and have chosen to look specifically at the issues of adapting to parenting and the problems raised by this. Whatever other problems occur, there are always likely to be implications for their relationships and interaction with their children and, therefore, for the children themselves.

We will begin by exploring the process of goal setting. This will include a consideration of the characteristics of useful and usable goals and the skills involved in deriving these. We will then looked at strategy planning, implementation and evaluation of outcome based upon the goals set.

Setting Goals
AIMS AND GOALS
Once parents have explored and have a clearer or more useful understanding of their situation generally and the problems they face specifically, they are likely to be in a better position to decide how they would like to change the situation and what they would like to achieve. This is the next task in the process of helping and is likely to involve decisions about their aims, by which we mean the general direction in which they would like to move, and their goals, which are much more specific and relate to more concrete objectives. For example, although the parents' aims might be to improve their relationship with their child or improve his/her behaviour, these might imply

any number of different specific goals or outcomes. It is necessary, therefore, to formulate goals so as to specify the meaning of the aims exactly. For example, improving the child's behaviour might include one or more of the goals of reducing the number of tantrums or crying episodes, getting her/him to help tidy up after meals, to attend to what the parents say, or comply with reasonable requests.

GOAL SETTING: THE PROCESS

In all cases, the process of setting goals should be done explicitly and in partnership with the parents. Where parents are asking for help, only they can know what they want to achieve, and they must therefore be consulted. No matter how expert, the helper cannot decide what someone else wants, and if he/she were to try to impose, it is likely to be unsuccessful, unless negotiated carefully with the parents, leading to their full agreement. Even when the goals may seem very obvious from prior exploration, it is still worth taking a little time to check them. This might involve simply putting the obvious into words (e.g. 'So, the goal is to stop him biting people/throwing toys in the house').

It is interesting to note how often professionals fail to complete this step, but doing so has a number of significant advantages. Firstly, it makes the goals explicit, and ensures that they are agreed by the helper and parents. Secondly, it allows any disagreement to be elicited and then negotiated if necessary until agreement is reached. Thirdly, it is likely to save time, because it ensures that all involved know what they are doing; it prevents confusion, and is likely to pre-empt later possible conflict. Finally, explicit discussion of the goals makes sure that the participants are working together appropriately in partnership. It is likely to augment the relationship, because it demonstrates the helper's willingness to continue to work in partnership with the parents. It also helps to ensure that the parents understand the process, are involved in it, contribute significantly to it, or even lead the decision making at every stage.

In many cases, however, the aims and goals are not necessarily obvious, and it is vital for the reasons above that they be determined by open and clear discussion. This may occur where there are multiple problems in the family, the problems are serious and complex, and where there is a need for longer term support. It is likely to be particularly true in situation where one is involved in preventive programmes targeting families at psychosocial risk (e.g. Puura, et al, 2002).

Where there are multiple problems, they cannot be tackled all at once, so that the first task becomes one of prioritising. This involves deciding which problems to tackle and in which order. Then the next step is to decide the goals for any given problem. However, since there may again be multiple goals, this process also involves a discussion about the order in which goals are to be pursued. This is especially true where goals are functionally related; here they have to be considered as a series, in which a particular goal can only be achieved once one or more subgoals have been attained, as is the case with the development of many complex skills. For example, the goal for a child of kicking a ball is dependent upon being able to judge distances, balance effectively on one foot and swing the other leg appropriately. Without attaining these subgoals, the final achievement of propelling the ball with the foot is impossible.

AN EXAMPLE

To illustrate these points, we will take a family, who were involved in a prevention programme, which began during pregnancy. By the time the baby was two months old (this was her second), the health visitor had got to know the mother (Mrs A) very well and was aware of a series of problems facing her. Although not really depressed, her self-esteem was low; she was having some health problems, and living in a rather threatening neighbourhood; her relationship with her partner was strained, and she also had little support beyond her immediate family. In addition she was having specific problems with her oldest child and finding it very difficult to relate to her new baby.

It was impossible to help her tackle all these problems at once, but the health visitor visited Mrs A at least once a week. She continued to explore the various problems, and began to try to prioritise them. Mrs A found it helpful to list and acknowledge all the different problem areas, and agreed that there was a need to focus and take areas in turn. They decided to tackle her own health problem first, because it was relatively easy to manage in the first instance, was causing her considerable pain, and much anxiety about what was wrong. The GP realising the seriousness of the situation responded well to her contact with him, and managed to expedite a referral to a local consultant.

While this was happening, Mrs A and the health visitor decided to focus largely upon the difficulties in the relationship with the new baby, because this was what was concerning her the most, and was contributing to her general low self-image. It was also agreed that the early stages of the baby's introduction to the world needed to be given priority, and were therefore given most of the attention initially, before going on to tackle the other more entrenched problems that had been around for some time, and were not going to be easily resolved. The health visitor also thought that adapting effectively to the baby would be a source of considerable satisfaction to Mrs A, whose potential improvement in self-efficacy would help her in considering the other remaining issues.

In relation to the baby, the obvious general aim was to improve the relationship. However, this was then translated into the following goals: to spend more time interacting with her; to enjoy the interaction; to reduce the amount of crying; and to be able to sooth her more quickly and effectively. These were thought to be realistic and manageable, although it quickly became clear that it would not be easy without the partner's help. A prior goal was therefore set which was to have him take care of the son for short periods during the day to allow her time to concentrate on the baby. In considering this goal together, Mrs A and the health visitor noted a difficulty, in that any such approach was likely only to produce an argument, largely because of Mrs A's resentment. Further discussion clarified a further goal in the series, that of finding ways to approach her partner productively.

We will consider the steps that were taken later in the chapter in relation to strategy planning and implementation. However, Mrs A was able to achieve all her aims within a few weeks. She began to enjoy the baby much more than she had considered possible, and she actually felt very good about what she had achieved. Her relationship with her partner improved a little and she felt that she wanted to tackle the difficulties she was having with her son. The general aims she set with the health visitor were again to improve the relationship between them, but also to improve his behaviour. As illustrated before, this led to setting a series of goals, which included spending more time with him, and to him staying in his bedroom and not calling out when he was put to bed in the evening. This again necessitated a prior goal involving her partner; she had to secure his cooperation in ensuring that they both acted consistently in relation to the bedtime routine.

SKILLS AND TECHNIQUES

In helping parents to set goals, all the skills and qualities discussed earlier in the book are relevant. We have already indicated that the process involves a continuing partnership if possible. However, the skills of attending, active listening, prompting, empathy, exploring, summarising and challenging are all essential and used throughout this stage to enable the parents to formulate, explore and decide explicitly on appropriate aims and goals.

In many instances there will need to be little discussion, but as in the case of Mrs A, all the skills were required to discover her views of what she wanted to achieve. This included challenging some of her ideas and negotiating alternatives, as well as helping her to express her goals in a useful form (see next section).

As always in making decisions, it is useful to begin with a range of options from which to choose. This can be facilitated when the goals are not obvious, by the parents and helper working together to make as long a list as possible of all the options they can imagine. This may be done by brainstorming, which is discussed below in the section on strategy planning. Egan (1990) suggests a number of techniques for helping people generate models of what they might like the future to look like as a way of helping to develop goals. These include: asking questions that are future oriented (e.g. 'What would life be like if this problem were resolved?'); encourage them to look at other people as models; help them look at the better times they have experienced; and even to search out new experiences. By discussion, these scenes can then be used to generate possible aims and then useful goals from which to select.

Having derived a list, each option can be evaluated and a decision made about whether it should be pursued. Those remaining can then be formulated in terms of the criteria below, if they are not sufficiently clear already. A way of evaluating them is to take each goal in turn and to list both its positive and negative implications. For example, a goal formulated as having her husband accompany her to hospital appointments was evaluated in terms of it helping her to cope with the journey and being more able to understand and remember what the consultant said. However, put against the loss of his earnings and the threat currently hanging over his job, this goal was rejected in relation to the aim of having more support from him.

CRITERIA FOR GOALS

Being aware of the process of setting goals and their nature is important in ensuring the parents' commitment to working to achieve them. We all set goals at various times in our lives, but may not pursue them with enthusiasm. Egan (1990) has explored this in detail and concludes that commitment is increased, if the goals are, for example, owned by the person, appeal to her/him, are chosen from a range of options and not forced, and will reduce crisis or pain.

Their value also lies in making all those involved clear about what is being attempted, in what period and in defining what constitutes a successful outcome. Formulating goals clearly helps to avoid, for example, problems such as happened in the following case. A family were trying to deal with their son's problem of soiling his trousers. Although the helper assumed the goal of reducing the frequency of the soiling over the next two weeks, this was not clearly expressed. The result was, therefore, that although the child was clean on most day within the two week period, the parents did not see this as a success, because they were expecting him to stop altogether.

The following are a list of criteria to be considered in setting goals in negotiation with parents:

EXPLICIT AND AGREED: We have made this clear already, but the first criterion of a useful goal is that it be made explicit and agreed with the parents. The major responsibility for the decision rests with the parents, so that it is in keeping with what they want and their values. The helper may have different views and should feel free to discuss and negotiate these with parents, but it is very important not to impose them. Where appropriate parents should be helped to consider both what they think they should do, and what they want to do, and to check this with other people (e.g. the family) if they wish. For example, a mother talked to a helper about her son's imminent death and said that she did not want him to be told. When asked what she thought she should do, it became clear that it was her husband who was insisting upon silence and not her. Having discussed it carefully, rather than living with the failure to communicate openly for the rest of her life, she addressed the issue directly with her husband, realised that they both wanted to talk to the son, and then decided to do so.

OUTCOMES: Each goal should be expressed as an outcome, target or an objective (e.g. 'I want to spend a little time with my husband each day'). The question is what is to be achieved, and this leaves open the means of achieving it, to be decided subsequently in strategy planning. Clearly the two issues relate closely, but it is better to decide what is really wanted without being constrained by thinking of methods.

CLEAR AND SPECIFIC: Goals should express an end-point that should be as clear and specific as possible. 'To get on better with my child' is a very general aim that may be better translated into one or more clear and specific goals, such as 'To have time each day when we enjoy something together and don't argue' or 'To reduce the number of times I tell him off.'

OBSERVABLE: Because aims are general, their achievement is not always easy to assess directly, whereas the intention is to formulate goals to allow parents to know clearly whether or when they have been achieved. The goal of 'Being able to recognise three words by the end of the week' can be easily assessed, whereas the aim of 'Being able to read' is difficult to judge exactly in terms of success. However, to be able to assess the achievement does sometimes require a clear idea of the point at which the parents begin. For example, 'Reducing the number of tantrums or times he soils' is only workable, if one knows the original frequency as a baseline against which to make a comparison.

REALISTIC AND ADEQUATE: To be useful, goals need to be realistic; there must be a reasonable expectation of them being achieved, and this has to be judged carefully in each situation. Expecting long term marital difficulties to be settled in a few days is unrealistic, whereas 'being able to have a conversation for 60 seconds without being sarcastic' might be possible. However, it also has to make a difference and not be set at such a low level that little is gained; helping a child to swear only 199 times a day as opposed to 200 contributes almost nothing and is therefore inadequate.

The importance of this is that one needs to maximise people's success if they are to be motivated to work at their problems. It is likely in many circumstances that they are seeking help because success has constantly alluded them. One needs, therefore, to help them gauge what is achievable initially, to be successful and then to build on this subsequently, with a series of goals. Again the importance of having a reasonable idea of baselines is obvious in doing this effectively, as is a careful assessment of whether the parents have the necessary resources (e.g. money, time or skills), because these are likely obstacles to the achievement of the goal.

TIME LIMIT: The final criterion for expressing goals appropriately is to include a realistic time period. This is to make it clear to all concerned when to expect some change, or at least when to evaluate the degree of success in attaining the goal. If a mother is to attempt to leave her desperately clinging child at a playgroup on his/her own, with all the distress that this will cause, then she should have some idea of how long it is likely to take, even if this has to be something of a guess.

Planning Strategies

Once goals have been clearly formulated, the parents and helper can begin to plan how they may best be achieved. This is a step that is often taken in more of a hurry than is necessary, again without considering all possible options. It is important to plan very carefully, if one is going to maximise the chances of success in achieving the goals set. Again this means trying to think of all the possible options, to consider the advantages and disadvantages of each, and to look for likely obstacles before finally deciding what to do. As always, the parents should be, and feel, fully involved in the discussion. It is crucial for their feelings of effectiveness that they not only make final decisions, but that they generate for themselves as many ideas as possible.

It is important not to attempt too much at any one time, so that if there are a number of goals, priorities need to be established for the order in which they should be tackled. This may involve planning for just one goal at a time before returning to focus upon the next. Nevertheless, if goals are closely related it may be valuable to consider more than one at the same time.

However, it is important to be careful not to overburden parents at the implementation stage, where there will be a limit to what they can do effectively at any particular time.

For a given goal, the parents and helper should work together to think up as many possible strategies as they can initially and not just to decide to use the first idea that comes to mind. The obvious advantage of this is that they are less likely to miss possibilities and more likely to make the most effective decisions. This can be aided enormously by a technique that we will call creative thinking.

CREATIVE THINKING

This is useful, because it is essentially an exercise concerned with encouraging creativity or divergent thinking. As in deciding goals, the idea here is to help the parents make explicit every conceivable strategy, so as to be able to select the best single or combination of options.

The method should be explained to the parents, who are then given the task, with the helper, of producing as many ideas as they can, until they have exhausted their creativity. They should be encouraged to let themselves go and not evaluate any of the ideas at this stage. They should just list them all, no matter how good, bad or far-fetched they seem to be at the time. They are asked to suspend logic or practicality at this stage, since evaluation will come later. If possible, it should be a pleasurable activity, in which the parents exercise their problem-solving skills and enjoy both the power of their thinking and even the silliness of some of the outcomes. It should not, however, be allowed to become boring and tedious.

The helper should contribute to the ideas, and add to the list, as well as generally being supportive and encouraging the parents to engage in the task and praising their efforts. However, it is to their advantage that as many of the ideas as possible come from the parents. This may involve helping them to clarify (without criticism) the ideas they have, as well as stimulating them to derive further ideas from combinations of those they have listed. The parents may be prompted by asking: what they have tried in the past; what other people have suggested or tried; who they might approach for advice/help; whether they know other people who are coping with similar problems; whether there are relevant organisations that may be useful and appropriate services to approach.

It is usually necessary to write down all the ideas as they are generated, as it can be impossible to retain all the options in one's head. Whatever is used (e.g. pencil and paper, flip chart, OHP or whiteboard), it should be clearly visible to both parents and helper, so that it can help their thinking.

This was done with Mrs A. (described earlier) in relation to the goals of: 1) her husband looking after her son so that she could spend more time in interacting with her baby daughter; and 2) finding the interaction enjoyable. The questions posed by the health visitor, therefore, were how could she get her husband to look after the son more and what she could do with the baby to enjoy their interaction. This led to two separate lists, some of the items of which are given here to illustrate.

Methods generated for getting the help from her partner included: just telling him to do it; nagging him long enough for him to have to do it; getting very angry; bargaining with him; asking him at a good time; giving him something in return; explaining to him what she was concerned about; just leaving with the baby; getting his mother to ask him; getting a new partner; getting something he would like to do with his son; and so on.

She also went on to think how she could make more time to interact with her daughter with or without her partner's help, and produced ideas like: talking to her all the time we are together; talking when she is awake; put her in a sling and talk while I do the housework; talk to her while changing/bathing/feeding; be with both children and get them to interact; and so on.

In thinking about strategies for increasing her enjoyment of the interaction with the baby, the listed included: to show her things; looking at her eyes and enjoy the colours; to try to work out what she is 'thinking'; to make myself smile at her; to try to get her to smile; to try to make her 'talk'; to imitate her and see what she does; to sing to her; to try and see what she can do; to touch her skin; to watch her; and others.

CHOOSING STRATEGIES

Having produced as many options as possible, the next step is to go through the list and evaluate each of them carefully, because even strategies that appear ridiculous or impossible may contain the seeds of a brilliant idea. Each item should be considered separately and explored for ideas that can develop from it. This can only be tackled by discussion, gradually eliminating options to leave only the most useful. The discussion need not be directed in any particular way, although it is useful to try to think through not only whether it would be successful, but also to think about how it would have the effects. One might even be more systematic by, for example, doing an analysis in which one considers the likelihood of success, as well as the costs and the potential risks (if any) involved. By costs we mean the effort, time, energy, skills, resources required, and of course whether these are available.

For instance, Mrs A, in considering eliciting help from her partner, quickly eliminated getting angry and nagging her partner, on the grounds that she tended to do this anyway and it had very little effect. The costs were high in terms of emotional effort and the risks included worsening the relationship. Ordering or telling him to play with his son was thought unlikely to work, because he hated being told what to do, and the risks of doing so would be increased resentment on his part, and a further endorsement of his view of her as demanding and bossy. By going through the list like this, it was gradually decided that it was best to approach him directly at a good time, to express how she was feeling and her concerns, and to ask for his support, without necessarily deciding how he might do this. It was further decided that she had to do it in a way that improved their relationship and did not antagonise him. She had to approach him when she was not too tired and that she had to keep calm and not express her usual irritation and anger. The discussion continued in this way, with a reasonable plan eventually being formulated. Although creative, it was quite a complex discussion in that the eventual strategy was derived from an amalgamation of a variety of the points, which were informed by others even though they were rejected.

In contrast, the discussion about the goal of enjoying the interaction with the baby was comparatively easy in that almost all the points made were of value. In fact, there was clearly too much to do at any one point, and what came out of the discussion was a realisation that enjoyment would really come from getting to know her, trying to understand her feelings and reactions, and trying to see and encourage pleasurable reactions in her. Whereas she had been thinking about getting enjoyment from what she was doing, she realised that this would actually come from the baby reacting to her positively. They decided that they should begin a couple of times a day, with her spending a few minutes each time looking at her daughter's face and eyes, when she was alert and peaceful, and trying to get her to smile and to 'talk', and then to react with pleasure to this. This was given further direction by Mrs A deciding to think about what the baby was thinking and feeling and to describe her own thoughts to the baby as she did so.

As these examples show, the list of options is a focus for the discussion. Having taken each idea in turn, some can be removed completely as unacceptable, impractical or ineffective. Others may be considered and modified somewhat or even lead to new options. The possibilities that remain can then be compared so that a final decision might be made about exactly what to do. This might involve making initial preferences between equally good options, implementing them together perhaps, or doing so sequentially. It is also useful to have what might be regarded as contingencies plans in case what one decides to do begins to go wrong. Mrs A, for example, had a number of equally good strategies and decided to just watch and try to get her daughter to react. It actually made her feel effective, however, to know that there were many other things that she could do at any point, including, for example, imitating her baby, singing to her, reciting rhymes, touching her and using massage.

The selection process may be helped by having in mind the same criteria described in choosing goals. They are likely to be most effective if they are agreed, made as explicit, clear and specific as possible, realistic and adequate, set within an reasonable time-limit, and with likely effects that are observable in some way. They clearly have to be acceptable to the parents, and within their resources and capabilities. The overall aim now, having tried to select the most effective strategies for the particular person in their specific context, is to implement them successfully in order to achieve the desired goals.

Implementation

To be effective it is important that those involved in the various strategies know exactly what they are doing, are prepared as well as possible and are supported while they carry them out. We will assume that this relates largely to the parents in terms of what they have to do, but the helper may be directly involved in seeking appropriate information or making a referral. If this is the case, then the helper must do exactly what they have agreed as quickly and effectively as possible, and keep the parents informed of the process.

In relation to the parents, the helper should do all that is possible to ensure that they are well prepared for what they have agreed to do. Although there is never a guarantee of absolute success, it is likely to be increased with detailed preparation. This should include giving the necessary attention to ensuring they have the skills and resources needed to carry out the actions and have considered the possible difficulties to be encountered in the process. For example, parents who are planning to reduce the frequency of a child's tantrums by ignoring them will benefit considerably from realising that the behaviour might well get worse before improving.

Having selected the strategies, parent needs to be clear about exactly what to do, and it may help if the strategies are written down as a set of instructions where necessary. It might also be important for them to rehearse what they are to do before they try to put them into practice. In the example of Mrs A, the helper actually encouraged her to interact with the baby in their session together, and watched what she did. As a result she was able to make a number of suggestions (e.g. to slow down and wait longer for the baby's reactions), illustrating them by interacting herself with the baby.

It was not possible to do the same in relation to the strategy of approaching Mrs A's partner, but a similar effect was achieved through role play, in which the helper initially took the role of the partner. This enabled Mrs A to try out a number of different approaches, while getting feedback from the helper. It also allowed her to play the role of the partner herself, so as to be able to experience being in the other position. In this way, she was able to foresee a number of difficulties and hence be prepared for them. It was decided that she should give her partner prior warning of wanting to discuss her difficulty and not to spring it on him. The role play also allowed her to see that she became threatened by hearing a contrary viewpoint, and reacted to this with immediate anger. She realised, however, that the interaction would be more effective, if she allowed her partner to say what he felt and to listen respectfully, because it left open the possibility of calm discussion.

Once the preparations are completed, then the helper's role is to provide support while the strategies are implemented. This may mean being available at pre-arranged times or accessible by telephone in order to talk through unexpected difficulties. It is quite clear, however, that most people need to be encouraged to carry out their plans and to sustain their efforts; many people do not do what they have planned, and those that do, may have considerable difficulty in keeping to them for long periods of time. They are likely to need frequent encouragement, and there need to be rewards for both their efforts and successes, including the praise of the helper. However, it may be beneficial for the helper to explore explicitly with parents the things that might sustain their efforts or demotivate them, so that they are forewarned. This support role requires all the qualities and skills advocated throughout the book, working in partnership, respecting them, attempting to understand what is happening, and exploring issues as they arise.

Evaluation

OUTCOMES

The next step is evaluation, where the helper and parents consider the outcome of the strategies adopted. In a sense evaluation of the helping process is occurring all the time, but here we are referring to a time in which the specific effects of their plans are explored. Although this is such an important stage, it is rarely given the time it deserves.

The major questions to be addressed relate firstly to the degree to which goals have been achieved and secondly the reasons for the outcomes. In particular, one should be concerned to: 1) celebrate success; 2) ensure that the parents' take appropriate responsibility for it; 3) consider the wider benefits arising, if any; and 4) see what can be learnt about the problem, about preventing further occurrences, and dealing with similar situations in future.

To illustrate, Mrs A was able to secure her partner's support, to spend more time with the baby, and to begin to enjoy interacting with her. She was full of praise for the helper, who accepted it, but also clearly described Mrs A's own more important contribution at every stage. They discussed the wider benefits, which included, for example: Mrs A feeling much more effective generally; a greater understanding between the parents; and a much more contented baby and older son. However, what particularly struck her was that the benefits had derived from improved communication, which had broken down somewhat between all members of the family, and that the most important element in this was the time taken to listen and try to understand the other person, whether her partner or the children.

Where strategies have been less successful or even failed, it is even more important to evaluate in a similar way. This involves: 1) acknowledging any success and at least the effort; 2) ensuring that the reasons for the outcomes are fully explored and understood; 3) consider whether there have been any changes at all in the wider context; and 4) see what can be learnt about the problem and the implications for revising the original strategies.

One can understand this as looping back within the process to an earlier stage. For example, to the stage of problem exploration or clarification, since the strategies used may have in themselves provided a greater understanding of the situation. It may be that the goals were unrealistic in retrospect and that they may have to be revised in light of the experience. It is possible that the strategies need to be revised or that entirely new ideas need to be considered, and, finally, although the strategies may have been appropriate, they may not have been implemented effectively or may have failed because of unforeseen obstacles.

HELPING RELATIONSHIP

Within this evaluation, there is also the need to consider the helping relationship itself, in order to decide whether it should continue or be changed. Even when strategies have been entirely successful, the next step may not be to finish meeting, but to loop back into an earlier stage of the helping process in order to explore and clarify other problems, for example, or to plan further strategies for different goals.

It is important to monitor the relationship periodically throughout its course to ensure that the needs of the parents are being met effectively. This means that there should be clear opportunities for honest negotiations about whether and how the relationship should continue. Although this is not necessarily simple, because of the potential for implying rejection or being rejected, it is enabled by a partnership in which respect and trust are paramount and the families' needs are central. It is also a point at which the skills of immediacy (see Chapter 9) come into their own, in the context of an acknowledgement of the difficulty of such discussion, and the need for absolute honesty.

Ending long-term helping relationships needs to be done by negotiation and mutual agreement, and may best be achieved through the gradual reduction of the frequency of visits. Nevertheless, it is important to give parents plenty of warning about the change, so that they have the chance to adapt to the new circumstances, considering the implications with the helper beforehand. The issue should not be avoided under the misapprehension that this will prevent potential hurt at separation. Allowing repeated warning gives the opportunity not only to explore how the parents will manage in the future without the helper, but is likely to prevent misunderstandings. It is not unusual for parents to be hurt and resentful at the prospect of losing a beneficial relationship, and they should be allowed to express and explore this. There is no way to prevent the possible disappointment, but discussion can make the process of parting a learning opportunity, and not an addition to parents' difficulties.

Dependency is always an issue with which one has to struggle. There are no easy answers, but if the helper is concerned throughout to foster self-esteem and self-efficacy, destructive dependency can be avoided by high-lighting the parents' own effectiveness and not the expertise of the helper.

In Conclusion

We have been concerned to look at the later stages of helping in this chapter and have presented a model related to the management of specific problems. This is not always necessary, in that being able to relate effectively to parents, exploring their situation with them, and facilitating construct changes may be all that is required to allow them to live more effectively. However, when there are specific problem we have presented a model involving four stages, giving examples to illustrate from the parenting area. These stages involve the tasks of helping parents to: 1) decide what they want to achieve in general and to set specific goals that relate to this; 2) select the most useful strategies for meeting these goals from the possible range; 3) implement these as effectively as possible, having made careful preparations; and 4) evaluate the outcomes and the helping relationship.

Although many of the worries faced by parents derive from the behaviour of their children, we have so far avoided giving specific strategies, because we believe that they are only of value if applied within the frameworks which we have outlined. There are, in fact, a vast number of possible strategies for dealing with children in general and the problems they can present, and we could now go on to describe a sample of these in a cookbook fashion. However, instead, what we should like to do in the next few chapters is to describe a model of parenting which might guide the ways of relating to children in general, as well as suggest a range of specific strategies on rational grounds. We will begin this by outlining a model of the task of parenting itself in the next chapter, before looking at parenting qualities and skills at different ages subsequently.

CHAPTER 11
A MODEL OF PARENT–CHILD INTERACTION

Introduction

In the previous chapters we have presented and explored all the stages of the helping process in the hope that this will guide the helper in engaging and working with parents generally. However, given that much of this work will involve the interaction and relationship between parents and their children, we should now like to focus specifically in the following chapters on the tasks and skills of being a parent.

Fundamentally parenting is an interactive process; it involves at least two people (parent and child) and is dependent upon the on-going interactions between them. If we are to provide effective help for parents and hence their children, then we need to have a clear understanding of the nature of this interaction. This applies whether one is concerned to work in a promotional way, whether the intention is to prevent difficulties, or whether help is aimed at enabling parents to deal with problems and difficulties that have already arisen.

We will begin with a overall description of the parenting task, before presenting a model of the parent–child interaction, drawing heavily upon the notions of construing elaborated in Chapter 8. We will then take each of the elements of the model in turn and consider them in detail. Finally, we will look at the implications of the model for the development of problems, introducing notions of risk and protective factors.

The Parenting Task

Parenting is essentially concerned with relatively mature people caring for their offspring from conception, through to their birth and on until the point at which they are able to function independently. Even then, there are likely to be strong emotional ties that continue throughout the lives of both the parents and their children. Although we will use the term parent throughout, we are aware that the task of caring does involve people other than the two biological parents, and will assume that the process is very similar, even if the caring role is taken on by other members of the community, including relatives, foster carers or adoptive parents.

The overall aim of the task is biological in the sense of ensuring the perpetuation of the species, and this involves: 1) the protection and hence survival of the immature offspring; and 2) the successful negotiation of the developmental processes, physically, socially and psychologically. The role of the parents, and other primary carers, is, therefore, to provide the circumstances in which children are safe and able to grow and learn appropriately, so that they can take an effective and productive place in society.

Given the complexity of the human, parental care-giving involves providing the conditions in which children can move from an immature state to one in which they have the behaviour, knowledge, ability, motivation and direction to negotiate the world successfully, both physically and socially. This includes being able to function effectively in a number of highly related areas such as: gross and fine locomotor functioning; learning and cognitive processing; moral understanding; social understanding and communication skills; the ability to cope and adapt emotionally; and educational and occupational knowledge and skills.

Although being a parent can be one of the most fulfilling pursuits imaginable, it can also be extremely demanding and highly stressful. It is a vital role, which is usually undertaken without explicit training or preparation of any kind. It requires 24 hour responsibility for another person seven days a week for many years. It is usually tiring in a practical sense, emotionally demanding, and may tax one's ability to understand the task at hand. It is, for example, frequently difficult to know what is the correct course of action to take, and there is rarely any definitive feedback on whether one has adopted the best course of action in the long term.

Even though it demands considerable effort, persistence and skill, the role of parenting is given relatively little support in the UK, for example, as suggested earlier in the book. The role has not been valued highly in our society, and, apart from the extraordinary emotional rewards that parents may gain from their children, it brings few, if any, immediate and tangible rewards. It is often taken on in addition to other existing roles, which are usually driven by financial and status considerations. Unfortunately, there is relatively little practical, educational or emotional help formally available from services, when required by parents. This means that prospective parent have either to be strong and self-sufficient in themselves or to have an effective informal support system surrounding them throughout this time.

Parents require the knowledge, skills, circumstances and energy to allow them to engage successfully in a diverse range of activities related to the child, from feeding and cleaning to playing and teaching. These will be described in the next chapter in relation to the work of Emde (1989), who sees these activities as reciprocal to the developmental tasks undertaken by the child. However, given the reciprocal nature of the task and the requirement for close synchronisation of parents and their children, it follows quite clearly that the interaction between parents and children on a moment by moment basis is the essential vehicle or mechanism by which it is accomplished. It is the way in which patterns of care are built and the development of the child is ensured. It is the way in which each comes to know and understand the other, but it is also the way in which problems may develop in the relationship. Because of its importance, we will provide a relatively simple model of the interaction to underpin and help make sense of our subsequent considerations of different aspects of parenting, including the qualities, skills needed, the problems that might arise and the strategies that might help.

Model of Parent–Child Interaction

Being a parent does not consist of ad hoc or arbitrary actions towards a child. It is a complex activity that involves both the child and the parent. It consists of the parent responding to the behaviour of the child, and in so doing attempting at any given moment to act as appropriately as possible so as to meet the child's needs in some way. The parent's actions cannot stand alone and must be understood in relation to the child. Parents can only be effective if they take account of the child, who is an active participant in the process, and whose behaviour must be a major determinant of what happens. This requires parents to be acutely aware of their children and involved in an ongoing process of monitoring and responding at any point according to their current state, needs, and characteristics.

Monitoring is in itself an active process, that is selective and directed towards what is important to the parents. However, if we take into account the model of construing presented earlier in Chapter 8, parents' actions or responses are not directly determined by what is observed, but by the sense parents make of what they see (i.e. their constructions of the events observed). In general, what happens, therefore, is that parents focus their attention on their children, giving considerable priority to them over other people or events. They interpret or construe the complex information presented by their children and respond according to their constructions. These constructions arise from a developing model or picture that parents have in their heads for anticipating their child. For example, the parent who picks up, cuddles and rocks the child is not responding simply to a cry, but to the construction that the child is distressed in some way, and has a need of some kind. What the parent then does will be determined by what she/he construes the need to be, and this could include hunger, for example, pain, fear, loneliness, discontent, or tiredness.

We have represented this process as the set of three boxes in the top half of the diagram shown in Figure 11.1. This is a variant of Figure 8.1, which we provided as a model of the parent–helper interaction, but can act as a model for all interactions between people whatever their relationship. As the current diagram indicates, we are assuming that the child (of any age) is going through exactly the same process as the parent in the interaction. He/she will be monitoring the parent, construing or making sense of what is observed and reacting accordingly. The child's response (whether a minimal facial expression, gesture or vocalisation) is then observed by the parent, who construes it and then responds accordingly, and the interactive cycle continues, with each participant monitoring, construing and responding to the other in turn.

FIGURE 11.1 PARENT–CHILD INTERACTIVE CYCLE

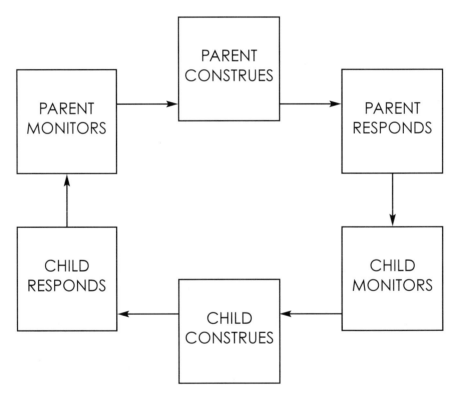

What the diagram shows is a system in which all parts are important for it to function properly. However, it still operates even if one of the participants stops attending to the other. For example, this might happen if the child goes to sleep or turns away from the parent and engages in conversation with someone else or to watch the television. The parent will still monitor what the child is doing (e.g. listening for sounds of awakening), construes what is happening (e.g. is happily playing) and responds accordingly (e.g. gets on with other tasks while the child is asleep or lets the child get on with his/her other activities independently). However, if the parent stops monitoring (e.g. because of postnatal depression or preoccupation with other problems) whether or not he/she is with the child, then the system may break down and have serious consequences for the child in terms of how he/she develops and what is learnt.

Certainly with very young children, the role of the parents is vital; without them the system would collapse. As children develop, they become more active participants, or even partners in the process, which is initiated and guided as much by the child or young person as it is by the parent. The parent, who asks an innocuous question of an adolescent and gets an angry reply or a rebuff, is likely to be highly aware of this process, because they may not easily make sense of the reasons for the response. Although in general, one might tend to assume parents to be more competent in maturity and ability than their children, and hence more able to control the interaction, children (even babies) are never passive recipients and do contribute significantly to the course of interaction.

To illustrate this, we will consider the newborn baby, as being at the least competent age. The idea that newborn babies are unable to interact in a meaningful way was the generally accepted view until recent years. For example, the philosopher, John Locke, in the nineteenth century presented the mind of the newborn as a 'tabula rasa' or blank slate, and the developmentist Piaget in the twentieth century described the neonate's behaviour as random and reflexive. However, a considerable body of research in the last three decades has shown quite clearly that children are born with the skills to enable them to play a social role, and to engage in this cycle of interaction (e.g. Bee, 2000; Murray & Andrews, 2000). These abilities will be described in the next chapter, but from birth, children are able and naturally inclined to monitor the parent (focusing on the face in the case of the newborn), have an inbuilt construct system (e.g. quite clearly discriminate social stimuli from others), and can respond even if this is at a low level of sophistication (e.g. quieten to the voice, show interest, move in rhythm). However, they develop very rapidly, and quickly become effective communicators.

PARENT MONITORING
We are using the word monitoring broadly to indicate that parents generally are involved in a constant process of surveying or checking their children, as

possibly the most important part of their world. When interacting directly with them, parents are usually using all their senses (vision, hearing, touch and smell) to determine how their children are. They are taking in information that can enable them to know what their children are doing, saying, meaning, thinking, feeling and needing.

This is not different from what parents do in interacting with anyone else in their lives. All people have to monitor each other in order to be able to interact and play a role in relation to one another, as we discussed when talking about the parent–helper relationship. We cannot interact with someone unless we take in information about them on a moment to moment basis.

What is perhaps different with children is that the role is particularly one of caring, and the stakes are higher. The monitoring function is, therefore, much more crucial and pervasive. In general children are more important than other people to parents, they are potentially more vulnerable (especially in the early years) and, therefore, parents are more likely to be aware to some extent of what their children are doing at all times. This is true not only when there is direct interaction between them, but also when the children are not in direct contact (e.g. on their own, with other people, playing or sleeping, even in a different room). There is a general monitoring function going on, even aided for example by sophisticated electronic listening devices, when child are put down to sleep.

This is particularly true in the early days, but it is unlikely to stop entirely even as children get older. The example in an earlier chapter of mothers construing their children's silence when out of their sight as, for example, 'up to no good' is pertinent here; they were monitoring their children even while separated from them and engaged in conversation. One might think, for example, of parents leaving their children for the first time with a baby-sitter, child-minder, or at school. The anxiety that this generates can be considerable, and is largely a function of not knowing what is happening to the child. In fact, it is interesting to speculate about the extent to which such concern continues even when children are old enough to leave home.

PARENTAL CONSTRUING
The next step in the interactive process is for the parent to make sense of the information derived from monitoring. Whether they are aware of it or not, parents are constantly processing all the information received in order to understand what is happening. This is part of the overall need we have to anticipate events, so as to respond appropriately and adapt. To do this, it can be assumed that, as described earlier, we each have a model or picture of the world in our heads (i.e. a set of constructions or construct system). For parents, one part of this larger picture will be a model or representation of their

specific child. In essence, it consists of everything parents know, feel or think about their child. It is a model that enables them to anticipate their children and understand what is going on. It contains, for example, their ways of discriminating the meanings of different cries in the young baby. A particular child's thumbing sucking might allow a parent to anticipate the child's need for sleep. Others will know from their pictures, that their toddlers will get over-excited in certain situations, not share toys, will enjoy an activity or get frightened.

This model enables them to predict their child's overt behaviour; for example, how well they will do in various tasks at school, what will upset them, or how they will react in general. However, it is also the means by which parents are able to understand what is actually going on inside the child's head. It is the way they make sense of their children's constructions; what they are thinking, feeling or meaning. It is the means by which they are able to understand the one word sentences their children use in their second year to express a wealth of different meanings, or their two word utterances a little later. For example, one mother understood the single utterance, 'Gog', not simply to mean 'dog' (or actually more generally any animal with four legs) but 'I want to stroke the dog'!

At the same time parents are evolving a picture of what it is like to be a parent. This is obviously highly intertwined with their model of the child, and is actually a model of how they should be as parents in relation to the child. It consists of the beliefs about parenting and is the means by which they can predict how they should react to their child, specifically or generally. It enables them to make predictions about the best way of handling different situations. Should they allow their children to have sweets? Should they use smacking as a means of discipline? Should they stay at home and not have alternative work while their children are young?

Once the child is born, both these aspects of the parents' constructions will be built up from their experience of the child and of themselves in the role of parents. Their model will continue to evolve as the child develops, becoming gradually more elaborate and complex as the child matures. However, the foundations are built prior to birth. Presumably most of us have a notion of what children are like and how parents should be, derived from our own experiences of being a child and of having parents. To this rudimentary model will be added constructions gained from our experiences of children and parents encountered by chance in our everyday lives or in relation to our families, friends and neighbours. One might even be affected by experiences derived from our studies and work, if in a relevant area.

Whatever the individual's model of children and parenting, its importance to the person is suddenly increased around the time of conception and pregnancy. Having made the decision to become a parent, whether by choice or accident, then one's model will reflect this in adapting to the new circumstances. Changes will quickly occur in relation to beginning to see oneself in the role of parent and the implications of this. These implications are likely to include changes in how one construes one's relationships to other people (e.g. one's partner or parents). One will begin to take more notice of parents and children, and hence build on existing ideas about, for example, what children in general are like. Prospective parents will also begin to formulate an image specifically about the child they are expecting. Their world view will change in many different ways over the period of pregnancy in anticipation of the birth.

At birth, the parents' developing construct system has to suddenly cope with and change to face the reality of life with a new baby. At this point, parents have their first direct experiences of their children and themselves in the parenting role, and changes in their constructions are likely to be considerable. As in any period of major adaptation, there may be considerable difficulty, particularly if one's previous constructions are idealised. The baby might not be quite the angel one was anticipating, and the reality of the child's demands and sleepless nights may not accord with traditional expectations of absolute fulfilment and contentment. One might not have anticipated the ways in which one's relationship with one's partner has to change as a result of the addition to the family. Such requirements to change are likely to be highly stressful and may account at least in part for the high frequency of depression experienced in the postnatal period and the level of parental disharmony and separation at this time.

Many constructions are likely to be found wanting and considerable change will need to be made to the system in the early days following the birth. For the parent this is a process of getting to know another individual intimately, learning how to fit in with this person, and providing the circumstances and opportunity for him/her to thrive. It is done, however, in the context of the total world in which the parents live and may be in competition with all other aspects of life that may claim the parents' attention. Adapting to parenthood does not occur in isolation, and the person continues to fit the task around all the other aspects of their world, including other children, for example, their partners, their work (especially in current times), and their home.

Parents' constructions play an enormous role in relation to how children are raised. The belief, for example, that a new-born baby cannot see or hear leads to very different parental behaviour from the construction that babies are highly attuned to the human voice and face. The construction that it is important to communicate with your baby will result in an entirely different approach to that which derives from a construction of young babies as not sufficiently developed to engage in social interaction. The construction that attending to crying will spoil the child results in behaviour contrary to that derived from a belief, for example, that crying is an important social signal and not to be ignored.

PARENTAL RESPONDING

How, or even whether, parents respond to their children in all situations will be determined by the processes outlined above. They will respond according to their constructions. If the child is construed as being hungry, he/she is likely to be fed. If she/he is seen as being deliberately naughty and physical punishment is acceptable, then he/she is likely to be smacked, for example, even if the parents' constructions of the child's motives are wrong. This becomes very clear if you watch a parent interacting with a child in early infancy. A nursing mother is likely to be still and quiet while a child is sucking at the breast, yet move more or talk to the baby when he/she stops. This clearly follows from her constructions about the direction of the child's attention and his/her needs. As a further example, in face-to-face interaction with her eight week old daughter a mother said the following over the course of several minutes: 'So what are you thinking then?'; 'How are you feeling?'; 'You're looking happy. Yes, you're smiling.'; 'You're not hungry for once'; 'You like that, don't you?' Even a fleeting change of facial expression was detected and interpreted; 'You weren't sure about that, were you?'

These words are the direct result of and outward signs of the construction process. It is going on constantly and not necessarily consciously, whether or not the parent is relaying her constructions back to the child or even interacting directly. If one listens to parents' conversation with their children, it is quite clear that the way they talk is directly related to their constructions of the child's understanding. For example, their utterances speed up, become longer, and become more complex grammatically and in meaning as the child's understanding increases. A cry will be construed as an indication of unhappiness, and will elicit a number of possible reactions (e.g. feeding, changing, putting to bed) depending upon the parent's construction. A more complex example involved a father who clearly construed his 4 year old son as clumsy or naughty, when he shouted at him for dropping a pile of his work papers on the floor. He instantly felt remorse, however, when he realised that the child had actually been trying to help by bringing the papers to him at his desk.

This last example illustrates very well our main point, that parental behaviour is determined in the cycle of interaction by their constructions. However, it also demonstrates the potential for change and even the change process, discussed earlier in the book. We talked about constructions as being hypotheses, that are tested and may change as a result of experience. This father was aware of his misjudgement, which arose from his general view of his child as difficult to manage, rather intrusive and naughty. What it taught him, however, was that his own ideas might not necessarily match those of his children, and that there is a need to try to determine the child's constructions in specific situations before reacting hastily.

CHILD MONITORING

As the parent responds to the child in direct interaction, in a reciprocal way the child monitors the parent, taking in information through all relevant senses (including sight, sound, touch and smell). Newborn babies, for example, can be seen to be staring at their mother's face for long periods immediately after birth, and will continue to do so subsequently in interaction, if they are awake and alert. The parents' face and voice are of particular interest and will attract attention more than other objects, which they are clearly able to distinguish (i.e. construe).

Children (even the newborn) will of course attend to other aspects of their environment, and novelty will be a determining factor to some extent. They tend to look for longer periods at what is novel and less at what they have seen before. This clearly indicates the construction process, which is basically about making discriminations between experiences. The face, however, in being such an ever changing picture, is likely to stay attractive to the infant, and particularly if it is responsive and therefore controlled by the attention and behaviour of the child.

For older children, the face remains a source of interest as it provides considerable information about the parent. In direct interaction, they watch the parents' face, listen to what they are saying, as well as the tone in which they are speaking in order to understand. Even when not interacting directly, in novel or slightly threatening situations (e.g. the sudden appearance of a stranger) children frequently check where their parents are for the security this brings, and as an indication of what sense to make of situations and therefore how to react.

CHILD CONSTRUING

Exactly like the parents, the framework of the interactive cycle assumes that all children are attempting to make sense or anticipate their world (i.e. construing) from the moment they are born (or even before). If we understand a construction as a discrimination between two or more objects or events, then children are by definition involved in this process immediately. They are able to distinguish successfully between different aspects of the string of experiences with which they are presented from the beginning of their lives. The ability to cry, as opposed to being silent, is itself indicative of a construction of internal states for examples. Newborn babies showing a preference for social events (e.g. faces and voices) is clearly a demonstration of their ability to discriminate and hence to engage in the construction process.

It is clear, however, that children's constructions are very different to those of adults in general. Understanding development is to a large extent about understanding the child's model of the world and how this changes with maturity. This is certainly the major task for parents, since their effective adaptation to their children hinges on their ability to see the world through their children's eyes. The more able they are to do this, the more effective they are likely to be in knowing their children's needs and responding appropriately.

This process is, however, made more difficult by the fact that the child's constructions, their ways of making sense of and reacting to the world, are ever changing. Their model, or construct system, develops rapidly from birth onward in both range and complexity, as is indicated by increased understanding and more differentiated responses to their world. In the very early days, changes can be detected almost on a daily basis, and the task of the parent is to adapt to these developments, to change his/her constructions about the child, so as to continue to meet the child's needs physically, emotionally, socially and intellectually and provide the circumstances in which the child can develop effectively.

CHILD REACTS

As in the case of the adult, children's constructions determine their behaviour, and their constructions will depend upon their developmental level and experience. The sense they make of situations determines their attention, interest, fear, startle, distress, pleasure, their words (e.g. 'Mummy's bag') or a particular action (e.g. kicking a ball). It is only through monitoring the child's behaviour in response to both their internal and external environments that parents can begin to understand their constructions. Whatever is going on in children's heads is unidentifiable unless they act or react. The less they do, or at least the less we can discern, the fewer constructions the child will be assumed to have. The author, Christy Brown, for example was assumed to be profoundly impaired, until a way was found to use his extremely limited response system to elicit his picture of the world and, as a result, to write an autobiography!

This example illustrates that children are able to learn (i.e. develop their construction system) simply by watching and listening to the events around them. However, the process is likely to be much more effective, if the situation presented to the child is regulated by and tailored to the needs of the child at the time. This is the task for the parent, and the interactive cycle is the only mechanism by which this can occur. It is only through monitoring effectively and interpreting their reactions appropriately that parents can respond in turn to make the changes necessary for children's current needs (e.g. to sooth when distressed; reduce stimulation when tired; to present interesting objects and events appropriate to their children's level when they are ready to play). It is only by attending constantly to children's cues and anticipating their needs effectively that parents may provide the appropriate circumstances for their children's needs to be met and their development facilitated. It is the only way by which the most productive learning opportunities can be ensured, including the circumstances for fostering the all important attachment relationship, upon which children's future understanding of people and their subsequent relationships are prefaced.

Implications for Helping

The model presented here has a number of implications for helping families. It is intended as a potential tool for all helpers to enable them to think about and understand the basics of parenting and to guide possible assessment and observational strategies in the context of promotional work generally, prevention and early intervention. Within these contexts it might also be of direct value to parents, if the helper were to share the model with them, so that their understanding of parenting and problem management skills may be enhanced in general.

We will elaborate this in the following chapters, but will concentrate here on the direct implications for understanding the development of psychosocial problems in the parent–child relationship and in the development of the child. Since there may be many reasons for the development of such problems, and since the same problem in different children may have diverse causal sequences, we will briefly consider the issues involved by presenting a basic model described by Carr (1999).

The Development of Psychosocial Problems

This model attempts to understand the development of psychosocial problems in terms of a complex combination and interaction of factors that might put children at risk or offer protection. These can be categorised as: 1) predisposing factors; 2) precipitating factors; 3) maintaining factors; and 4) protective factors. These terms are used to ensure caution in understanding causal links. Causes are rarely simple, obvious and direct, and effects of specific events are rarely invariant. It is extremely difficult, if not impossible, to be certain about the ways in which problems are created, especially in retrospect, but there is evidence to suggest that the presence of the following factors may act to increase the likelihood of problems (risk factors) in the parent–child relationship and in the child or increase resilience.

PREDISPOSING FACTORS: These are risk factors which predispose children to the development of problems. They involve personal factors deriving from the child's biological and psychological make-up. Biological factors include, for example: genetic vulnerability: prenatal circumstances, such as maternal illness, smoking, alcohol or drug use during pregnancy; perinatal complications (e.g. premature birth); or physical injury or illness in the postnatal period. Psychological factors include: low intelligence, temperamental difficulties, low self-esteem and low self-efficacy.

There are other predisposing factors that Carr describes as contextual. These include early parenting and attachment problems, exposure to early problems in the family (e.g. psychosocial or relationship problems in the parents), and early stresses (e.g. adverse separations from parents).

PRECIPITATING FACTORS: These are specific adverse events or circumstances that might directly trigger the onset of psychosocial problems in children. Although they may not be identified in relation to all problems, there are many possible factors that might occur here, including, for example, specific stresses such as bereavement, aggression or abuse, illness or injury, change of school or parental separation or divorce.

MAINTAINING FACTORS: Once problems have begun, it is assumed that there are a host of variables that might operate to maintain them. These can again be classified under the headings of: 1) biological, 2) personal and 3) contextual. Biological factors include poor health or specific conditions that can operate to interfere with the ability to deal with psychosocial problems. Personal maintaining factors include, for example, low self-efficacy, problematic constructions in relation to causal circumstances, and poor coping strategies in relation to problem solving and mood regulation. Contextual factors include parental, family and general social problems that make it difficult to remedy the problems; for example, psychosocial problems in the parents, poor coping strategies, low self-esteem, marital discord, poor parenting practices, poor social support generally, poverty and disadvantage.

PROTECTIVE FACTORS: These are any circumstances that help protect the child against the development of psychosocial problems, prevent further deterioration once they have arisen, or might aid attempts to resolve problems. Again these can be classified as: 1) biological, 2) personal and 3) contextual. They are in many ways the opposite of maintaining factors and include good physical health as the biological; high intelligence, high self-efficacy, good problem solving and emotion focused coping strategies as examples of the personal; and good parental and family functioning in a supportive social context as contextual factors.

PARENT–CHILD INTERACTION AND PROBLEM DEVELOPMENT

We will discuss these factors further in the next chapter in relation to promotional and preventive strategies. Such risk and protective factors might operate in many different ways, and we should like to briefly illustrate possible general mechanisms within the model of the cycle of parent–child interaction. All the factors are likely to impinge directly or indirectly on one or more of the six elements of the interactive cycle, and then potentially over time to have adverse effects (in the case of risk factors) upon all the other elements. This will be true whether the factors arise initially in the child, the parents, or the wider context. The more risk factors there are, the fewer protective factors, and the more elements affected, the greater will be the likelihood of significant disturbance and the occurrence of psychosocial problems in the child and the parent. Although all six elements are important, it is adverse changes to the constructions of the parent and child that are perhaps the most significant, since these will potentially have long-lasting implications for the cycle as a whole if central constructions (e.g. about the self) are adversely affected, distorted, or become fixed or rigid.

To illustrate possible mechanisms we will take a few examples of predisposing factors and make suggestions about how they might influence the interactive cycle beginning from different initial points. For example, children may have difficulties monitoring their world generally, including the behaviour of their parents for a number of reasons. The most obvious is where the child is blind or deaf, but this might also arise because the child is unwell and chronically preoccupied with internal events, such as pain and discomfort. Whatever the reason, the child's ability to take in information about situations, and particularly the parent–child interaction are likely to be impaired. This will have important adverse effects upon the further development of their construct system, with implications for being less well attuned to the parents in their reactions. The parents in turn will have more difficulty in adapting to the child through interaction and might have continuing problems in understanding their children and reacting effectively to them.

Even if they can monitor the world effectively, where children have damage to or dysfunction of the central nervous system, resulting from disease, trauma, or prematurity, for example, their ability to develop effective constructions of the events they experience will be compromised. Particular difficulties specifically with the construction of social events is evident in children with autism. They lack what is generally referred to as a theory of mind, which in essence is a set of constructs for making sense of the constructions of others. All these will have consequences for the behaviour of the child and hence for the parents monitoring it. They may react less or more slowly to the parent or they might show behaviour that is difficult to understand (e.g. not looking, not talking, head banging, continual rocking). What they do will be less well synchronised to the interaction with the parents, and as a result parents will have difficulties in making sense of the child's behaviour and of course more trouble in interpreting the child's picture of the world.

As we have seen children vary in temperament, and some, as noted by Thomas and Chess (1977) show patterns of behaviour that are much more difficult than others. They might sleep little and be irregular in routine, for example, they might be difficult to feed, fussy and fretful, cry frequently and be less able to adapt to novelty. As a result, again the task for the parent will be more arduous. They will have much more difficulty in anticipating (i.e. construing) the child. Although they are likely to have to give more time and energy to the child, they are less likely to be rewarded for the effort. They may have difficulties in bonding with the child, and over time begin to construe the child negatively, and themselves as less effective in the parenting role. As a result they may become less inclined to care, less attuned to the child with consequent further effects upon the child as the cycle of interaction evolves. The children will, for example, have experiences that are less well synchronised with their needs and possibly much less positive, and hence have difficulties in developing constructions about security, trust and self-worth.

At whichever point these child risk factors are initiated, subsequent negative effects will be ameliorated in the parent by the kind of protective factors described earlier. If the parent has high self-esteem, optimism, independence and effective problem solving skills, for example, and the support of family and or wider community, then she/he is much more likely to be resilient, to be able to cope with and adapt to the difficult circumstances.

On the other hand, if there are also predisposing risk factors in the parents, then the outcomes are likely to be worse for the parent–child interaction and hence the development and adaptation of the child. This might occur, for example, where parents fail to attend to their children or do not monitor them appropriately. This is likely to result from their attention being distracted by the whole range of potential stresses that may impinge upon them (e.g. housing problems, money difficulties, marital disharmony). They may be so preoccupied with a violent partner, their own personal health problems, and/or having insufficient money to afford essentials, that their ability to attend to their children effectively is severely reduced. This might also be associated with depression and a reduction in awareness generally, or because of other mental health problems, including substance misuse.

Whatever the reasons, failure to monitor the child effectively will result in missing cues from the child, misinterpreting his/her behaviour, limiting the parents' ability to understand the child and develop appropriate constructions, and obviously a failure to synchronise effectively or meet the needs of the child. The parent's behaviour is likely to be less warm, consistent, contingent and appropriate. As a result, following the interactive cycle, the children involved will have an experience that is not attuned to their developmental needs, with negative consequences for their developing picture of the main people in their lives, their relationships in general, and their own place and value. The notion of secure attachment has been given increasing prominence in the developmental literature, and it is these effects on the child's constructions that will lead to the various patterns of insecure attachment behaviours that in turn make parenting more difficult. Such a cycle also helps to explain the long-term adverse intellectual and emotional implications for children of postnatal depression in the mother.

Parental monitoring, their ability to attune to their children and their parenting generally are also highly determined by the constructions parents have about themselves (e.g. self-esteem and self-efficacy), their children and the parental role. Problems in their constructions might arise from a number of sources, but particularly the parent's own experiences as children. If they were themselves raised under adverse circumstances, where they were neglected, exposed to parents who were inconsistent, harsh and punitive, or experienced outright abuse, their own constructions of parenting may be adversely affected, compromising their ability to synchronise their behaviour effectively to their own children. Their ability to construct appropriate models and hence adapt effectively to the parental role will also be constrained by factors such as limited intellectual abilities, drug and alcohol misuse, and severe mental health problems, included deluded beliefs. Social isolation, discordant relationships in and outside the family, and associated negative beliefs about oneself are all likely to lead to constructions of children and parenting that are far from effective.

All such factors are likely to have severe effects upon the constructions parents bring to the care-giving situation, and the further development of them in terms of understanding the needs of their specific child as he/she develops. They might be fixed and rigid in their beliefs, parent- and not child-centred, lacking in understanding of children's needs, and unaware of the need to adapt to developmental changes in their children. The more negative the effects upon the parents' constructions, the more difficulties will occur in attuning their behaviour appropriately to their children. Their parenting style will be intimately affected by these constructions. They may lack warmth and respect for the child, be inconsistent in discipline, coercive as opposed to working in partnership, neglectful or harsh and punitive. There may be an absence of routine, inadvertent reinforcement of difficult behaviour in their children, and inappropriate criticism. All such effects upon parental behaviour will provide a poorer experience for their children, whose constructions of themselves and their world will be influenced adversely, with continuing knock-on effects around the interactive cycle and for their interactions with other people.

In Conclusion

We have discussed the tasks of parenting and presented a model of the parent–child interaction, taking account of the construction processes of both the parent and child, as crucial elements. Our intention was to provide a relatively simple way of understanding the interactive situation, which can be regarded as the essential vehicle for the appropriate development of children generally. The model provides a means of thinking about ongoing interactions moment by moment, as well as enabling some understanding of the changes that might occur over longer time periods. We have illustrated the use of the model by considered questions about how the interaction might be disrupted and psychosocial problems might develop over time. In doing so, we introduced notions of predisposing, precipitating, maintaining and protective factors, and briefly described how some of these might operate within the system by impinging upon the various elements of the parent–child interaction.

The points we have made in the chapter have clear implications for understanding parenting and the derivation of problems. As such it is hoped the model provides guidance for potential helpers working with parents in a range of situations, whether promotional, preventive or in response to problems that have already arisen. It is likely to be useful in terms of the exploration stage of helping in suggesting the areas and issues to be explored and the possible causes of problems and mechanisms by which they might operate. It gives a basic framework for the development of a clear understanding of specific problems or their future development. It should also give some direction in terms of establishing the aims and goals of intervention which might focus upon any or all of the different elements of the interactive cycle. Finally, it is likely to be helpful in guiding the search for appropriate strategies to prevent, ameliorate or manage a variety of difficulties. What must be clear, however, is that the constructions of the parent and child are crucial and can only be explored and elicited in collaboration with them, in a partnership which is dependent upon their expertise and willingness to share.

With these ideas as the basis, we will now go on in the next chapter to think specifically about early parenting, including strategies for enhancing the interactive cycle.

CHAPTER 12
INFANCY AND EARLY PARENTHOOD

Introduction

Parenting is principally concerned with ensuring that children are protected and cared for. They can then grow, mature, remain healthy, and successfully acquire the skills, knowledge and experience which will allow them to survive and prosper in the world in which they live.

Each family is unique by virtue of the distinctive qualities, characteristics and relationships of its members. Children are born into and brought up within many different types of families. In many families, they live with their mother and father. However, children also live in households where there is only one parent, and where their parents are divorced, separated or remarried. Children live in families where their parents are heterosexual, and sometimes where parents are gay and lesbian. Children live in large families, small families and extended families. Some families are characterised by their sense of stability and continuity, whereas others change and evolve, while some even shatter.

Irrespective of composition and history, pregnancy and the subsequent birth of a child, particularly a first child, herald a profound change in the life-cycle of adults and the family. For many, it is one of the most significant, challenging and life-changing events experienced. The preceding stages of human development are principally concerned with undertaking the journey into maturity and adulthood, and becoming established in the world. This encompasses many different tasks and events. In the earliest stages, this includes making one's own first attachments and relationships, developing a sense of self, and acquiring physical, psychological and social skills. The child moves on to attend, and then complete, school, and make friends outside of the family. In growing older, the adolescent further develops personal, as opposed to family, interests and knowledge, and takes on adult roles such as beginning work. As well as changing and loosening ties with one's own immediate family, the young adult develops intimate and sexual relationships, selects partners, and experiments with relationships for their long-term strength, durability and compatibility. These developmental efforts provide the opportunity to establish stable adult relationships and, for many, they also provide the emotional and practical basis for having children.

The physical, psychological and social beginnings of life start during pregnancy. As the foetus grows physically, so the life begins to take root in the mind of the mother, the father, the wider family and social network. With the birth of a child, the adult becomes a parent and faces a series of adjustments and changes to create and sustain family life and to accommodate their new offspring. These changes affect emotional attachments, roles and responsibilities, patterns of income and expenditure, and the use of time and routines. At the heart of this is the requirement of parents to meet the infant's needs for safety, care, security and stimulation. It should also be said that these transitions are not solely confined to the immediate parents, but involve the extended family, friends, work colleagues and others. This new found status touches everybody.

The transition to parenthood is seen in sharpest relief when adults become parents for the first time. Some assume that once parenthood has been achieved, the process of adjustment and adaptation is over. It is, however, continuous. It requires further adaptation to the growth and development of the first child, as well as, to the birth and development of subsequent children. Each member of the family will need to alter and adapt as the family of three becomes a family of four, or five, or more. None of these transitions is ever likely to be straightforward. First time parents may struggle with the changes required to move from adult to parent. Whereas in coping with a second or subsequent child, the parent may need to find ways to balance time and attention between siblings, to help siblings' adjustment to one another, further financial pressures and increased emotional and physical stress.

This chapter is concerned with the very first stages of this life-long process. It is primarily concerned with the transformation of adults into parents and the care and nurture of the newborn baby and infant. It will look at some of the important tasks that await the new infant and their caregivers, the array of abilities that infants possess, and how parents and infants interact and develop their relationship. The chapter will also consider how personal, family, social and cultural factors can affect the outcomes of these processes.

The Developmental Tasks of Early Parenting

There are many ways of describing and understanding parenting. For a long time, there was a concentration on practical activities and physical care, such as, feeding, changing and clothing the newborn baby. This was partly because the psychosocial abilities of infants were believed to be quite limited. As a consequence, babies were seen to possess few needs beyond the physical. Practical care activities are also more obviously and directly connected with assuring the physical survival of the baby.

Less general attention has been given to the fundamental role that parents and other primary carers have in responding to and nurturing the social and emotional development of their children during these early stages of life. Among exceptions to this, are those who work within the fields of psycho-analysis, attachment and infant development. These writers, researchers and clinicians, from Freud onwards, have paid considerable attention to the emotional and cognitive world of the infant. The elaborate and changing nature of these theories will not be dealt with in detail here. In broad terms, these theories initially concentrated on the sexual and aggressive characteristics of human beings. The focus then shifted to the importance and value of intimate, personal relationships, not only for protection and survival, but also for psychosocial development. More recently still, advances in developmental research have broadened our knowledge about the capacities, capabilities and skills of infants. An underlying constant in these ideas is the central and fundamental importance of the relationship between the primary carers, often the mother though not always, and the infant.

From within these traditions comes the work of Emde (1989) who emphasised the notion that the baby cannot be considered in isolation from the parent, and that the fulfilment of needs has to be understood in terms of 'an interpersonal matching of regulatory systems in development – the infant's and the caregiver's' (p. 34). He proposed that the practical, psychological and social activities which go to make up the care and nurture of an infant fulfil a number of crucial developmental functions for both the parent and the infant. Emde has characterised these functions as a series of tasks which will be outlined in detail below. Each of the tasks is described in terms of what it fulfils for the infant and the parent. The tasks are not mutually exclusive, many of the activities and actions of parents and their infants will achieve aspects of different tasks simultaneously.

ATTACHMENT-BONDING

Attachment is the term used to encapsulate the desire shown by the infant to be near the primary care giver, the feelings of security, safety and peace, which are apparent when near, and the distress caused when separation occurs or is threatened. The nature of attachment may vary from secure, insecure to disorganised. It is persistent and can even be impervious to insensitivity or abuse by the attachment figure (Murray-Parkes, Stevenson-Hinde & Marris, 1991).

Bonding refers to parental feelings of intimacy and closeness for their baby, a deep emotional connection and relationship which transcends time, place, demands and events. This affectional bond is one way in which parents are able to anticipate, concentrate upon and meet the needs of their infant. It also enables them to tolerate and withstand the inevitable demands of parenting as they intrude on their own personal needs.

VIGILANCE-PROTECTION

Although more limited than adults, neonates and infants possess a wide range of skills and abilities which enable them to monitor and sense changes within themselves and their environment. Infants are, for example, sensitive to pain, hunger, tiredness, and changes in temperature and light. They interpret and react to physical and emotional discomfort and threat, and alert caregivers through cries and other responses. For example, a baby will check for the presence of the mother and will eventually become distressed at separation from the security this provides.

At the same time, the parent has a responsibility to protect and maintain the physical and emotional safety and integrity of their baby. This means providing the best possible conditions to reduce the chances of danger and threat. This involves being aware of signs of change in the infant's bodily and emotional state, good hygiene, supervising older siblings, and safe sleep practices. Parents also need to ensure that they themselves are able to manage their own tiredness, feelings of frustration or otherwise.

PHYSIOLOGICAL REGULATION-PROVIDING STRUCTURE

The infant is equipped with only a rudimentary ability to control biological functions, such as, temperature, hunger and feeding, and states of consciousness. Physiological regulation becomes more possible as babies mature, learn to use their environment and become more able to make their needs known. For example, the infant begins to use hunger cries to communicate the need for feeding, or kicks the covers off when too warm.

The parent meanwhile helps the baby gradually to gain and exercise control over these bodily processes. For this to happen, the parent needs to develop consistent and reliable ways of responding to and guiding the needs of the infant. Over time, the parent's behaviour then becomes familiar to the infant, and the baby has the best chance of learning how to respond. For example, the mother will help the baby to feed and suckle when hungry in a way that satiates the baby's appetite, but does not lead to the discomfort of being overly full or full of wind. In a similar vein, a parent may use a winding down routine when putting the baby down to sleep. This relaxes and calms the infant, and signals to the baby what is about to happen next.

AFFECT REGULATION-EMPATHIC RESPONSIVENESS

In a similar way, the parent anticipates and monitors the feelings and emotional state of the infant. For the infant, these feelings are truly outside of verbal awareness and governed by fundamental experiences, such as, calm/distress, comfort/discomfort, safety/threat, trust/mistrust, and familiarity/unfamiliarity. The parent attempts to understand and make sense of the infant's feelings and act accordingly. It is important that parents act to provide care, nurture or stimulation. However, it is crucial that these actions and responses are in tune with, and reflect, the needs of the infant. The parent must separate their own feelings from those of their baby. In their actions, parents must prioritise and respond to the needs of their infant rather than their own. From these interactions, infants are given the chance to experience their feeling state changing and can then slowly learn to gain control of it for themselves. For example, this may mean picking up and soothing the baby in response to signs of tension and distress. At the same time, the parent tries to understand the source of upset. Equally, it may mean playfully engaging an alert and attentive infant, and subsequently adjusting the level of stimulation as the baby either enjoys or tires of the interaction.

LEARNING-TEACHING

The parent is, initially, the primary means for infants to acquire knowledge and experience about the world and themselves. This is most likely to occur when experiences are offered consistently and sensitively by parents in ways that are manageable and understandable to the baby. Parents then guide their infant through these experiences, so that their baby can become familiar with what happens to themselves in the world around them. In a way, the parent almost thinks for the baby. These countless, repeated and shared experiences enable the infant's mind to grow. With the acquisition of rudimentary knowledge and memory, the infant can begin to depend upon their own mind and resources. For example, when showing signs of hunger the mother will, time after time, guide and help the infant to latch on to the breast and suckle. In doing so, the infant gradually learns that discomfort, crying, feeding and comfort go together. These physical, emotional and behavioural experiences begin to link, merge and develop into fundamental constructs and, with this, a growing sense of self.

PLAY-PLAY

The parent and infant playing together can be a mutual source of enjoyment, pleasure and stimulation. Rather than being given over to special times for play, games with infants are often accomplished as part of other activities, such as nappy changing and bathing. The role of parents in playing with infants often involves mirroring, building on, and developing the actions and responses of the baby. This type of social play is usually based upon playfully adapting and altering familiar routines to create a sense of anticipation and fun that builds towards a joyful and exciting climax. Games are likely to alter and change according to the preferences of the infant and parent, and the developmental abilities of the infant. The mutual pleasure derived from such experiences deepens attachments and bonds, reinforces knowledge and expectations, as well as, promotes the possibility of enjoying the unexpected.

SELF-CONTROL-DISCIPLINE

With a growing ability to exert control over biological and emotional systems, the baby has the chance to develop rudimentary self-control. This may, for example, be noticed in an ability to momentarily restrain distress at being hungry, while the mother prepares to breastfeed. At the same time, while remaining responsive to the baby's needs, the parent has the role of slowly introducing demands from the outside world. This needs to be accomplished in ways that are both tolerable and tolerated by the infant. In doing so, the parent has the task of providing structure that is consistent and familiar to the infant, but which also anticipates and encourages conformity to the personal and social needs of the family. For example, the baby will be encouraged to adapt to sleeping for longer periods at night by changes in feeding patterns, keeping the lighting low and by resisting any efforts of the baby to initiate play and stimulation.

The picture that emerges from Emde's ideas is one of parents and infants inextricably bound together, navigating a course through fundamental human processes. Everything that occurs between them is imbued with the potential to influence the nature and shape of these developmental tasks. This journey, and its outcomes, will be dependent upon the needs, characteristics, skills and abilities of all those involved.

There is evidence to suggest that parents who are observant and sensitive to the needs of their child, are loving, can interpret and make sense of the world from the infant's point of view, and respond in familiar, consistent and careful ways are more likely to fulfil the developmental tasks of parenthood successfully. These parental abilities and qualities resonate with the characteristics of the helper outlined in Chapter 5. They help the parent to develop a loving bond with their dependent baby, to solve problems with the infant, and to acquire a rich array of practical and emotional parenting skills. At the same time, these tasks stimulate and encourage the skills, abilities and behaviour of the infant so that they can grow, develop and flourish. For example, in receiving sensitive, responsive care and nurture an infant develops a sense of trust and security. The gradual acquisition of control over one's body and feelings helps the infant to develop a sense of self. This is a self which is composed of a mind that retains ideas, familiarity with the world, and a rudimentary understanding of how to influence it.

In contrast, a very different picture is likely to emerge when parents find it difficult to feel warmth and affection towards their baby, hard to grasp and understand their baby's needs, and do not provide the most appropriate caregiving. This may be, for example, because parents remain unaware and indifferent towards the infant's needs. Alternatively, they may be preoccupied by their own needs and prioritise these above those of the infant. As a result, they may not be alert to potential sources of danger and threat, and they may be unable to guide, enjoy or help the baby to manage the demands of the world. In consequence, infants may not have the chance to develop a sense of security and attachment, of trust and familiarity in the world. They will have little opportunity to learn to control their own body, emotions and environment, and these will have profound effects on their emerging sense of self and constructs of the world.

The developmental outcomes of the infant are fundamentally influenced by the qualities and characteristics of the parent. They are also, however, dependent upon the skills, abilities and characteristics of the infant themselves. In recent years there has been a number of advances in knowledge about the abilities and skills of neonates and infants which have increased our understanding of very young babies. These will be described in the next section.

The Skills and Abilities of Infants

Often, among professionals and parents alike, there is a concentration on the eating, sleeping and crying habits of infants. Without doubt, babies feed often, around 10 times a day at first and, even before birth, they show distinct periods of rest and activity over the 24 hour cycle. In the first few weeks, babies spend about 15–16 hours of the day asleep, although they will be asleep for no more than about four hours at any one time. They are usually in an awake and alert state for only 2–3 hours per day. As far as crying is concerned, babies cry for anything between half an hour and two and a half hours a day. This peaks at about six weeks and usually decreases from this point onwards.

This section sets out to give a broad overview of the extraordinary array of physical, psychological and social abilities that neonates and infants do actually possess. In doing so, one needs to acknowledge the enormous variation that exists between infants. This is not surprising, since they are, after all, human beings with all the foibles and idiosyncrasies of the rest of the human race.

MOTOR SKILLS AND REFLEXES

In terms of physical development, the newborn possesses many basic reflexes, such as, blinking, pupil dilation, sucking and swallowing. They have involuntary muscle movements used in, for instance, breathing, digestion and circulation. Infants possess a number of primitive reflexes which fade with time, some within weeks (e.g. walking reflex) and others over months (e.g. startle response).

Even at birth, infants can turn their head to one side and make crawling movements. They first acquire control and co-ordination of head and torso movement. This control gradually extends to the arms and legs, and then fine motor skills, such as, the co-ordinated use of fingers and toes. At three months, young infants can usually sit with support, and push their head and shoulders up when lying on their stomach. By nine months, infants can usually crawl, sit unaided, pick up small objects, and walk with the aid of furniture.

Even though co-ordination is limited at first, there is evidence that early movement is purposeful and not random. For example, there appears to be a synchronised and harmonised interplay between the verbal and non-verbal behaviour of a parent and the movements and responses of their baby when the two are communicating and relating together intensely. Infants also show early signs of trying to reach and grasp at people and objects; and will turn their head towards sound, particularly familiar voices.

PERCEPTUAL SKILLS

Before birth, the foetus responds to tactile stimulation and shows recognition of the mother's voice. At birth, neonates can hear, locate and turn to all sound within range of the human voice. The newborn baby is most responsive to the human voice, and quickly learns to discriminate familiar voices, especially that of the mother, assuming she is the primary caregiver. They can also distinguish basic tastes and smells, including the odour of the mother.

Vision is initially very good, but focused at about 30 centimetres. The infant can track a slowly moving object with head and eye movement within weeks of birth, and shows greater attention to the human face, again especially the mother's. Visual attention is not random, but tends to focus on contrasts, for example, light and dark, and corners and edges. Infants can also match faces to voices within weeks, and there is some evidence that they can imitate facial expressions.

At three months, infants have well developed peripheral vision, depth perception and soon grasp that the things that they can see have physical substance. Full visual acuity is usually developed by 12 months.

LEARNING CAPACITY

Along with building a sense of themselves and the world in which they live, other main learning achievements in the first two years of life include understanding about cause and effect (i.e. 'If I do this, then that happens.') and learning about object permanence (i.e. 'Things still exist even when I can't see them.'). Infants acquire knowledge simply through experience and social interaction, and this is accelerated when experiences are more frequent and consistent. Other major ways of learning are initially through the infant feeling and manipulating objects in the mouth, and later feeling in the hands, as well as, learning through trial and error. The progress and amount of learning depends upon the cognitive abilities of the infant and, as suggested earlier, the type of care and stimulation offered by parents and others.

Babies change and develop their behaviour in response to their environment. For example, when infants are given a bottle of sweetened drink they will begin sucking. This is not surprising, and alone does not merit attention apart from a passing note about the value or otherwise of giving sweetened drinks to infants. However what is of more importance, and a simple demonstration of the infant's capacity to respond to the environment, is what happens when the offer of the bottle is preceded by a simple touch to the infant's forehead. The infant will learn to associate the stroke of the forehead with the appearance of the bottle so much so that eventually the mere stroke of the forehead will produce sucking movements without the bottle being present. Evidence such as this shows that infants will respond to learning patterns based on classical conditioning.

The newborn can learn very rapidly through operant conditioning. Infants learn within the first few weeks that specific actions bring about interesting events, and they will change their behaviour and learn to do things in response to positive and negative reinforcement. For example, they can learn to set a mobile in motion when rewarded for turning their head, or using a series of kicking movements. They will also often react with great pleasure as they see the effects and impact they have on the world.

While sugary drinks can be a powerful reinforcer, so is the mother's behaviour, including her voice and heartbeat. For example, mothers tend to be more socially responsive to displays of positive emotions; they are more likely to notice, smile and show interest in their baby smiling as opposed to other less positive behaviours. As a consequence, these behaviours are positively reinforced and are more likely to re-occur. In contrast, negative emotional expressions by infants are often not given the same level and type of positive attention and reinforcement. Perhaps as a consequence, expressions of negative emotions by infants have been found to decrease over the first year.

A final source of new knowledge and experience comes from the infant's capacity to copy and imitate the expressions and movements of other humans. This is evident within days of birth. Certainly by the end of the first year, infants inspect their mother's faces to gauge the appropriate emotion for ambiguous situations.

As their learning increases, infants quickly show an ability to organise their experience into patterns. Like their elders, they will show surprise, and sometimes distress, when things occur which do not conform to their expectations. For example, they may become upset when exposed to a combination of their mother's face and a different voice. Such patterns of learning illustrate the infant's ability to acquire and use experience so that they learn, change and develop. In effect, they form constructs, which help them to become familiar with, make sense of, and anticipate their world.

SOCIAL AND COMMUNICATION SKILLS

Infants communicate, express their needs, and show interest in others from birth. Crying is the most obvious means by which they do this and it enables them to show distress, attract attention and secure care. They also show disgust, contentment, interest, attention and a desire for closeness. These skills emerge and evolve quickly during the first few weeks, while parents at the same time begin to distinguish between their baby's cries (e.g. distress and hunger). Facial expressions reflecting pleasure, such as smiling emerge from 4 weeks, those reflecting sadness and anger at around 4 months, and signs of fear following separation emerge after about 7 months.

From birth, infants show preferential, sustained attention and interest towards other humans, especially primary caregivers. For example, they respond differentially to human voices as distinct from other sounds. The mother's voice is highly attractive and it can even be recognised in the womb by the foetus. Infants will also respond more strongly to the human voice than other sounds while asleep.

Babies like to look at and concentrate on human faces and face like patterns. They will spend longer looking at their own mother's face than the faces of other women. This preference appears to go beyond just interest and seems to be part of the wider processes involved in making and maintaining a primary attachment with a parent.

Babbling begins at 3–4 months, and from 7 months is used as part of purposeful interaction, as well as, for personal amusement and play. Interaction even prior to babbling is stimulating and enjoyable for the infant, and provides the basis for later verbal and social communication. These early interactions show the basic characteristics of human communication. They involve turn-taking, synchrony and shifts in intensity. Young babies use mouth, tongue and lip movements, as well as, movements of the arms and legs during these interactions.

The process of infant communication is interpersonal from the very beginning. For example, as infants show social interest and behaviour, parents monitor and interpret these signs and signals in order to understand and make sense of what the baby might want or need. The response of parents and other carers to the social communication of infants is crucial to the further development of such skills.

One universal means of heightening communication between adults and infants is the use of 'motherese'. This simplified form of adult speech is slower, uses shorter sentences, higher voice pitch, deeper intonation, concrete content, and repetition and expansion of the infant's preverbal communication. Preverbal communication needs to be carefully managed by the parent. Parents gradually learn to initiate 'conversations' during periods when their baby is awake and alert. The type and intensity of these interactions must be adjusted to the mood and temperament of the baby, there are some general requirements of parents. These include regulating the 'conversation' by responding in sufficient time to maintain the baby's attention, giving plenty of time for him/her to organise a response, and avoiding movements and noises which might alarm or disrupt the child's concentration. Parents also need to be sensitive to the fact that although early interaction can be highly stimulating for infants, it can also overload them if continued for too long.

TEMPERAMENT

Children are unique at birth and do show strong individual or temperamental differences, as they are known. There have been a number of efforts to identify and categorise the main differences between even very young infants. Pioneers in this area are Thomas and Chess (1977) who described three broad types of temperament, related to nine specific underlying dimensions. The easy temperament child is seen as calm and enjoys interaction, is tolerant of new experience and situations, and establishes behavioural and physiological routines without difficulty. The slow to warm-up temperament child is described as often taking time to respond to stimulation, as low in activity level and taking more time to adapt and accept new situations and routines. The difficult temperament child, in contrast, is described as often uncomfortable, sensitive and irritable, finding it difficult to establish and adjust to routines and tending to avoid new situations. Tolerance, sensitivity and responsiveness are particularly important parental qualities for helping children with a difficult temperament to adjust to and negotiate life demands and expectations.

As discussed by Bee (2000) the validity of these dimensions has been questioned. For example, the original research was not carried out with neonates, the ratings of temperament by parents and observers may not always agree and a lot of the work is based upon information from parental questionnaires rather than direct observations of infants. Nevertheless, work on temperamental characteristics is still being pursued, and more recent approaches are suggesting five basic dimensions of: activity level; approachability/positive emotionality; inhibition/anxiety; negative emotionality/irritability/anger; and control/task persistence (e.g. Caspi, 1998).

To conclude this section, we have outlined some of the knowledge currently available regarding the abilities and skills possessed by infants. There is a great deal more information available and very useful sources are Bee (2000) and Murray & Andrews (2000), who present the social skills of babies graphically via videotape stills. Here we have tried to illustrate how even the youngest babies appear to have not only a profound desire for personal, human, social contact, but also an array of emergent skills and abilities to bring this about. These characteristics give the infant the best chance of having their needs for care, safety and stimulation met. The nature and extent of these skills will differ from infant to infant, that is, from person to person. What, we hope, is also apparent, is that their needs are met through a complex process of interaction between them and their parents.

Parent–Infant Interaction

In Chapter 11, we outlined a general model of parent–child interaction based upon a constructivist approach. In this section, we will concentrate on the implications of this model for early parenting and parent–infant relationships. Our model proposes that there is a continual cycle of interaction between parents and children involving their observations, their constructions (including their thoughts, feelings and beliefs), and their actions, reactions and behaviour. This interplay may vary in focus and concentration, but it is going on all the time. The process is, by and large, outside our immediate awareness; it happens automatically, without conscious effort, and is primarily governed by our constructions.

These cognitive, emotional and behavioural processes are an essential part of being human, of being a parent, and of being a child. The processes enable parents to be sensitive, understanding and responsive to their children. They encourage children to articulate, show and express their needs, as well as, help them to make sense of the actions and reactions of their parents and the world around them. These processes provide the mechanism through which the ties between parents and children deepen and the tasks of parenting and child development can be accomplished. However, there will be times in all relationships when interaction is problematic. These problems may be short-lived, confined to particular aspects of the relationship or more profound and deeply ingrained. They may arise, for example, when parents and children are insensitive or unwilling to recognise the signs and signals sent out by each other, when their constructs conflict in ways which are difficult to reconcile, or when actions and reactions are unwanted, unhelpful or incompatible.

This general model of interaction is perhaps easiest to grasp when parents and children are able to communicate verbally and non-verbally, when they can think about and explain their own thoughts and feelings, and when they have a skilful and familiar repertoire of behaviour. This chapter, however, is concerned with infancy and early parenthood, the period of life when the cycle is just beginning to build and develop. The mother and father, who may have no previous experience of being parents, are faced with their infant, who, quite literally, has no experience of the world. All are inextricably linked at the very first stage of their lives together. This time of novelty and beginning does not mean that the parents and their infant bring nothing to their new relationship. As we have seen earlier in the chapter, both parents and the infants bring a whole range of skills, abilities, beliefs, desires and needs. Each of which will influence and affect the individual components of their interaction.

It is probably right to assume that an infant's monitoring, constructions and behaviour are governed almost entirely by the necessity to ensure that their needs are met. It is also true that an infant's capacity to monitor themselves and their environment is limited by their individual and developmental abilities, as well as, by their varying states of consciousness. However, as we have seen, even at birth, infants possess sufficient skills and abilities to sense and react to how they feel, as well as, what is going on around them. These perceptual skills function selectively, in the interests of the infant and seek deep connections with other humans. For example, infants can notice when their desire for closeness and proximity to their parent is, or is not, being met. They can notice when they feel physically comfortable, or uncomfortable. What they do not yet possess are sophisticated abilities to understand, comprehend and make sense of their experience. For example, neonates may initially not be able to understand whether the discomfort they are experiencing is a result of hunger, a temperature, indigestion, irritability or something else.

In terms of construing, an infant's experience of the world begins during birth. Infants quickly start to absorb, learn, change and develop as a result of what happens to them. These capabilities enable them to begin to anticipate and remember, and to organise and build a rudimentary sense of themselves and their world. In so doing, their mind, their constructs and self begin to emerge, fashioned from their innate characteristics, their experiences and relationships.

In a similar vein, the capacity of infants to act and react is limited by their motor control and co-ordination, and their understanding of themselves and the world. As a consequence, they are highly dependent upon their carers for ensuring that their needs are met. As we have already outlined, infants possess an array of social and communication skills which enable them to be highly successful, if not very sophisticated, at achieving their purpose. For example, infants may not be able to feed themselves, but they can notice that they feel uncomfortable and cry so that they get help. The parent will then interpret the cries and feed the baby. A fundamental task for the infant is to begin to link their monitoring of themselves and their world with their growing knowledge (i.e. their construct system) and with their social skills and actions. These links enable infants to begin to focus attention on the most important and valuable things around them; they help them to anticipate and make the best, most accurate and useful sense of what is going on. The links also enable them to use responses and actions, which will ensure that their needs are fulfilled in the most quick and effective way.

The dependence of the infant on the care and nurture of their parents highlights the way that the parent and infant components of the cycle of interaction are intertwined. At times, these components seem to merge and can be difficult to separate and distinguish. Infants need, at first, the help of their parents to detect, notice and guide their experience. For example, parents detect and hear the cries of their baby and put this together with other information such as when the baby last fed, last slept, was last changed, the nature and type of cry, the temperature of the baby in order to interpret, make sense of the cry and respond.

For this process to be as successful as possible requires parental empathy and attunement, as well as, the close monitoring of the baby. Infants, especially at first, will often be within the parent's eyesight for much of the day, and parents usually become highly sensitive to even slight changes in their baby's state, behaviour and appearance. In doing so, they learn which of their baby's signs and signals is most important for them to attend.

While the infant is learning and developing constructs of the world based upon their singular experience and needs, the parental components of the cycle are governed by constructs which are related to both the new child and parenthood, as well as, other broader issues. These include the events and processes of pregnancy and the birth, expectations of parenthood, and the needs of the infant. They also include the personal needs, goals and ambitions of the parents, their family circumstances, wider personal and family relationships, as well as, social and cultural issues. The usefulness, accuracy and viability of parental constructs will initially be tested in pregnancy, but this will reach a new level of intensity with the reality of caring for a newly arrived baby.

These new information, knowledge, skills, feelings and experiences will need to be drawn into and accommodated within the parent's construct system. The nature, strength and flexibility of these constructs will profoundly influence the type and quality of care and nurture provided by parents. How this occurs and progresses provides the foundation for parents' adaptation to their new role; it determines the quality of their relationship and bond with their new baby, and the nature of the care and stimulation that they can provide. For example, even standing over the cot watching the sleeping infant can intensify a parent's beliefs in the beauty, wonder and uniqueness of their baby. On the other hand, for a parent who is struggling to adapt to their new role, such experiences may reinforce their problems in coming to terms with what has happened, and may provoke the parent's feelings of inadequacy and resentment.

The nature and content of these constructs drive the way parents look after their children. Parents respond from moment to moment, and these responses build into longer-term patterns of behaviour and interaction, which need to be considered in terms of not only what occurs, that is, the *content* of care, but also how it occurs, the *process* of care. The content of care includes all the practical, emotional and developmental activities such as feeding, reassuring, playing and communicating with our babies. The process of care is concerned with the way these activities are carried out. For example, the degree of sensitivity of parental attention, the consistency and stability of parental care, the level of rapport and synchrony between parent and infant, as well as, the emotional tone of the interaction.

In this section we have sought to illustrate some of the major issues for parents and infants as they begin to relate, adapt and undertake their developmental tasks together. Even at this early stage, each component part of the cycle of interaction is alive with influence and possibilities. The outcomes of this process will depend upon the capacities, capabilities and constructs of those involved.

Risk and Resilience

For almost everyone, becoming a parent is complicated, demanding and far from straightforward. However, evidence suggests that certain personal, family, social, and environmental characteristics appear to help parents and infants as they negotiate their developmental tasks. Families exposed to such characteristics are less likely to experience difficulties. These characteristics are known as resilience, or protective, factors. Similarly, there is also a range of known risk factors that are associated with an increased probability of developing psychosocial problems at this early stage.

The mechanisms by which these risk and resilience factors operate and affect the building blocks of early parenting and infant development are multiple and complex. The lives of most families are composed of a balance of both risk and resilience. Generally, the level of vulnerability is determined by the extent and number of risk factors to which a family is exposed, rather than the effects of specific risk factors alone (e.g. Zeanah, Boris & Larrieu, 1997). Families exposed to several risk and few resilience factors face a more arduous task. They are therefore more vulnerable to the development of psychosocial difficulties than those not so affected.

Resilience factors include: good individual and family health; easy temperament and average or above average intellectual abilities in the child; high parental self-esteem; good problem solving and emotional coping skills; secure and warm family relationships; more general social support; accurate knowledge and expectations of parenting and child development; positive emotional experiences in parents' own childhoods; and good access and relationships with helping agencies.

It is perhaps not difficult to imagine how these characteristics might help promote successful adaptation and adjustment. For example, a healthy, well-supported parent may be in a good position to withstand tiredness and the other physical demands of parenthood. A bright, confident and knowledgeable parent may be good at developing useful and effective ways of dealing with the uncertainties and difficulties which arise with the care of their baby. Equally, a smiling, responsive, easily settled baby may boost the confidence and competence of a parent. It is reasonable to assume that parents who benefit from these sorts of resilience factors are better placed to negotiate the transition to parenthood successfully. They are also more likely to be able to concentrate on the tasks of parenting with their infant, and to interact and care for their infants sensitively and responsively.

In contrast to this, Figure 12.1 contains a list of well-known risk factors. These include characteristics of the infant, the pregnancy, parents, parent–infant relationship, wider family relationships and social support, environmental factors, and life events. Listing these risk factors makes their potential for triggering and maintaining difficulties immediately apparent. It is not difficult to appreciate, for example, how a sickly baby or one with a difficult temperament may place additional pressures on parents and their relationship. Equally, a parent who has to cope with, and sort out, their own personal and family problems is likely to be distracted from the tasks and processes involved in meeting the needs of their baby. We will illustrate the impact of risk and resilience by considering a specific example:

Hayley was nineteen, worked as a shop assistant and lived in a high rise flat, which she shared with her sister. Hayley had known her boyfriend, Tony, for just under a year. The relationship had had its ups and downs. Because Tony drank heavily and could become aggressive, when Hayley found she was pregnant, she thought seriously about having a termination without telling him. However, she eventually decided that having a baby

FIGURE 12.1: RISK FACTORS KNOWN TO INFLUENCE INFANT MENTAL HEALTH

Child
- Premature baby.
- Small for dates.
- Physical illness or disability.
- Constant crying or other difficult behaviour.

Pregnancy
- Unwanted pregnancy.
- Immature/young mother.

Parent-Infant Relationship
- Lack of feeling for the baby.
- Problems in interaction.
- Adverse parenting (e.g. punitive/coercive, rejecting or negligent).

Family
- Adversity in parents' childhood.
- Marital/partner discord.
- Parental physical illness.
- Parental learning difficulties.
- Parental mental health problems.
- Parental substance misuse.
- Parental criminality.
- Four or more children
- Isolation/lack of social, emotional and practical support.

Social, Environmental and Cultural
- Poverty.
- Financial problems (e.g. debt).
- Unemployment.
- Housing problems (e.g. homelessness, neglect, overcrowding).
- Environmental problems (e.g. neighbour disputes, threat of crime).

Life events
- Major recent life events such as divorce, bereavement, trauma.

would bring Tony and her closer together. She hoped that he would come to love the baby as much as she would and that they would become more committed to one another as a result.

During the pregnancy, Hayley went through periods of being tearful and feeling down, mainly because she had doubts about whether she had made the right decision. Tony showed little interest in Hayley's welfare towards the end of the pregnancy; he spent more time going out with friends. When she was feeling down, Hayley, as always, turned to her sister, Karen, for support and a shoulder to cry on. Karen accompanied her to antenatal appointments and classes. This motivated Hayley to attend. Karen also helped out financially, buying extra clothes and equipment for the baby.

Hayley had her baby, Robert, in hospital and was discharged quickly. She was keen to breastfeed, as she wanted to follow the advice of her midwife, with whom she got on well. However, in the first few days, Hayley found it difficult. She persevered with feeding, but became worried that she was responsible for the feeding problems. Robert was also difficult to settle and woke frequently. Hayley became exhausted from lack of sleep and increasingly tearful, as well as, resentful towards Tony who offered little support.

There are in this example a range of features and circumstances which may raise Hayley and Robert's vulnerability to developing problems. From the information given above, it would seem that Hayley's relationship with her boyfriend, even before the pregnancy, was not particularly good. She had doubts about the pregnancy and suffered from low mood. After the birth, she looked after Robert almost entirely alone and was exhausted. Robert was not easy and found both feeding and settling difficult. The flat was also crowded after Robert's arrival, but it was also in a high rise block, which made it difficult for Hayley to go out with him.

In terms of resilience, however, Hayley had a good relationship with her sister who provided both practical and emotional support. She became committed to Robert in spite of her mixed feelings during pregnancy. She had also formed a good relationship with her midwife. It is difficult to predict in any absolute sense: 1) whether Hayley will go on to have more parenting difficulties than other parents; 2) whether Robert is at greater risk of psychosocial problems; and 3) what the difficulties might be. On balance, however, the risk of problems seems high.

The accumulation of risk factors, such as, low mood, exhaustion, and relationship problems are likely to make it difficult for Hayley to remain sensitive and empathic to Robert. With her fatigue and unhappiness, she might find it difficult to pay attention and monitor Robert's needs, especially when he is not particularly easy in temperament. She might begin to construe Robert as intentionally difficult, or as a sign of her own incompetence. She could even begin to feel that Robert, like Tony, does not really love her. These and the pressures of living in an overcrowded high rise flat could begin to feed off each other and exacerbate her unhappiness and tiredness. As a consequence, Hayley might begin to shut herself off from her child. She could easily become irritable with him and not give him the loving and responsive care that he particularly needs. It might be difficult for her sister to remain sympathetic to Hayley's low mood and their relationship might become difficult, and for similar reasons the relationship with her boyfriend might disintegrate further.

Alternatively, the outcome may not be quite so ominous or problematic. Hayley's close relationship with her sister may provide her with a vital source of support. She might to able to talk about her problems and concerns with her sister. This could give her considerable emotional support, as well as help to challenge some of her negative constructions. If the relationship were to remain strong, and Karen is strong enough to cope, then she might also be able to help Hayley recognise her strengths. Together they might be able to devise useful ideas about the best way of dealing with Robert's feeding and settling, as well as her own tiredness and problems with Tony. In addition, since Hayley also has the capacity to develop good relationships with professionals, such as her midwife, she might be able to seek out and elicit the support she needs. In particular, her health visitor might help her to address some of the problems with Robert which might further build up her resilience through increased self-efficacy.

Knowledge about risk and resilience allows us to identify some of the factors in the lives of families that can significantly influence the outcomes of early parenting and infant development. This can be used to guide the helping process, particularly exploring and understanding the presence and possible influence of these factors within the circumstances of individual families. These are issues which will be addressed in more detail in the next chapter.

In Conclusion

Here in this chapter we have concentrated on some of the important features of the earliest phase of a child's life. We have highlighted the inherent demands on people as they move into the role of parent, a transition that at birth confronts them with a reality from which there is no return. From this point onwards, parents and their newborn babies are immersed together in an array of tasks which shape and direct the physical, psychological and emotional development of the infant. The outcomes of these tasks are very much dependent upon the constant, on-going interaction between them, and this is, in turn, influenced and determined by the characteristics infants bring into the world, the adaptation of the parents, and the support or otherwise derived from the family's wider social, economic, and environmental circumstances.

Infants possess an extraordinary range of social, perceptual and learning abilities, which are present at or soon after birth and develop rapidly thereafter. These enable infants to participate in a synchronised interaction with their parents in which the child's overall development and well-being is the outcome. This includes the development of a child's sense of themselves as a person in relation to others and the world of which they are a part. This interaction involves both parent and child being absorbed in a process of monitoring, construing and responding to each other. It is this cycle of interaction which forms the foundation for the relationship that develops between the parent and their infant, and the pattern of care, nurture, stimulation and protection provided for the infant.

It is quite evident that parents and infants will bring their own, individual innate and acquired skills, abilities and other characteristics to these processes, and they do so within a very wide range of environmental contexts. Some of these characteristics and environments will protect and safeguard the progress and development of the family, while others will increase and intensify the likelihood of parent and infant problems. With this as the background, we should like to go on in the next chapter to look at ways in which community practitioners and others can promote adaptation to parenthood, prevent difficulties from arising, and help parents manage problems when they do occur.

CHAPTER 13
PROMOTION, PRIMARY PREVENTION AND EARLY INTERVENTION

Introduction

One of the themes that runs through the constructivist approach like that of Kelly is that humans feel more secure and comfortable with the familiar. They at least know where they stand. In contrast, change and adaptation is intrinsically taxing and unsettling. It can disrupt and disturb; it is less predictable than the familiar. While the parenting of infants is replete with wonderful possibilities, it is also laden with the inherent demands of change. New parents acquire deep-rooted responsibilities. They have to care for and nurture their infants. They have to modify their relationships with each other and the world outside, as well as, build a relationship with their new baby. At the same time, infants, simply and most extraordinarily, have a whole new world around them. It is with these experiences that both parents and infants face the unavoidable and continuing prospect of change. These experiences grip, stretch and challenge our constructs and our understanding of our children, our world, and ourselves. At the same time, they thrust new knowledge, skills and discoveries upon us. They provide and require new ways and priorities for attending to and acting in the world. All this occurs at a time when the physical and psychological resources of parents may be sapped by tiredness, exhaustion and, above all else, unfamiliarity.

Although many find this transition stressful, it is testimony to what it is to be human that many parents and infants are able to negotiate it relatively unscathed. However, some families, as we have seen in Chapter 12, are more vulnerable to problems because of the presence of risk factors and the absence of resilience. Some of these families will develop substantial difficulties which will have important and detrimental effects in both the immediate and longer term. Despite this, the traditional concern of the many professionals involved with families at this stage of life has tended to be the physical health of the pregnant mother and the biological development of the foetus, the practical management of the birth, and the health of the newly arrived baby and mother (Fundudis, 1990). On the other hand, contact with families during pregnancy and early parenthood provides a excellent opportunity to promote the psychosocial well-being of parents to be, parents and their infants.

This chapter will begin by looking at ways in which professionals can encourage and facilitate the best possible start in life for newborn babies and infants. It will then move on to consider how to identify and support vulnerable families so that, where possible, early difficulties can be prevented. The final part of the chapter will concentrate on early intervention, and the use of particular strategies within the Parent Adviser approach to help parents manage problems, if they develop in this crucial phase of life.

Promoting Parent and Infant Well-Being

The promotion of parent and infant well-being is essentially concerned with encouraging and guiding parents to use the personal, family and social resources available to them, so that they are best able to meet their own and their infant's needs. The promotion of psychosocial health should begin before birth and continue thereafter. The aim is to foster the circumstances and characteristics which increase family resilience and enhance the development of the infant. The main areas include: facilitating parents' general adjustment to parenthood, encouraging their understanding of the psychological, emotional and social needs of infants, and helping parents to relate effectively to their baby. Promotion, therefore, involves practitioners in prompting all parents to be aware of, and plan for, the changes brought about by parenthood. Parents should have the chance to consider what they know and what they do not know. They should have the opportunity to think about their own feelings, expectations and needs, and those of their baby, as well as, their strengths, concerns and worries. Promotion, in other words, provides the impetus for all parents to begin, and to consolidate, their positive adaptation to the changes and demands that lie ahead. This requires the loosening and reorganising of the parent's constructs, and the acquisition of the necessary practical, emotional and monitoring skills.

Promotional issues during pregnancy include consideration of the health of the mother and that of the foetus, and any previous difficulties or complications, such as, miscarriages and still births. They should also cover the parent's feelings about becoming pregnant, being pregnant, and how they expect to feel after the baby has arrived. It is also an opportunity to encourage the mother and father to begin to see the baby as an individual. This allows parents to play with their constructs of the baby in pregnancy, and to develop the idea of the baby as a real person.

The extent and quality of personal and family support is also important, and includes all the people to whom parents can talk and involve in their pregnancy, and their reactions. It may be important, even at the antenatal stage, to encourage parents to think about how they will cope with the arrival of their baby and what changes and demands they anticipate. This includes the possible impact of the baby's arrival on the mother, the father, and the family. Discussion and exploration of this type may allow parents to voice their concerns and worries, as well as, to touch upon wider issues like money, housing and family relationships.

After the arrival of the baby, key promotional topics include: the process, procedures and experience of the actual birth itself, its effects on the mother and those around her; and, the mother's feelings for her newborn baby and the response and support of the immediate family and social network. Of equal importance is the concern and preoccupation of the mother and father for their baby, including their sensitivity, understanding, care, communication and relationship with the baby. It is also important to encourage parents to think about how they may cope and manage the difficulties and problems of early parenting such as crying, tiredness and irritability, feeding and sleep problems, as well as, wider issues such as practical household tasks, and significant financial or other worries.

Families, for a whole range of different reasons, will express and articulate each of the areas outlined above in enormously varied ways. Perhaps more importantly, given the extraordinary nature and effects of being pregnant and becoming a parent, each of these issues will be felt in an individual, personal and intimate way by each and every single family.

There is a whole range of opportunities which offer the chance for psychosocial promotion during pregnancy and early parenthood. These vary from routine antenatal and postnatal checks and contacts, to parent preparation classes and postnatal groups. Many of these contacts may be brief and limited in scope. This book is founded upon the notion that people only really talk openly and deeply with others when there is a climate of understanding, a relationship of trust, and an opportunity to feel encouraged and empowered. Rather than excluding the use of the Parent Adviser approach, the nature and circumstances of many of these contacts highlights the importance of community practitioners having excellent communication and relationship building skills. These characteristics are as vital to promotional work as they are to all other aspects of the helping process. It is important that practitioners have the necessary knowledge about the psychosocial issues of early parenting and infancy, so that they can fulfil their role and responsibility to offer accurate and relevant information and ideas. It is essential that they also have the interpersonal skills and abilities to create meaningful relationships with parents and parents-to-be, so that psychosocial promotion is undertaken in ways which are acceptable and effective for parents. Exploration and discussion which is based on an understanding of the individual parent and baby, offered at the pace of the family, and supported with relevant leaflets, books and videos is likely to be more effective than generalised and didactic instruction.

It is probably not the role of professionals to become immersed in efforts to resolve the issues of adaptation faced by the majority families, but to provide, through promotional approaches, the encouragement, stimulation and momentum which enables parents to manage the issues for themselves. The vast majority of parents will, with these promotional efforts, the support of their family, other new parents and their wider social network, then be able to negotiate and manage the demands that adaptation to parenthood requires of them. There is, however, a vital role to be undertaken in supporting families who are exposed to significant risk factors, so that serious problems can either be prevented or managed successfully. Before dealing with the issues involved in prevention and intervention we would like to illustrate one particular approach to early promotion with which we have been involved.

The European Early Promotion Project: An Example of a Promotional Approach

The European Early Promotion Project (Puura, Davis, Papadopoulou, et al, 2002; Roberts, Loxton, Campbell et al, 2002) was based in locations in Cyprus, Finland, Greece, the Federal Republic of Yugoslavia and the UK. It set out to provide a pro-active, non-stigmatising and universal psychosocial promotional approach in combination with a primary prevention and early intervention service. The Project consisted of systematic antenatal and postnatal contacts with all families. These contacts used semi-structured interviews developed from the work of Tsiantis et al (1996) and modified by Professor Veronika Ispanovic-Radojkovic at the Institute of Mental Health, Belgrade and colleagues (see Davis, Cox, Day, et al, 2000). These promotional contacts also provided the basis for an assessment of family need. Ongoing help and support was then offered to families who were vulnerable to or experiencing difficulties. The assessment of need, the prevention and early intervention activities of the Project will be described in more detail later in the chapter. This section will concentrate on the Project's promotional aspects.

Primary health care workers offered the approach to all women expecting their first or subsequent child in the areas served by the Project. The UK site was in Lewisham, south London. The service was provided by health visitors working with their usual caseload; they received additional training and supervision in the Parent Adviser approach and the use of the promotional interviews. The antenatal visit was conducted at home at around the thirty-sixth week of pregnancy. It was usually the parent's first meeting with their health visitor and provided a valuable opportunity for relationship building.

The interview consisted of a series of open-ended questions, each of which prompted an exploratory discussion of the emotional, psychological and practical issues that could impact on the parents, their unborn children and family relationships. The areas explored in the visit covered many of those outlined in the section above. These included: the parents' feelings and self-image during pregnancy; her anticipation of the labour; the changes happening in the family; the support the mother wanted and anticipated; her image and expectations of the baby; the likely effect of a new baby on the mother, her partner, other children and the extended family; and wider practical issues.

One of the most thought-provoking questions used in the interview was 'How do you imagine your baby now?' Parents often took time to respond, finding it interesting to consider that their unborn child might already have an individual personality. This also frequently evoked warm feelings towards the developing baby. The aim of the interview was to reinforce positive and realistic responses and thereby build parental confidence and competence in areas of strength. It also provided an opportunity for parents to think about and explore any worries or uncertainties, and, in doing so, to identify and begin to address any areas of concern. When negative feelings were expressed during the interview, the mothers were encouraged to share these with their partner, a friend or family member.

The second promotional visit was conducted by the same health visitor at home about four weeks after the birth. The same open-ended, respectful and relationship based approach was used during this visit with the baby present where possible. The health visitors based this visit on a second semi-structured interview, which explored the birth, the mother's adjustment to her new situation, her concerns and the impact of the new baby on the family, their relationships, and future expectations. Potential problems were explored with the mother, who was encouraged to think through the use of her existing resources and social network to address the issues. Every opportunity was taken to encourage the mother's understanding of her baby's innate skills, abilities and communications. The health visitors also took time to consider the parent–infant interaction and to give positive feedback on the mother's communication and relationship with her baby. Many mothers found it fascinating that their babies tended to listen to them carefully, not interrupting their speech, but waiting for a gap to respond with vocalisations or body movements.

Parents generally welcomed and benefited from the antenatal and postnatal promotional contacts. Beyond this promotional purpose, the visits served at least three other important functions. Firstly, they provided an opportunity for the health visitors to establish supportive helping relationships with parents. This acted as a foundation for any later contacts between the health visitor and family. Secondly, the open dialogue and focus of the promotional interviews provided the health visitors with an understanding of how individual parents were adapting to the changes evoked by pregnancy and the subsequent birth of their baby. And thirdly, the contacts enabled the health visitors to gauge the level of risk and resilience to which individual families were exposed. The promotional visits, therefore, helped health visitors to recognise families who were at risk of developing difficulties. This enabled the health visitors to target their resources more effectively towards those in most need.

Prevention

Supporting and helping parents so that they can give the best possible start in life to their infants is not just about promoting the adjustment of all parents and families. Infancy is an optimal time for the prevention of problems. Promotion, prevention and early intervention are approaches which can sometimes be difficult to distinguish and often overlap. The primary prevention of early parenting and infant psychosocial difficulties has two key aims: firstly, to reduce the extent and impact of risk factors to which families are exposed, and, secondly, to build and increase the strength and availability of family resilience and protective factors. By addressing these issues, it is intended that families are enabled to be in a more robust and less vulnerable position to deal with the demands of parenthood. They can then direct their efforts and energy towards the care, nurture and stimulation of their newborn babies without being distracted, preoccupied or worn down by sources of risk.

Evidence suggests that carefully organised preventive home visiting can successfully tackle many of the problems faced by children, parents and families at risk of developing complex psychosocial problems. Over 100 evaluations of home-visiting programmes have been published to date. The evidence from some of these evaluations indicates that home-visiting can produce beneficial effects on infant and maternal health in the medium and long term, including reductions in abuse and neglect (Hardy & Street, 1989; Olds, Henderson, Tatelbaum & Chamberlain, 1986). Programmes have been shown to improve resilience and reduce vulnerability through, for example, improving parental knowledge of child development and parenting (Taylor & Beauchamp, 1988), improving language and cognitive development of children (Bryant & Ramey, 1987), and improved mental health as adolescents (Aronen & Kurkela, 1996). Long term follow-up has shown, for example, reductions in maternal criminal behaviour (Olds, Eckenrode & Henderson, 1997). There is also evidence of benefits on the life course of the mother and family including reductions in the number of subsequent pregnancies, reduced dependence on state benefits, and increased uptake in employment (Olds & Kitzman, 1993). These positive results need to be balanced by the fact that some programme benefits have been limited to a subset of families, usually those at most risk. Other studies have produced only small and inconsistent improvements (e.g. Gomby et al, 1999; Olds, Hill, Robinson et al, 2000).

Services need to be organised, and staff trained in ways that increase the likelihood that vulnerable families are recognised as early as possible so that extra help and support can be offered. Core organisational features of effective home visiting programmes are shown in Figure 13.1 (Elkan, Kendrick, Hewitt et al, 2000). To be successful, primary prevention needs to be organised and provided within existing universal services. This integrated approach then provides the platform, and the means, by which to identify families who are exposed to higher levels of risk. This assessment of need should happen as early as possible in pregnancy, as it maximises the time available prior to the birth to help families deal with their vulnerability.

FIGURE 13.1 CORE FEATURES OF SUCCESSFUL HOME VISITING PREVENTION PROGRAMMES

- Early identification and screening through universal service.
- Target families in highest need and relate help to the level and extent of need.
- Support initiated during pregnancy.
- Voluntary participation.
- Home based provision.
- Case management supervision and support.
- Facilitation of parenting knowledge and skills.
- Frequent visiting.
- Appropriate helping relationships formed with parents.
- Programme delivered by trained workers.
- Integration with existing services.

Providing preventive support of this nature is not easy. These approaches are best provided by trained community health and social care practitioners who work within service systems, who can provide them with regular case management, supervision and support. The practitioners also need to work closely with specialist child and adult mental health, social care and early years services to ensure that families in highest need have access to additional forms of intervention and support.

Preventive approaches should avoid compulsion and coercion of families at risk. In fact, the genuine participation of families is vital to their success, and vulnerable parents should be actively and warmly encouraged. This is more likely to happen when practitioners are able to provide easy, convenient and frequent home contact from before birth, and when practitioners have the skills and abilities to develop working methods that are founded upon partnership with parents and mutual trust .

In order to operate within services that prioritise preventive support for vulnerable families, community practitioners have to feel confident about identifying, assessing and understanding the nature and extent of individual family need. We will, therefore, now describe an example from the European Early Promotion Project of one system for identifying and assessing family need.

The Assessment of Need

The presence of particular risk factors does not specifically predict the nature of child and family difficulties. As outlined in the previous chapter, the vulnerability and need of individual families depends upon the number and impact of risk factors, and the protective influence of any resilience factors present. The identification, recognition and assessment of need is therefore not an exact and precise process. It depends upon the circumstances of the family and the interplay between the risk and resilience factors present. The helper also needs to have the opportunities and skills to establish a good enough relationship with the family so that their circumstances can be adequately explored. The helper also requires the chance to think through and understand the implications of the vulnerabilities identified and share these views with the parents involved.

The health visitors involved in the European Early Promotion Project used the Needs Checklist (Davis, Cox, Day, et al, 2000) to help them identify factors known to influence the development of psychosocial problems in infancy. The Needs Checklist is not a diagnostic instrument, but a screening tool designed to act as an 'aide-memoir' for the health visitor. It consists of a list of well known risk factors, as described in Figure 12.1. Each risk factor on the Checklist was rated using a three point scale, not present, possibly present and definitely present. The Checklist was completed after both the antenatal and postnatal promotional contacts by the health visitor. A final decision about the level of need was not made until after the postnatal visit.

Our experience in the UK shows that the health visitors who used this approach were more sensitive to recognising family need than a group of health visitors working a in similar, neighbouring area using their routine approach. For example, the trained health visitors judged 54% of families to be in need, whereas the group of untrained health visitors judged only 24% to be in need. At the same time, an index of need derived from the content of independent research interviews identified 68% of families in the intervention group, and 71% of families in the comparison group, to be in need. It would appear, therefore, that the families of the trained and untrained health visitors did not differ in their levels of need according to the findings of the independent index. However, the trained health visitors identified about twice as many families as in need. When compared against the research index of need, the trained health visitors were also significantly more accurate in their judgements of need than the untrained group. The accuracy rate was 68% for the trained, and only 49.5% for the untrained.

The promotional contacts and assessment of need provided the basis for a mutual understanding to develop between the family and the health visitor. Families assessed with 'No Need' in the intervention group of the Project continued to receive routine health visiting services. Those identified as in 'Some Need' were offered additional supportive home visits based on the Parent Adviser approach to help manage their difficulties. Once a shared view of the families needs had been reached, the health visitors went on to help develop goals and plans in partnership with the parents involved to address specific risks and vulnerabilities. Families with exceptionally high need, for example, psychotic symptoms in the parents, severe physical problems in the child, a history of child abuse and neglect, were referred to more specialised services. These close interagency links were an essential part of the overall system

We have used this example from the European Early Promotion Project to illustrate one way to help health visitors identify and support vulnerable families. It is possible that this system could have been improved if midwives had also been trained and involved in the use of the Needs Checklist at the 'booking in' stage of pregnancy. This may have identified families in need at an earlier stage and ensured that they received preventive help more quickly and for a longer period before the birth. It may also be useful to amend the Checklist by adding a list of key resilience factors. This would encourage those using the Checklist to focus on the strengths and resources available to families, as well as, their vulnerabilities.

Working with Families to Prevent Problems

We have emphasised that effective primary prevention is reliant upon particular systems of care being in place. To be successful, primary prevention also depends on the skills and qualities of the practitioners involved. Practitioners need to understand the core stages and processes of helping, and to be able to build sound and productive partnerships with parents. Much of this book has already been taken up with describing the Parent Adviser approach to these fundamental aspects of helping. We would like to illustrate how this general approach can be applied to primary prevention.

A trusting parent–professional partnership needs sufficient time and appropriate conditions to develop. Regular and consistent contact with parents early in pregnancy provides the ideal opportunity to develop this type of safe and stable relationship. It is unrealistic to expect that parents, particularly those facing distressing personal problems and difficulties, will talk openly and confidently with helpers whom they have only just met or meet infrequently. Such contacts are likely to slip into a question and answer format led by the professional. This is an approach which may provide some, limited information to the helper. It will not usually offer the openings and opportunities by which the parent and the helper can explore the parent's circumstances in-depth. It is unlikely to lead to a deep understanding of how the parent's present circumstances may prompt and maintain difficulties during the early stages of parenthood. It will also make it difficult for helpers to use their knowledge and ideas to best effect.

Understanding the features and circumstances of a family's life, including risk and resilience factors, should be a process of shared exploration. This may, for example, entail talking through the relationship and family difficulties that a couple are experiencing, as well as, all other problems. It may then consider the implications of these for coping with the demands of parenthood and looking after the needs of their baby. Developing this type of commonly held view provides the foundation from which to identify and negotiate priorities and goals for preventive change. In practice this means working out with the parent how they would like their lives and circumstances to change and improve in realistic and achievable ways so that parenting and caregiving will be easier and less problematic. It is only at this stage that it is conceivable to develop and implement plans and action that achieve the two priorities of primary prevention; firstly, to help parents deal with the circumstances that are likely to make the subsequent care and nurture of their infant more difficult; and secondly, to help them improve the amount and quality of emotional and practical support available to them, develop suitable parenting qualities, skills and knowledge, as well as other sources of resilience and protection.

When the stages of helping are explicitly laid out in this manner, they can appear time consuming and potentially frustrating to those who want to prevent suffering as quickly as possible. The time, effort and success of prevention depends upon the nature and complexity of the risks faced by individual families, the qualities and characteristics of the parents and the helper, and their relationship. Our approach highlights the intrinsic value of working together with parents. Sometimes this type of relationship is achieved very quickly, because it is exactly what the parent wants; sometimes it is even initiated and driven by the parent. At other times, however, it will take time for a true working partnership to develop.

Although we have emphasised the need to begin primary prevention during pregnancy, it is important that these efforts continue into the postnatal period. The birth of the baby not only tests the robustness of these efforts, but also, as we have illustrated earlier, introduces new forms of risk. These additional factors include traumatic birth, maternal depression, and infant illness or disability. The arrival of the baby also provides further, new types of resilience, such as, the parents' affectional bonds for their newborn, the baby feeding and settling easily, family and friends providing good practical and emotional support. It is important that the helper continues to explore and understand these issues, so that they can provide appropriate support to vulnerable families as these events and processes unfold during the days and weeks after birth. The frequency of this contact should again be determined by the individual needs of the family.

By way of illustration we should like to return to the case of Hayley, the young mother, her boyfriend, Tony, and their baby outlined in Chapter 12. An antenatal assessment of need would have revealed that Hayley had very mixed feelings about her pregnancy; she had periods of tearfulness and was feeling low. She and her partner also had relationship difficulties. Furthermore, Hayley was living on a low income, in potentially unsuitable housing. In resilience terms, Hayley had a close and supportive relationship with her sister.

To be effective, a helper would need to explore all these issues with Hayley, and, if possible, with Tony, so that their significance and implications for their pregnancy and the birth could be understood. This would help to clarify any changes the couple could make before the arrival of their baby. For example, through the exploration of Hayley and Tony's relationship problems, it may have emerged that Tony too had mixed feelings about the pregnancy. He may have really wished to settled down with Hayley, but was worried that they were both too young to cope with parenthood. He may also have felt that having a baby would jeopardise his chances of going to college and a better future for the couple. As a result, Tony may have become increasingly frustrated, angry and aggressive, using drinking as a way of coping.

With help, the couple may have agreed goals to improve their communication, to agree the way forward for the pregnancy, to make longer term plans as a couple, including college courses, and to sort out the suitability of their living arrangements. Having agreed joint priorities and goals, the couple may then have needed further support to develop and implement their plans of action. For example, this may have required the health visitor to help the couple to talk through their thoughts and feelings about the future of the pregnancy. This might have helped Hayley and Tony to understand each other better, as well as, improve their communication. It may also have helped them to make a shared decision about the pregnancy.

Alternatively, with exploration, a different picture may have emerged of a couple with more substantial problems. For example, Tony may have felt that he had no responsibility towards Hayley or the pregnancy, and he may have refused to meet with the health visitor. Under these circumstances, the role of the health visitor would have been to work with Hayley alone to explore her situation fully and to help her to decide the best possible way forward. For example, if Hayley decided to proceed with the pregnancy on her own, then the health visitor would have tried to help her to identify suitable goals and strategies for herself and her baby, including developing further sources of practical and emotional support and dealing with housing and financial matters.

Although such efforts in the antenatal period may be valuable to families, it is not always the case that all difficulties will be prevented. Personal and family situations are likely to evolve and change with the birth and development of the baby. Support needs to be diverse, consistent and on-going within a general system of care as described, for example, in Chapter 1. However, since we have stressed the importance of the parent–infant relationship, we will focus upon specific strategies for attempting to facilitate and improve parent–infant interaction.

Early Intervention Strategies

Early intervention is a broad term that is used to cover many different aspects of care. Our use of the term here covers the provision of help and support as problems begin to develop, as well as interventions that can be offered during the earliest periods of life. Early intervention is intended to ensure that problems are managed swiftly, so that they do not become ingrained and well-established. However, it must be said that not all the problems of infancy are likely to be overcome from interventions solely provided by community practitioners. For example, parents with substantial and extensive problems, which put themselves, their infant or others at risk, are likely to need the help and support of a wide range of agencies, such as, child and adult mental health services, social services, community health and relevant voluntary agencies.

All sorts of psychosocial difficulties can arise during infancy. These may be related to adjustment and transition; for example, parents may find it hard to accept the changes in lifestyle and responsibilities that parenthood demands. Problems may be connected to the wider needs of parents; for instance, parents may not grasp and understand their baby's needs because of their own learning disability, or they may remain unaware and indifferent to their baby because of postnatal depression. On the other hand, early problems can arise because of the needs and characteristics of the baby, including a variety of illnesses and disabilities, or specific difficulties with, for example, frequent, lengthy and intense crying that is difficult to soothe.

Each of these, and the many other problems which can arise at this stage of life, will make the developmental tasks of parenting more difficult to negotiate. They may also interfere with the growing relationship between the parent and infant, and the care, nurture, protection and stimulation that this offers. It is not within the scope of this book to consider all the possible strategies available to address the problems of early parenting and infancy. Rather, we would like to concentrate on three very specific types of strategy which can be used to improve parent–infant relationships and interaction: 1) parent observation activities; 2) positive touch; and 3) early play.

Each of these aims to affect and improve the relationship and interaction between parents and infants using slightly different methods. They are similar, however, in their potential to affect the different components of parent–infant interaction. For example, each of the strategies aims: 1) to help parents become more observant and sensitive in monitoring their children; 2) to be more empathic in being able to interpret and make sense of the world from the infant's point of view; and 3) to acquire a wider, more responsive and consistent repertoire of skills to care for and nurture their infants. In implementing the strategies and exploring their effects, parents can also be encouraged to incorporate what they have learnt into their wider caregiving practices. These changes may then help troubled parents to develop a deeper affectional bond with their baby; improve their confidence in tackling other demands and stress, and cope better with the emotional demands of parenting.

As parents use the strategies, they will also stimulate and influence the infants' monitoring skills, their subsequent constructions and emergent behaviour. For example, the strategies will encourage infants to become more alert, attentive and prepared for interaction. These methods will also help them to develop a more stable, predictable and secure sense of themselves, their relationship with their parents, and the world around them. They will also facilitate the organisation and co-ordination of the perceptual, social, cognitive and motor abilities of the infant.

These strategies need to be suggested, used and negotiated with parents as part of the overall helping process advocated by the Parent Adviser model. In other words, the strategies should be developed and implemented in partnership with parents, on the basis of a shared understanding of the family's difficulties. The intention is that the strategies will help parents to reach their goals for change and will be used as part of their plan of action.

It is hoped that the methods to be described here will add to the knowledge, skills and expertise that helpers bring to their relationship with parents. A key part of this partnership, and the helping process more generally, is how helpers ensure that their knowledge, ideas and suggestions not only correspond to the needs of the parents but are also genuinely useful to them. This is more likely to occur if the helper's suggestions and strategies are offered in a tentative and invitational way so that they appear as possibilities rather than imperatives. This will promote a parent's sense of choice and participation. The parent may then find it easier to incorporate the suggestions into their own ideas. They may also find it easier to decline them, if they do not fit with their own needs.

Any plan of action that the parent and helper develop together needs to be realistic and achievable. A plan that is composed of a series of small, agreed steps which are clearly laid out and thought through is more likely to be successful. The practicalities of a particular strategy should be talked about beforehand so that both the parent and helper can anticipate and deal with any perceived problems or difficulties. Time also needs to be arranged and set aside for the parent and helper to continue to meet regularly, so that they can explore and review the implementation and progress of the plan. The overall plan, as well as the specific strategies being used, can then be altered and improved where necessary. This type of regular review is a crucial part of helping parents to achieve their goals. It helps parents to appreciate their successes, gives them encouragement, and enables them to look at the more general implications of the strategies for their parenting. It can also identify any problems with the overall plan of action, as well as with implementation.

Parent Observation Activities

The ways in which the inherent nature and abilities of an infant are expressed and shaped is unique to each infant and the family of which they are a part. Infants are naturally social and drawn to other people, particularly their primary caregivers; babies are more likely to look at, turn towards, listen to and respond to their mothers than anyone else. Since the parents' understanding and sensitivity to such characteristics and needs forms the basis of their caregiving and the child's subsequent development, it is important to ensure that their understanding is as developed as possible, and it is this that is the target of parent observation activities. This section will look at the ideas that underpin these activities, the types of infant behaviours and characteristics that can be used, the role of parents and helpers, and some suggestions about their successful use.

The general approach to parent observation activities is grounded in the work of Berry Brazelton (for example, Brazelton, 1992; Brazelton & Nugent, 1995). It has subsequently been incorporated into a number of intervention systems, including PIPPIN (Parr, 1999), for example, and the promotional interviews of the European Early Promotion Project described earlier. The basic idea is that parents spend structured periods of time concentrating upon, prompting and exploring the skills and abilities of their baby. At their core, the activities aim to bring the distinctive and individual nature and qualities of their baby alive for parents. In doing so, the activities help parents to appreciate, understand, and respond more appropriately to their infant's needs. The exact nature of the tasks will depend upon the parents and baby involved, the nature of their problems, and the intended goals for change.

Although called parent observation activities, the overall aim of the strategy is not just for helpers to guide and encourage parents so that their monitoring becomes more sensitively attuned to the signs, reactions and behaviour of their baby. It is assumed that these changes in awareness, and the experience as a whole, will subsequently affect both the parents' constructs of the baby and their behaviour, and subsequently the development of the infant.

The infant characteristics used as the basis of parent observation tasks can include their visual and auditory abilities and preferences, motor and communication responses to parental prompts and stimulation, as well as their arousal states and moods. For example, parents could be encouraged to observe their baby's reactions to changes in facial expression. They might begin by adopting a blank expressionless face, then open and close their mouths and eyes, smile broadly or poke out their tongue. These expressions are chosen because they are highly likely to evoke greater interest and reaction from the baby. Alternatively, they could monitor the amount of attention the baby gives to the mother's face compared with the faces of other adults, such as, the helper. As the baby gets a little older, parents might also be encouraged to make slow predictable movements of their head from side to side across the infant's field of vision. This will help them to realise and experiment with the baby's ability to track and follow movement. It should be remembered that parents need to be close to their baby when using any of these visual prompts so that infant is able to focus and clearly see what the parents are doing.

In the same way as experimenting with babies' visual capacity, observation activities can also focus on their responses to sound. For example, parents might observe reactions to their own voice in comparison to other voices and noises. They might explore the baby's reactions to 'motherese' in comparison with other sounds, such as more adult speech or a monologue. Then again, parents could concentrate on the social and communicative efforts and responses of their infants. For example, they might observe the vocalisations, leg kicks, arm waving and other early signs of infant communication that often occur as a co-ordinated response to sustained parental attention.

Other observational activities might include monitoring the infant's moods, preferences, reflexes and other behaviours, such as, rooting, sucking and hand to mouth behaviour. For example, parents could watch how the baby appears when calm and alert in contrast to when unsettled, restless or irritable. As part of the activity, the parent could observe the baby's facial expressions, muscle tone and responsiveness in these different emotional states. Alternatively, they could keep a note of what appears to trigger and maintain the infant's moods, for example, what calms, consoles and soothes, and what irritates and upsets the baby.

The following is an example of the use of an observation activity as one aspect of the intervention with a depressed mother, Angela. She had become increasingly withdrawn, low in mood and energy. She had lost confidence in herself and found it difficult to spend time with her four week old baby, Naomi. As a consequence, she frequently failed to notice the baby's signs of interest in her, and had come to believe that Naomi did not readily respond to, or love, her. This exacerbated Angela's low mood and she began to avoid close contact with Naomi.

Angela really wanted the situation between herself and Naomi to be different. In particular, since Angela wanted Naomi to be more responsive towards her (her goal), her health visitor thought that some observational and prompting activities might be useful. She thought that these would give Angela a chance to see how her own behaviour could invigorate and energise Naomi's interest in her. As part of the plan to help, Angela's health visitor agreed to spend some sessions with Angela and Naomi so that they could get to know each other better. At the first session, the health visitor encouraged Angela to hold Naomi in her arms rather than have her in the Moses basket as was usually the case when she visited. She then asked Angela to watch her daughter's reactions closely, particularly the direction and quality of her gaze when the three of them were together. The health visitor commented on the increased time Naomi spent looking at her mother in comparison with other objects in her field of vision, including the health visitor.

The health visitor then encouraged Angela to change her facial expressions and watch Naomi's reaction, which was of increased attention and interest. Angela was surprised and gratified by this, but was not sure that the reactions were just by chance or because the health visitor was present. They explored this and Angela decided to repeat her observations with Naomi over the following days and to discuss them at the next visit.

In this example, the observational activities prompted and encouraged Naomi's natural social interest and preference for her mother. The activities also gave Angela a new experience of her baby. When repeated, with the guidance and support of her health visitor, these new experiences helped to challenge Angela's constructions about feeling unloved and Naomi being unlovable. This helped Angela to feel closer to Naomi and to value herself more as a parent. These and other similar activities helped Angela to change the way she related to her daughter more generally; they increased her sense of pleasure, satisfaction and self-efficacy and were eventually associated with improvements in Angela's general mood.

As in this example, parent observation activities are unlikely to be effective if they are undertaken on an ad hoc or casual basis. It is better if they occur regularly and systematically. They need to take place at a time when the parent and the baby can concentrate on each other. Parents need to relax in a situation that is free from distractions (e.g. loud noise, music, television and the presence of other children). The baby should be awake, alert, and not hungry or unsettled. Once parents have gained confidence and enthusiasm, they can begin to experiment with the conditions, circumstances and environment used for the activities. For example, the baby's responses and attention to the mother could be observed while the television is on, or when other distractions are present.

The length of the observational activities will depend upon the age of the infant and the content of the activity. For example, an activity which simply involves regular parental observation, such as watching the baby's mood, may happen more frequently, perhaps several times a day. Activities that involve stimulation and interaction with the baby should be relatively brief in duration to avoid tiring or over-stimulating her/him. These activities can be highly arousing for babies and they can easily become overloaded. Signs of this include the infant turning her gaze and becoming self-absorbed, changes in facial expression, such as frowns and grimaces, or even possetting.

As with all strategies, if parents are to experiment between visits, the role of the helper is to work with the parents to enable careful planning of the observational tasks and anticipation of any problems. They need to decide what activities are going to be used, when, where and how. At first, however, helpers should be present during the observational activities and share them with the parents. In doing so, they can coach, encourage and tentatively guide them in what to do, as well as help interpret their observations of the child. Parents may need gentle help and assistance to adjust and modify the type and intensity of the observational activities so that they suit the mood, temperament and responses of the individual baby. This might include encouraging them to slow down, for example, and give time for the baby to respond to what they are doing. It might also include helping them to avoid abrupt movements and noises that might alarm the baby or disrupt its concentration. This should be done, however, in partnership, without being intrusive or dominant. Care should also be taken to avoid a situation in which they take over and simply demonstrate their own superior skills in relating to infants.

Beyond planning and implementation, the helper has an essential role in exploring the experience, meaning and implications of the activities with the parent. This exploration needs to be based on the wider skills and qualities of the Parent Adviser model as described earlier in the book. When exploring observation activities, it is perhaps most useful to begin by encouraging parents to describe what they noticed during the activity, including both about what they themselves were doing and the reactions of the baby. This helps to gauge and understand the parent's constructions, which can then be discussed, explored and elaborated as appropriate. This might involve the helper in steering parents towards aspects of the activity which are particularly pertinent to their goals.

When undertaking observation activities without the helper present, parents should, if practical, write down or record their observations. This can help jog their memory, when talking the activities through with the helper, but it can also give a record of how things change over time.

Such observational activities and associated discussion are intended to challenge parents to change their constructions; to learn about their children's behaviour and ability. For example, a parent who saw her baby as continually crying and demanding discovered from her observations that she cried much less than anticipated. However, it can also give parents an insight into the baby's experience or constructions. For example, parents who finds it difficult to empathise and identify with their baby could be asked about the experience of the activity from their baby's point of view. This could be prompted with questions, such as, 'What do you think your baby saw?'; 'How do you think she/he felt?'; 'Your baby seems to like it when you do that, why do you think that is?' This type of exploration may enable parents to realise, for example, that their baby is a person with a mind and to begin to see how that mind might to operating.

The activities also give parents the chance to try out new ways of responding. For example, parents who initially feel their baby's behaviour is somehow knowingly wilful and difficult may come to realise that he/she is sensitive to noise, for example, or becomes unsettled with too much stimulation. As a result, they might decide to reduce the levels of ambient noise (e.g. sounds from the television) or to accommodate their new understanding by being more gentle, not suddenly intruding, but watching what the baby is doing. They might learn to avoid over-stimulating her/him in spite of their own desire for closeness and interaction. They might also come to realise that the baby's crying is a communication, indicating, for example, the need for relaxed and gentle soothing and not a tense, impatient and distressed response which serves only to exacerbate his/her discomfort.

Throughout these exploratory discussions, it is often helpful to focus, explore and build upon perceptive observations made by the parents and responsive interactions between them and their baby, as opposed to picking up on problematic behaviour. This is likely to help the parent feel more positive and builds upon what they are doing well. There will, of course, always be exceptions to this, since it is not always possible to ignore negative interactions. However, even here, such sensitive issues can still be approached in a respectful, warm, constructive and empathic manner.

These observation activities are based upon the parent systematically prompting, watching and reacting to their infant's behaviour. This type of approach will suit some parents and may be particularly helpful during the very early stages of infancy. However it will not match the needs of all parents. We will now turn to consider a different approach based upon the guided use of touch.

Positive Touch

Parents instinctively hold, rock, touch and stroke their infants. Different methods of touch are an age old and routine part of infant caregiving traditions in many parts of the world. Recent empirical evidence suggests that infant massage has been found to increase growth, improve parent–infant interaction and change infant and maternal behaviour (Field, Grizzle, Scafidi et al, 1996; Malphurs, Larrain, Field et al, 1996; Onozawa, Glover, Adams et al, 2001). Infant massage techniques have become commonly available in the UK through self-help books, such as McClure (2000). They are often incorporated into postnatal advice and workshops. Infant massage is used to help parents manage some of the minor illnesses and problems of infancy (e.g. colic). It is also now a part of the care given to premature infants and those with special needs. However the use and application of infant massage in these circumstances requires appropriate training and supervision.

The focus here is on the use of touch techniques as a purposeful strategy to improve the relationship and interaction between parents and their infants. The idea is that parents' regular use of touch with their babies, accompanied by guided exploration with the helper will enable them to concentrate upon the infant's responses, as signs and signals of the baby's experience. By seeing these as communication, parents may become more receptive towards their infant's needs, and interpret and respond to these more appropriately. For example, parents may begin to derive pleasure and satisfaction from seeing their baby relaxed and comfortable. This may begin to deepen their bond with the baby and boost their own confidence as a parent. Intrusive parents may learn to slow their touch strokes or gently bring the routine to a conclusion in response to their babies' signs of disengagement and discomfort.

Such changes in parental receptiveness are likely to have considerable benefits for the relationship and for the child. However, positive touch alone may have much to offer. For example, babies may enjoy the stimulation and relaxation, develop a greater awareness of their own body, improve their muscle tone and suppleness, as well as, improve the co-ordination between their senses, thoughts and actions.

This section will cover the preparation and setting required for the use of positive touch, and the general skills, techniques and processes involved. It will also look at the role of the helper in negotiating, coaching, and exploring the use of positive touch as a strategy for change. Readers wishing to learn more about infant massage and specific techniques are encouraged to contact a trained and qualified infant massage practitioner in their local area. Alternatively, they can contact the International Association of Infant Massage UK Chapter for advice and information.

The use of positive touch requires parents and helpers to think about a range of practical issues. For example, although touch may be used all the time in many different circumstances, it may be helpful for parents to find a regular period in the day to concentrate on this activity. This obviously needs to be convenient for the parents, and at a time when the baby is awake and receptive. Many young infants seem to prefer the morning but, as they grow older, positive touch can become an important part of the bedtime routine.

Before commencing a touch routine, it is important to gauge the mood and feelings of the baby. Prompts and signs of engagement from the baby consist of a bright-eyed focused expression, calm attentiveness, and relaxed arms, shoulders, palms and posture. Although they may be soothed by the routine, infants who are uncomfortable or distressed are unlikely to engage or benefit. Signs of this might include gaze aversion, yawning, arching the back, grimacing, anxious tongue poking, unsettled crying, falling asleep, and stiff, tense legs and arms. In a similar vein, parents also need to be in a focused and relaxed state with sufficient time for the routine. Being rushed or distracted will certainly not help them to respond sensitively to their baby's cues, nor encourage the baby's attentiveness and composure.

In general, infants should feel safe, warm, comfortable and at ease. Noise, harsh lighting and draughts should be avoided, as well as anything that is likely to unsettle or disturb the child (or parent for that matter). Since they may not like being completely undressed, very young babies can at first be stroked through or underneath their clothes, though older children may enjoy being unclothed. The child might be comfortable in a variety of positions, including lying on a soft, padded baby mat, sitting cuddled on the parent's lap or being cradled between the parent's legs, while sitting cross-legged on the floor, or with legs extended and the back supported. However it is done, parents also need to be comfortable or they will be distracted and not enjoy what they are doing with the child.

It is important to have the necessary equipment readily to hand. This includes a soft towel, nappies, extra clothes, wipes and suitable massage oil, if it is being used. It is quite useful to keep the oil in a small lidded container or bottle so that it cannot be spilt. Mineral oils and vegetable oils can both be used for massage, and should be poured onto the parent's hands a little at a time until sufficient, rather than directly onto the baby's skin.

Both types of oil have advantages and disadvantages. Mineral oils, for example, are safe due to their purity; they contain no allergens and do not irritate the skin. They have a long shelf life; cleanse and moisturise the skin; and are relatively inexpensive. However, they do not penetrate the skin and leave it feeling greasy and slippery. Many mineral oils are also rather strongly scented.

Vegetable oils are less greasy and more easily absorbed into the skin, leaving it to function naturally. Almost all are odourless and they are good for softening the skin. On the other hand, not all vegetable oils are safe for infants. Some cold pressed oils may be of poor quality and contain contaminants, while others, for example, nut oils, can cause sensitisation to the skin as they contain allergens. Vegetable oils also have a shorter shelf life, vary in quality and are more expensive.

Having found a quiet comfortable place free from distractions and intrusions, parents should take a few moments to relax and compose themselves. This can be done, for example, by taking a few gentle, deep breaths, perhaps repeating the word 'Relax' slowly and quietly to themselves as they exhale. As they do this, they can begin to focus on the infant and keep other thoughts at bay. It is wise, particularly with very young or sensitive babies, to simply place a resting hand somewhere on their skin, as a way of introducing the activity and soliciting their permission. This gives the opportunity to gauge the mood and interest of the baby, and helps her/him to anticipate and prepare for the touch routine.

In the first few weeks, most babies only need a few gentle strokes while they are being cuddled and cradled, without particular attention to any one area of the body. After three months or so, they will probably begin to enjoy longer routines. Parents should start a positive touch session with slow rhythmic strokes, the speed and timing of which should be regulated by the infant's body signals. The parent's hand contact should be unhurried and smooth, and the strokes should mould to the shape of the baby's body. The parent should try to concentrate and sense the mood, muscle tone and movement of their baby. As this happens, the parent will begin to feel the baby's active co-operation, participation and involvement in the routine through the sensation of touch.

A range of touch strokes and movements can be used. Examples of these include milking strokes of the arms and legs. When using this stroke for the arm, the baby's wrist is held in one hand. The parent then makes a bracelet shape around the arm with the other hand. This hand then gently slides from the shoulder to the wrist. The movement is repeated with the parent's hands alternating as they slide in one flowing motion down the baby's arm. While using this type of stroke, the parent should be careful not to lift the baby's body. The stroke is used in a similar way with the baby's legs. Paddle wheel strokes use the palms of the parent's hands to stroke the baby's tummy, with one hand following the other in a fluid rotating movement. The 'I love you' stroke is also used on the baby's stomach. Using the right hand, the parent makes a single downward stroke on the left side of the baby's tummy. This is followed by drawing an upside down 'L' shape going from the baby's right to left. Finally, the parent makes an inverted 'U' shape going from the baby's lower right side, up and around the tummy button, and down to the left side of the tummy. The parent can repeat the words 'I love you' as they go through the stroke.

Gentle circular movements can be used around the baby's jaws and hands. For example, the baby's hand is held by the parent who then uses circular movements of their thumb to gently rub the baby's palm. Babies' feet can be massaged using strokes with the index finger from the base of the toes to the heel whilst the baby's ankle is gently supported with one hand. More detailed information about these and other strokes should be sought from a trained and experienced infant massage practitioner as appropriate.

Once the parent has gained a little confidence, and the baby is familiar and comfortable with the experience, the parent can begin to experiment with the strokes and routine. For example, the stroke pressure can be adjusted from lighter to firmer, and the rhythm from slower to faster. The parent can try using different areas of the hand, from finger tips to the flat of the hand. The routines can also incorporate still touch and momentary rests between strokes. Babies generally find tentative, fluttering, ticklish strokes or poking uncomfortable, and these should be avoided. The touch routine should always end with the habit of winding down, using gentle soothing strokes and cuddling, followed by a quiet, still time between the parent and infant. Once the baby has become used to positive touch, the parent might also have music, which the infant is likely to find relaxing, playing quietly in the background.

Practitioners should be aware of the limitations, contraindications and cautions in using positive touch with infants. These should be fully discussed with parents. For example, the infant's skin should always be tested for sensitivity, particularly when using vegetable oils. Caution should be exercised when using strokes. Positive touch for infants differs from adult massage. For example, it is important not to use forcing movements, or to be too vigorous or firm. Parents should always remain sensitive to their baby's cues, and they should halt when the baby shows any signs of discomfort or disengagement. The parent and practitioner should always discuss the health of the baby before beginning to work in this way. Touch routines should be avoided when a baby has a high temperature, and specialist advice should be sought if a child has a serious medical condition. Obviously skin conditions (e.g. eczema), cuts or infections need particular care.

The use of positive touch as a strategy for helping to improve parent–infant interaction should adhere to the principles of the Parent Adviser approach outlined earlier. For instance, positive touch should be used within the context of a sound helping relationship. It should not be imposed, but implemented within the helping process, like any other possible strategy, to achieve goals that have already been agreed with the parents. As always, planning and implementation should be adjusted to the individual circumstances and needs of the parent and infant. Parents should certainly understand the aims and purpose of the methods they use. This should be ensured by the helper, who also has a role in explaining, coaching and guiding the parent to use positive touch techniques, as well as, exploring their effects on the parent, infant and their relationship.

Again an exploratory approach should be used, as described earlier in relation to parent observation activities. The focus and direction of this exploration should be based on the parent's needs. For example, when using positive touch with parents who lack confidence in responding to their baby, helpers should encourage, praise, explore and help parents to elaborate their observations of their infant's reactions. This might include the parent's attention to their baby's prompts and cues, and their sensitivity to infant's growing familiarity and response to touch. The parent could also be encouraged to try different ways of using touch strokes. Whatever is done with a specific parent and child, the intention of exploring the situation in this way is again to help parents observe and understand their children better, discover different ways of handling and caring for them, and recognise their own skills and competence.

Early Play

Positive touch uses a predominantly physical and non-verbal approach in attempting to improve parent–infant interaction. In contrast, early play, the final method of intervention to be considered in this chapter, highlights the use of songs, rhymes and other verbal activities. We will look briefly at some fundamental aspects of parent–infant play, explore examples of the play activities that parents commonly use with their babies, and then look at issues for both parents and helpers, when play is employed as part of a purposeful strategy to improve parent–infant relationships.

Play, itself, is an everyday occurrence. These seemingly ordinary and routine activities are rarely given a second thought by many. They are, however, an essential part of the lives of parents and children. They provide the opportunity to share the intrinsic value of fun and enjoyment together. On the other hand, play is also used by parents to occupy, distract, and alter infant moods. For instance, a parent may start singing a cheerful, jolly song to capture the interest and attention of her baby, who has become tired and fractious on a long car journey. On another occasion, a lullaby may be chosen to calm and soothe the baby. Most importantly of all, play provides parents and infants with opportunities to make vital discoveries. They have the chance to learn, practise and develop their skills and abilities with each other. The experience of seeing and feeling an infant communicating during play can have a powerful effect on the parent. It can create new levels of intimacy, as well as, strengthen and enrich the relationship that exists between them.

At its best, play, like other forms of interaction, involves a continuous interplay between the thoughts, feelings and actions of the parent and infant. Play is often initiated and guided by the parent, but is it primarily centred on the needs of the infant. The direction and endpoint of the play depends upon the attention, interest and reactions of the infant. In essence, the parent has to sense the baby's interest in the parent's initial playful prompts. These, for example, might be the first lines of a rhyme, or the shake of a rattle or other toy. The parent will pause momentarily, waiting for the baby's response and, at the same time, gauge the meaning of this response. If encouraged by the baby's reactions, the parent then builds upon and augments these responses using repetition, exaggeration and magnification. When their ideas and desires correspond, a playful rapport will develop between the parent and infant, and then deepen. In the midst of this ebb and flow, it then becomes difficult to see clearly who is initiating and leading the play, and who is following and responding.

Through play, infants learn to focus their attention and build concentration. It helps them to co-ordinate perceptual and motor abilities (e.g. hand-eye co-ordination) and to acquire and practise preverbal, social and communication skills. Playful interaction can prompt emotions such as, delight, surprise, excitement and satisfaction in the infant. The intensity of these interactions enables them to become familiar with and rehearse the content of play activities. For example, they learn to recognise the melodies and actions of nursery rhymes very quickly. At the same time, they become used to and comfortable with the emotional quality and nature of the parent's play.

During play, parents need to watch and listen to their infants closely, so that they can judge their reactions and feelings accurately. This monitoring enables parents to alter and adapt their playful behaviour to suit the infant. This adds to the parents' knowledge (or constructions) of their baby and of themselves. It also, inevitably, changes their behaviour. For example, through play they may see how their baby enjoys excitement and surprise, and will subsequently begin to weave this more into their playful activities. In contrast, other parents may realise that their baby is easily unsettled and alarmed, and, as a result, will manage surprise much more carefully to avoid startling and upsetting him/her. Parents often show their pleasure and enjoyment during play through smiles, strokes and cuddles, which are adult responses that infants find especially stimulating and pleasing.

The most common forms of play that parents use with infants involve songs, rhymes and games, although with the availability of Book Start and other similar schemes, books are also becoming an increasing part of the repertoire. There is an almost endless, and ever expanding, variety of known nursery rhymes and songs. Songs and rhymes bring together words, melody, rhythm and movements in seemingly straightforward ways. Though apparently simple, they are able to convey and evoke a whole range of feelings, emotions and responses. Some, for example, 'Rock A-Bye Baby' and other lullabies have slow, soothing melodies and rhythms. Singing songs such as this can almost effortlessly induce gentle rocking motions and feelings of calm. Others, for example, 'The Wheels on the Bus' and 'The Grand Old Duke of York' have more lively and vibrant tempos which encourage energy, movement and activity. The uncomplicated words and form of these nursery songs mean that they are easy for parents to remember. But perhaps more importantly, their simplicity is attractive to infants and enables them to be understood, recognised and remembered. For example, even quite young infants become tense and excited as they anticipate a particularly enjoyable part of a fun, action song. Songs and rhymes are ideal for improvisation. For example, parents can exaggerate pauses during a song to create feelings of anticipation and reactions of surprise. Alternatively the tempo of a favourite song can be gradually slowed to calm and soothe a baby.

Songs and rhymes also incorporate other forms of play. For example, rhyme, simple actions and anticipation, as well as, tickling are combined in games such as 'Round and Round the Garden' and 'This Little Piggy'. Other verbal activities include infant-led communication games in which the movements and sounds of the baby are copied and imitated by the parent. In games such as these, the parent might improvise by repeating the sounds of the baby and gradually changing them to make words and other interesting noises. Even more simply, infants can be included and involved in everyday conversation. The parent can talk about and describe what they are doing during routine ordinary activities. The subject of conversation, for example, might be changing the baby's nappy, or doing the washing up. The vital component is the inclusion of the infant as an active participant in the conversation, for example, by leaving space and time for the baby to respond. This type of activity can sometimes take conscious effort on the part of the parent as growing up often involves learning to keep thoughts to oneself.

Other games which rely less on verbal communication include 'Peek A-Boo', water play, and the use of toys, rattles and safe interesting household objects. 'Peek a Boo' essentially involves the infant seeing the parent's face repeatedly disappear and then reappear. It might begin with the parent sitting close to the baby. Once the baby's interest has been captured, the parent then covers her face with her hands for a few moments. The parent then opens her hands, revealing her face, accompanied by a call of 'Peek a Boo'. The game tempts the infant's interest in the disappearance of the mother's face, then surprise and relief at its reappearance. Once repeated, the infant begins to anticipate, predict and become excited about the return of the face.

Many babies love water, although some do not. It is a fascinating source of multi-sensory stimulation, in terms of what it feels like, the way it moves, its sound and the way light reflects and sparkles on its surface. When very young, a parent can just gently wash the water over the baby's tummy when having a bath, talking and sharing the feelings and stimulation. As the infant gets a little older, parents can encourage water play using spoons or containers in the bath. The toys and utensils can be chosen so that some float, while others sink. Once again, the parent's role in these non-verbal games is one of helping and assisting the infant's play; carefully adding to and enhancing the ideas of the infant rather than being either passive or overly intrusive.

Parents can also assemble a 'treasure basket' for their baby. This is simply a small box of developmentally appropriate toys and objects which are interesting and enjoyable to the infant. The box only needs a few items in it at any one time, and these can be gradually changed, with new ones added and others removed.

While these games and their effects will be useful to all parents, the purpose here is to look at how they can be utilised as part of a purposeful strategy to help parents improve their interaction with their baby. The core processes by which this can be achieved are similar to those described for the parent observation activities and positive touch. These will now be familiar to the reader and we reiterate them here at the cost of being tiresome. However, early play strategies need to be used at the appropriate stage of the helping process once a good enough relationship has formed between the parent and helper. Early play activities can then be carefully used as part of a parent's plan of action to improve their relationship with their infant and to overcome their problems.

Ideally, parents should set aside regular specific times in the day to use the agreed play activities with their infant. This, of course, does not preclude play at other times. In fact, the idea is that the successful use of planned early play would encourage and improve the quality of spontaneous play at other times. Rather than simply encouraging parents to play and interact as a general strategy, our approach assumes careful planning of their activities with specific times each day set aside for them. This helps parents to concentrate on the task at hand for short periods at least and to learn something of play. However, it also facilitates their skills of observing or monitoring their baby and attempting to be empathic (in terms of trying to make sense of the babies' constructions). It can foster the development of a reflective approach to their own constructions of the baby and their role as parents, and enables them to experiment with new ways of responding. Above all, if the activities are usually fun and enjoyable, then it will encourage parents and children to look forward to continuing such activities and will cement their relationship.

Play sessions need to be set up at times of the day when the parent is relaxed and the infant is alert and settled, without distractions or other demands. The sessions may, at first, take place with the helper present, so that she/he can provide encouragement, exploration of the different skills and strategies involved, and discussion of the experience. Many parents are often quite self-conscious about their voices and will sometimes suggest using tapes rather than actually singing themselves. However, it is important to talk this through, highlighting the value and preference that the baby has for the mother's own voice.

While we have given a few play ideas above, these are only by way of illustration. The choice of play activities should be determined by the developmental and individual needs of the infant, as well as, the preferences of the infant and parent. In fact, it is best to encourage parents to come up with their own ideas and activities. This can become an exploratory activity in itself, and is often pleasurable for the parent and helper. Most adults, even those who are not yet parents, will remember and piece together songs, rhymes and games from their own childhood. This promotes the active participation of the parent, and shows respect for their ideas. It is also likely to generate suggestions with which the parent is more comfortable, familiar and, probably, confident. They are therefore more likely to put them into practice.

As with other strategies, parents need to be sensitive to the engagement and disengagement cues of the infant. It is helpful for parents to become used to some set activities with their infants before encouraging improvisation. At an appropriate stage, parents also need to think about how to incorporate play activities into everyday routines; for example, learning how and when to use songs and rhymes during feeding, changing, getting dressed and settling.

In keeping with the approach taken with the previous strategies, helpers have a role in facilitating the parent's use of early play activities with their infants. However, it is equally important to then explore the parents' experiences of these activities with them. As described earlier, these exploratory efforts should be guided by the parents' own goals and based upon an awareness of the cycle of parent–infant interaction.

To illustrate this exploratory process, we will outline below a short piece of dialogue between a parent and helper. The parent, Jackie, had trouble forming a bond with her son, Aaron, in the weeks after he was born. She talked the problem over with her health visitor, when Aaron was about three weeks old. It appeared that the problems arose partly because Jackie found it difficult to believe in herself. She also felt frequently criticised and undermined by her own mother. With the help of her health visitor, Jackie decided that she needed to get to know Aaron better, and to feel more confident in herself. As part of the plan to achieve this, Jackie decided to have regular play sessions with Aaron. Initially the health visitor was present during the sessions, encouraging, guiding and exploring with her what she was doing and experiencing. Jackie then began doing the sessions on a daily basis and discussing progress during the health visitor's weekly visits. At first, she was quite hesitant during the play and frequently believed that she was doing something wrong. However, with careful, gentle encouragement and exploration, she became quite used to the process. The dialogue below comes from a visit with her health visitor after Jackie and Aaron had been doing the play sessions for a few weeks.

HV: How have your play sessions been going this week?
Jackie: They've been going alright. I think we've managed to do them most days this week like we agreed.
HV: That's really good; it can't always be easy. What have you been doing?
Jackie: Well, this morning we did some singing. We did 'Wheels on the Bus' and then we did 'This Little Piggy', and then 'Twinkle Twinkle

Little Star'. He got really excited during 'This Little Piggy'.

HV: Ah. What was Aaron doing when he got excited?

Jackie: Oh, his eyes lit up. They were all bright and shiny, and he really started wriggling when I tickled him. And then he started to kind of wave his arms in the air. He looked so cute.

HV: Its sounds like he had a great time. It sounds like you had a good time together. How did you feel during the songs?

Jackie: Well, at the time, I really enjoyed them too. It was good to feel that we were having a nice time together at last. At times, it's felt like it was never going to happen.

HV: How do you mean?

Jackie: Well. When Aaron was born, I just felt that I couldn't cope. I had thought there would be a magic spark and I would feel great. But it didn't happen. I was tired and exhausted. And my Mum was constantly at me. I felt useless and I thought it was never going to go away.

HV: What about when you were playing yesterday, how did you feel about yourself then?

Jackie: It was different. I could really see Aaron looking at me. Like he really wanted to be with me. We were really having fun together.

HV: How does that make you feel?

Jackie: (eyes becoming tearful): It makes me feel much more like a proper Mum. More how I would like to be, but never thought I would. I feel like he wants me, and loves me. And I feel like I can start loving him back.

In this brief dialogue, the health visitor initially concentrates on and explores Aaron's reactions during the play session. As things have gone well, it gives the opportunity for her to highlight Aaron's enjoyment. It also concentrates attention on Jackie's sensitive and pleasurable observations of her son. This in itself could have been explored further. However, the health visitor chose to use a series of simple, prompting questions to focus on the mother's feeling about herself during the play session. This was a key issue for her, and the purpose of these prompts was to explore, and then reinforce, the positive changes that have occurred in how Jackie felt about herself and towards Aaron. On the basis of this dialogue, the health visitor might then move on to get a sense of how confident the mother felt about her changing perceptions of Aaron, of herself and their interaction.

In this section, we outlined the potential value for using early play as a method for improving the interaction and relationships between parents and their infants. It is likely that early play strategies, as well as, the other two approaches that have been outlined above, will be used as one aspect of a parent's overall plan of action. The complex nature of many problems means that these strategies will often be used in conjunction with other methods and approaches so that the goals of a family are met.

In Conclusion

In this chapter, we have highlighted the valuable role that community practitioners have in working with all families to encourage effective parent–child interaction, enhance family adaptation, and strengthen their ability to manage the demands and stresses of parenthood. In addition to this promotional function, we believe that community practitioners are extremely well placed to identify and work with families who are at risk of developing problems. In essence, this means providing targeted preventive help so that families can deal successfully with the risk factors to which they are exposed and, at the same time, build and reinforce sources of resilience. Finally, it is important that practitioners are able to provide help and support to parents so that the problems that do arise during this early phase of family life can be tackled as soon as possible, and before they become entrenched.

This chapter has also outlined and illustrated a range of methods and strategies, such as, the promotional interviews and the Needs Checklist of the European Early Promotion Project, and the use of parent observation activities, positive touch and early play. These various tools and methods may be incorporated into any number of different promotional, prevention and intervention approaches. However, it is crucial that they are applied within the context of effective helping relationships. The success and usefulness of these methods will depend upon the nature and circumstances of the family, the stage of the parent–helper partnership, and the skills, qualities and knowledge of the helper.

The effectiveness of these approaches will also be reliant upon the type of service system in which an individual practitioner works. Successful approaches to promotion, prevention and early intervention need to ensure that there is sufficient contact with all families. Services need to ensure that vulnerable families are identified as early as possible, and that such families are able to receive frequent, home based support from pregnancy onwards. Practitioners themselves need to be encouraged to prioritise the kinds of early intervention approaches we have outlined, but, furthermore, they need to be adequately trained initially and subsequently receive ongoing supervision and support from experienced colleagues.

Prevention and early intervention programmes provided on this basis can reduce the chances of children suffering complex, long term problems. However, there will always be some parents and infants who will need the sustained help and support from more specialist services and agencies. It is therefore important that the links and access to such services are straightforward and efficient.

The successful negotiation of this early period of life provides infants with an extraordinary and profound relationship with their parents. From this, children are able to develop a fundamental and secure sense of themselves and the world around them. The parents, at the same time, can become established and skilful in their nurturing and caregiving role. However, important developmental challenges lie ahead for them both, and the next chapter will move the journey of parents and children beyond the first twelve months and into the toddler stage.

CHAPTER 14
PARENTING TODDLERS AND YOUNG CHILDREN

In Chapter 2 we began by looking at the needs of parents and children and acknowledged that the task of parenting is not necessarily easy in any circumstances and that with any additional stresses it can become very difficult. As we set the scene we presented strong arguments for a general system of care in which all parents should have access to support at all stages of the developmental process. Whilst acknowledging that most parents cope most of the time, there is a large number for whom extra support should be available before more serious problems arise.

When we considered the aims of helping we were concerned to ensure that parents were listened to so that they could clarify and explore their problems in order to facilitate the well being of their children. To do this effectively helpers have to work in ways that enable parents; ways that reduce their vulnerabilities and increase their abilities and resources. We understood this in terms of strengthening their self-esteem, self-efficacy, social skills, social and practical support and their problem solving skills. In addition, a key concept to all of this was the establishment of a partnership with the helper that facilitated the process of helping and sustained it throughout.

In the last two chapters we began to consider the task of parenting, which we underpinned by a model of interaction between parent and child. This is a model that fits the innate social characteristics children bring into the world, enables their needs to be met, and requires parents to be highly attuned to their infants. This interaction is of paramount importance for the child's development. We have already explored issues to do with parenting in the first year. In particular we focused on an understanding of the adaptation to parenting, and on seeking ways to promote the parent–infant relationship, prevent subsequent problems, and intervene appropriately where necessary.

What we intend now is to consider the task of parenting toddlers and young children from 12 months of age to about eight years. Clearly the relationship of the parent and child will have been established at least initially in the all-important first year. However, as children become more mobile, develop ever-increasing verbal skills and are subject to influences other than the home, the task appears to become more complex. Parenting in this context is not an easy job and one for which little or no training is given.

Therefore, what we should like to do is to explore a model of parenting, so that the reader can be guided in providing more effective help for parents in both preventing and dealing with common problems.

We will begin by presenting some ideas about overall qualities that relate to parenting appropriately, and then look at some of the specific skills needed to be with children and to enable their development.

Before continuing, however, we should like to make clear, without labouring the ideas throughout, that we are proposing a model of parenting that is based upon and parallel to the models underlying the Parent Adviser approach. Central to this, as described earlier in the book, are a set of frameworks to do with people anticipating or construing each other, a process of helping initiated ideally by a relationship in the form of a partnership, and a set of qualities and skills to establish the relationship and pursue the process. Although it may not be an exact fit in all respects, we are asking the reader to apply all these frameworks to the context of parenting and to see to what extent the models of the parent–helper situation are useful as a way of guiding parents. This was true in the last chapter and will continue now within the context of somewhat older children. However, the task as described in relation to infants, the importance of the interaction, the understanding of risk, resilience and ideas about prevention should not be forgotten in the present context.

Key Qualities of Parents

We have seen in chapter 11 that the parenting task is one of protecting, nurturing and fostering the overall development of children. Central to this task is a process of being aware of the child's needs at all the different stages of development and trying to provide for them appropriately. The basic skills of how this is accomplished will be analysed later in the chapter, but we assume that there are general qualities in parents that facilitate the processes and the practice of their skills.

There is considerable research on the characteristics of parents and the effects of these on children. This includes, for example, the work of Maccoby & Martin (1983) on parenting styles, which are shown in Figure 14.1.

These four styles can be understood in terms of two basic dimensions of: 1) love, warmth or acceptance versus rejection; and 2) control or directiveness versus permissiveness or absence of control. Interestingly, these styles have been related to outcomes for children's development. As described by Bee (2000) the best are for children of authoritative parents, who are loving and warm, but do have clear rules and set limits on the behaviour of the children. This style seems to be associated with children who have higher self-esteem, are generally better adjusted, and are more independent, compliant, and outgoing.

FIGURE 14.1 TYPOLOGY OF PARENTING

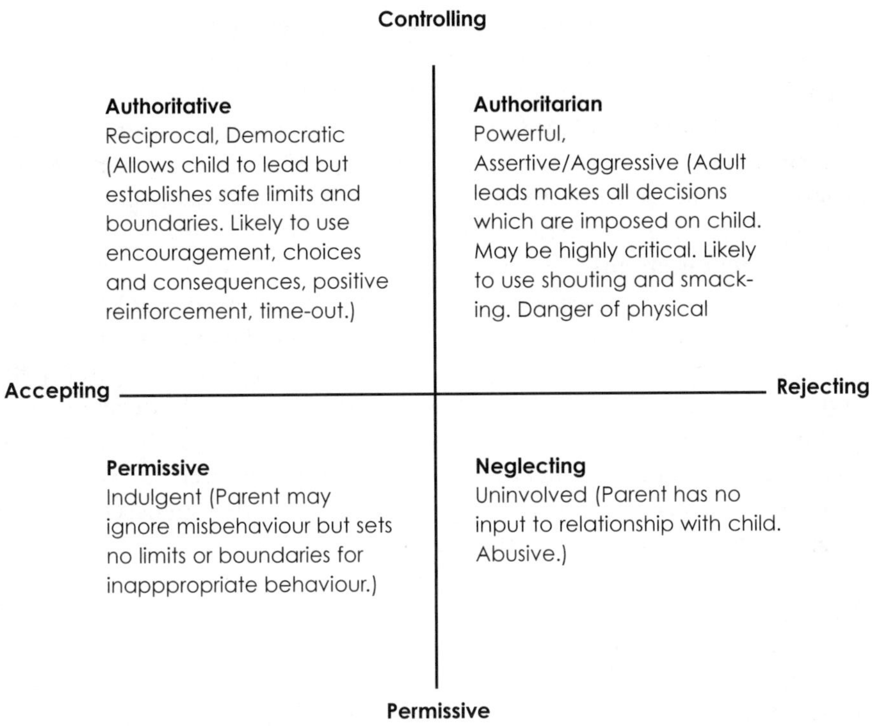

Controlling

Authoritative
Reciprocal, Democratic
(Allows child to lead but
establishes safe limits and
boundaries. Likely to use
encouragement, choices
and consequences, positive
reinforcement, time-out.)

Authoritarian
Powerful,
Assertive/Aggressive (Adult
leads makes all decisions
which are imposed on child.
May be highly critical. Likely
to use shouting and smacking. Danger of physical

Accepting ─────────────────────────── **Rejecting**

Permissive
Indulgent (Parent may
ignore misbehaviour but sets
no limits or boundaries for
inapppropriate behaviour.)

Neglecting
Uninvolved (Parent has no
input to relationship with child.
Abusive.)

Permissive

(adapted from: Maccoby & Martin (1983))

Children from authoritarian families, with parents who show little love or warmth and are authoritarian, directive and demanding, are more likely to be lower in self-esteem, to be less skilled with their peers, and to do less well at school. Children from permissive or indulgent families are likely to show some negative outcomes, in being, for example, more immature, less independent, less likely to take responsibility and to do less well at school. However, the worst outcomes are clearly with children who are neglected in terms of parents who are neither warm nor demanding. These are likely to show significant disturbance in peer relationships, to be more impulsive, and more antisocial, for example.

These kinds of findings have been further explored in relation to the concept of attachment, which has derived considerable significance in the developmental literature following the pioneering work of Bowlby (e.g. 1969) and Ainsworth and others (e.g. Ainsworth, Blehar, Waters & Wall, 1978). A good account of this is again given by Bee (2000). What seems to be clear, however, is that the formation of a secure attachment is associated with better outcomes for the child in terms of sociability, self-esteem, and psychosocial adjustment, for example, and may be related to parenting qualities and behaviour. Children with secure attachments, for example, are more likely than those who are insecure to have parents who express their warmth towards them, are sensitive to their needs and responsive, as opposed to distant, inconsistent or even abusive.

It is evident from this work that there are core qualities necessary for parenting and that these impact upon children in highly significant ways. We have been struck by their similarity to the qualities of helpers, described earlier in Chapter 5. We will, therefore, explore these further here, firstly for simplicity, but more importantly, because of the assumed effects of these qualities (as discussed in the helper context) on the relationship with children, understanding of them and their situation and the facilitation of a beneficial process of change and development in them. Although described here separately they are all highly interrelated.

RESPECT

Throughout the book we have stressed the need for respect as a major attribute of helpers. Since we discussed it at length in chapter 5, we will say relatively little about it here, only to say that it is a vital quality for parents, if they are to provide as best they can for their children. In terms of Roger's (1959) notion of unconditional positive regard, it indicates a superordinate view of their children as important and of special value and worth. This is not just what might be called love, but also implies a construction of them as people to be treated as such.

The importance of respect in parents has been underlined by the United Nations convention on the rights of the child. This tells us, for example, that children have the right to respect and freedom from all forms of violence, belittling, and cruel punishment. They should be involved in decisions that affect them, have personal privacy, and be allowed to say how they feel, and what they think and want, providing it does not impinge on other peoples' rights. They have a right to information that would make life better for them, good food and health care, rest and play, and for those with special needs, to live as full a life and as independently as possible.

This declaration clearly has implications for the role of parents. Most significantly, it extends the focus from the care of children in a physical sense to them as people. It means, therefore, that even as babies, parents and others should treat children as worthy of time and attention, helping them to express themselves, and listening attentively to what they say.

If parents demonstrate respect for children in this way, believing that they are valuable, important and capable, they are likely to grow up believing this about themselves. This is likely, therefore, to enhance their self-esteem, self-confidence, and self-efficacy, and to increase the chances of them becoming happy, independent and mature adults, capable of forming close and loving relationships with others (Bavolek, 1990, Pearce, 1991). In terms of helping parents, the most important implication here is for them to construe their child as a person to be treated as they themselves would wish to be treated by others.

RESPONSIVENESS OR SENSITIVITY

This quality is emphasised by many authors in the developmental literature. Bavolek (1990) understands it as the process by which unconditional positive regard is established. Herbert (1988) and Schaffer (1977) for example, give strong emphasis to it, relating it to important outcomes including secure attachment. It follows closely in our view from the notion of respect and its significance is clearly indicated in the interactive cycle described earlier, where the processes of monitoring children closely, being sensitive to them and their needs and being prepared to respond as quickly and effectively as one can were highlighted.

In essence this quality implies giving importance to the needs of the child, attending closely to these and being open to the child's experiences. It implies a detailed attempt to understand children and their needs, and to be appropriately responsive to them, putting them high on the parents' personal agenda. A key to this is the parents' understanding of the developmental processes.

KNOWLEDGE OF CHILD DEVELOPMENT

Just as the helper's technical knowledge and expertise are crucial to the helping processes, so the parents' knowledge of children is a vital part of parenting processes. In chapter 12 we saw how a baby is born ready for social engagement and ready to form a close bond with its parents. It is through this attachment that their development is facilitated and they begin to learn about, or to elaborate their own construction system of their world. Throughout childhood this construct system is very different to that of their parents and is at the same time developing rapidly. The task for parents is, therefore, to grasp and adapt to the system of the child.

As listening is the vehicle through which one begins to understand in the helping process, so an obvious way to understand children is to listen to them in the broadest sense. Nevertheless, if parents are to have realistic expectations of their children in order to anticipate what they require, then knowledge about children and their development will enable this to happen. For example, it might help them to know in advance that children are social from birth and that interaction is vital for their development. Such knowledge might help them know that crying is an important communication mechanism and not a deliberate attempt to annoy them, which is a faulty construction with important repercussions for the parent–infant relationship. Knowledge of child development will help parents make more accurate constructions of their children that are helpful both to the relationship generally and to the expectations of the skills and behaviour that the child can develop at any given age.

There is so much more known today about child development and a great deal more than the space here allows. Further in depth exploration is recommended for the interested reader (see for example, Brewer, 2001; Bee 2000).

EMPATHY

This refers to the parents' willingness and ability to put themselves in their child's shoes, to feel with the child, and to see the world from her/his point of view. This must include understanding the value and importance they attribute to events as opposed to imposing one's own. For example, it is easy to trivialise issues that really upset children, when in fact their crying is a signal of something important to them. Patting them on the shoulder or even hugging them and saying, 'Shsh, don't cry' may not be particularly helpful. Crying is possibly just what they need to do before they can talk about the particular problem that is bothering them. Allowing a child to cry can be difficult and painful for some parents, especially if they have had a traumatic childhood themselves and painful memories from it, but only through respecting and understanding the child's feelings can one begin to respond effectively.

Demonstrating empathy is crucial to spontaneous, compassionate parenting, and involves responding physically (e.g. with hugs) and also with verbal acknowledgements of how a child might be feeling. Attempting to verbalise children's feelings is important in a number of ways. For example, by helping a child to identify and name what they are feeling, parents are likely to increase the child's ability to verbalise emotions themselves rather than simply acting them out. Speaking to children who have just had a tantrum about how angry they felt may help them to talk about their feelings on the next occasion and not simply to throw a tantrum.

Empathy is also likely to help children to feel understood, and is important for the development of a trusting relationship with the parent. If it is demonstrated to them throughout early and middle childhood, it is likely to keep open the lines of communication throughout more difficult years of adolescence. Bavolek (1990) identifies it as the single most important quality required by a parent and as critical for the overall growth and well being of the child.

WARM ENTHUSIASM

This quality is closely related to respect, but suggests that the expression of one's valuing of children should include overt affection, joy and eagerness. Such warmth is an important way of indicating the core interest that parents have for their children, and many authors and researchers have identified warmth, love and affection, closeness and intimacy as essential for the psychosocial health and development (Bavolek, 1990; Skynner & Cleese, 1994; Schaffer 1977).

Parents demonstrate this quality by a keenness to be with their children, delight in their development, their ideas, their creativity and by taking pleasure in their company. It is communicated to the child through all aspects of the parent's behaviour, but especially the medium of touch that is calm, gentle, nurturing and affectionate (Bavolek, 1990). The zest a parent has for the task will demonstrate itself through an ability to laugh at themselves and with their children. Although parents might realise the enormity of the task and the responsibility on them, they can still retain a sense of humour, and it is important for parents to ensure plenty of opportunities to have fun with their children while they are growing up and after. Humour can diffuse difficult situations and will be a model for the children not to take themselves too seriously. Gentle teasing can be a source of fun, if not allowed to get out of hand; learning to laugh at oneself is part of growing up and may be related to the development of humility (see below).

Fun and enjoyment is highly motivating for children and parents. It contributes to the development and quality of the parent–child relationship and is likely to communicate a considerable amount to the child, in terms of their constructions of themselves, other people and their relationships.

GENUINENESS

We have defined genuineness earlier as a complex quality related to an openness to the experience of oneself and others. The need for this in parents is as crucial as it is for helpers. In relating to children it is important to be open to their experience and the meanings they attribute, and to do this accurately with as little distortion as possible. This requires, of course, that they are accurate in construing themselves, as otherwise their views of others and especially the uniqueness of their children will be coloured.

This quality implies, therefore, the need to demonstrate to children that parents are real, honest and sincere, and not pretending or playing a role for whatever purpose. It means being truthful, reliable and open with children. Parents who are genuine will keep promises and not make idle threats, especially when it comes to discipline and managing difficult behaviour. They will be consistent without rigidity; they will do what they say, but will be open to negotiation with the child should this be necessary. This ability will arise from the capacity to be themselves and to respond spontaneously in an open and natural way.

Apart from Rogers (1959) genuineness has been identified by a number of authors as important in the development of relationships with children (e.g. Bavolek 1990; Skynner & Cleese 1994). It is important for children to be able to learn to trust others and themselves. A child living with a parent who is genuine in their approach will know what to expect from the parent and will develop feelings of security. However, they will also be acutely aware of a lack of genuineness and this has significant implications for the development of all their constructions of others and the extent to which they are to be trusted and what they do is meaningful as intended. If parents are not genuine, then the relationship with the child will suffer and all attempts to manage his/her behaviour will be reduced in effectiveness. Rules will be flouted, communication and negotiation will be sterile, and encouragement through praise will not only lose its effectiveness, but might even be discouraging as the parent's expressed view (e.g. 'You are wonderful') will not be believed, or will not accord with what the child knows and will give an ideal to which he cannot aspire.

HUMILITY

This is particularly important in parents, because of the tendency to require perfection for one's children and the prevention of constantly failing to meet inappropriately high standards. They need patience with themselves and with their children, so as not to fall short of their ideals. Humility is likely to ensure that parents do the best they can, but acknowledge their limitations, both physically and mentally. They need to be aware that they can and do make mistakes, that they might not know how to deal with lots of situations with their child, and that they can only do what they think is best. They should, however, try to learn from their mistakes and to involve their children in the process so that the parents can work in partnership with them and learn from them what to do.

Parents who have humility are likely to recognise and admit the necessity of having their own time for rest and relaxation. They will acknowledge realistically the need for time away from their children in order to meet their own

WORKING IN PARTNERSHIP WITH PARENTS

needs, for their own sake, but so that they can continue to meet the needs of their children. Couples can support each other in this, but lone parents may have more difficulty in finding the support that they require. Friends and family have a vital function in the provision of such support, although many parents may need considerable encouragement to take time for themselves and to attend to each other (if they have a partner) in order to relax and to renew their energy and enthusiasm for the task in hand. They, too, need to be listened to and to have their problems taken seriously as emphasised throughout this book.

Humility will enable parents to admit mistakes in their relationships with their children, to forgive themselves, and not to be afraid to communicate about this to their children where appropriate. A self-awareness of how their own upbringing impacts on their ability to parent can be particularly helpful in this respect. Children are wonderfully forgiving, and by parents saying sorry to them, when they know they have been unreasonable, provides a good model for them. It is helpful for children to know that parents get things wrong. It can be a valuable lesson for them also to be realistic about themselves, willing to learn and to be self-reflective. Humility also allows parents to admit superiority in the child when this is realistic, and hence negates thoughts about having to be perfect, or even to get into competition or be defensive.

PERSONAL INTEGRITY

To have humility parents need to be secure and strong in themselves. Personal integrity, therefore, is being included here to refer to the need for the emotional, inner strength needed to tolerate the anxieties that parents naturally have regarding their children's development, well-being, and emerging independence at all stages of the developmental process. It is used here to refer to the parent's capacity to cope with the arduous task of parenting, physically and psychologically, and to support their children through all their problems, retaining an objectivity to problem management, whilst respecting involvement of the child in developing and implementing solutions.

It also involves in parents a self-awareness to monitor, identify and manage their own feelings (e.g. anger) for the good of their children. They need the ability to put their children's needs before their own, and require considerable personal resources to do this. This is particularly true when there are other stresses in their lives (e.g. financial, personal, in relationships) from the whole range of possibilities, and especially when their children add to these, by constant crying, for example, or by any other of the gamut of behavioural difficulties potentially exhibited by children at all stages of development. However, self-awareness is likely to have very general effects on the parents' ability to manage, plan their lives appropriately and to minimise stresses, which will undoubtedly arise (e.g. not organising a children's birthday party in the evening of a day on which they have had to work, so that they are focused on the task and not tired and hungry).

Personal strength or integrity is particularly necessary when it comes to managing children whose behaviour is unacceptable. It is needed to enable parents to remain objective, to analyse the situations involved, to decide what to do, and then to implement a system that will set rules for the child and keep to these. As we saw at the beginning of this chapter, it is the children of the authoritative parent who have the best outcomes and so parents need to be appropriately directive in setting rules and limits, while accepting and respecting the child as a person. If parents are vulnerable themselves for whatever reason (e.g. preoccupied with their own problems) they are unlikely to be able to respond appropriately and sensitively to their children in this way.

Integrated with the other qualities described here, personal integrity is crucial to the whole process, enabling the context for parents to cope with the complex and potentially stressful task of parenting, and providing a secure relationship with the child. With clear limits, this in turn gives a secure base from which the child's emerging independence can be exercised, and a model of how to be in the world, including how to manage problems generally.

Personal integrity, like all the other qualities mentioned here, is not a characteristic that can be assumed, but is something to which one might strive. It is, however, very much dependent upon the context of support, within which the family exists, as well as their own worldview, and may vary considerably over time.

Parenting Skills

Having suggested some important core qualities in parents, we will go on to explore more specific skills involved in raising children effectively. Although these may be learnt and improved by practice, we believe that they follow to a large extent from the qualities we have just outlined, and are given meaning in a general way by them. Nevertheless, we will explore them in some detail to see what parents can do specifically to facilitate the development of secure and loving relationships with their children, so that they can grow to independence and contribute effectively to their world and form their own mature and loving relationships.

We will consider the skills of playing, encouraging, listening, exploring problems and problem solving with children in the present chapter, before continuing in the next chapter with ways of deliberately helping children to change, when their behaviour is considered unacceptable or inappropriate.

The skills to be discussed here are basic to all parenting, and important for facilitating children's development and preventing problems from arising in the child. They are, however, also important as core skills of behavioural management to be considered in the next chapter. There is considerable agreement about their nature and importance in the parenting literature (e.g. Webster-Stratton, 1992; Quinn & Quinn, 1995; Sanders, 1992). For us they are significant in relation to their function of facilitating the parent–child relationship and in enabling the cycle of interaction described in Chapter 11. They ensure that parents continue to understand their children, in spite of rapid change, continue to respond as appropriately as possible to them for meeting their needs, and finally to help them learn the skills they need, including those of relating to others and managing problems.

Before describing these skills, it may be useful to reiterate our assumptions about the nature of the relationship. Earlier we explored the concept of partnership in the helping relationship, and will assume throughout the following discussion that the same model applies to the parent–child relationship. It entails the assumption that they are both working closely together, that they both have knowledge or expertise, and that the outcomes are most effective if these are shared as much as possible. This means the parent having some framework for what is required of them in terms of the aims of the task, but also requires them to be led by the child, to work at his/her pace, and to begin from an understanding of his/her picture of the world. Although parents may seem to be most powerful, the child's power to determine what happens should not be forgotten and should be respected. Negotiation will certainly be required to resolve conflict, but it is important they be working towards the same aims, and that they do this as far as possible by skilled communication, mutual agreement, and shared understanding.

The Skills of Playing with Children

It is generally considered important for parents to play with their children to establish and develop their relationship and to provide the context for effective development and learning. A few minutes play each day is thought to help build a warm relationship and to reduce the power differential between adults and children (Webster-Stratton & Herbert, 1994). If adults can use their imaginations alongside the child, let her/him lead and direct the game, it is likely to make them feel valued and important and builds solidarity in the relationship. Play helps children learn who they are and to develop ideas about the world around them. It is a vehicle for spontaneous self-expression and creativity, and is associated with improvements in psychosocial adaptation; for example, children who engage in joint activity with their parents and imaginative and creative play with parents are less likely to have behaviour problems (Galboda Liyanage, 2000; Webster-Stratton, 1992). It helps children in developing their expressive and receptive language skills, as well as their social skills generally, their problem solving and their self-efficacy. Above all, it is about having fun and likely to increase the desire of the participants to be with each other.

Michael and Terri Quinn (1995) have likened playing with children to listening to them and have named the associated skills as 'play listening'. Listening well to someone as we have seen earlier in this book requires a number of different skills. It means attending carefully and responding sensitively to the person's verbal and non-verbal behaviour. Above all it means letting them take the lead and tell the story at their own pace in their own way. Because play is so much a reflection of this, it may be useful to think of play as another form of listening.

We will consider each of the skills and requirements more closely: having fun and enjoyment, attending sensitively (attunement), allowing the child to lead the interaction, understanding and interpreting, commenting, encouraging, and the ability to use imagination. Although described separately, as with the qualities discussed earlier, they are all intimately linked and likely to occur together.

HAVING FUN AND ENJOYMENT: Activities which are enjoyable are likely to have a number of benefits and this is what parents should seek regularly with their children if they can. If they are enjoyed, then they will become repeated and a continuing source of pleasure and learning. Young children might enjoy physical play, for example, and a 'rough and tumble' on the floor; allowing them to overpower the adult can be great fun and build their confidence. They may enjoy sporting games (e.g. playing football), cards, word games or whatever. The essence, however, is to have fun, and this will be different for each child. Parents, therefore, need to know what their children will enjoy, but clearly need to allow them to choose, since they are likely to select what will be enjoyable for them now. However, this can easily be neglected, if parents do not allow the time for it specifically, feel they have to direct what their children do, or always feel they should teach their children, instead of allowing them to discover what they need to know for themselves.

ATTENDING SENSITIVELY (ATTUNEMENT): In play, an essential skill for parents is that they actively and sensitively attend to their child in all aspects of their behaviour. These are the same skills described earlier in the book for helpers (Chapter 5), and involve the thoughtful monitoring of what the children say (once verbal), but also what they show in terms of their vocalisations, direction of gaze, facial expression, tone of voice, body posture and movements.

Sensitivity to these are the basis for knowing and understanding what children are experiencing in terms of their thoughts, feelings, intentions and needs. As such they are the determinants of what the parent should do for or towards the child at any moment to be helpful in achieving the tasks of parenting and meeting the child's needs.

Monitoring and attending carefully is clearly needed with babies, whose ability to communicate is limited, and who require caregivers to be sensitive to their needs, to read the cues they give, and to act appropriately to help them achieve their goals (e.g. stop hunger, reach an attractive toy). However, it is essential at all stages, in order to know their children and ever adapt to their changing needs. Play, therefore, might vary from them interacting directly with actions or words, to sitting quietly and unobtrusively with the child, sharing the enjoyment with one's attention, and anticipating when to help or intervene with a descriptive comment when appropriate.

UNDERSTANDING AND INTERPRETING: This is the process by which the parent seeks to comprehend and make sense of what the child is doing, thinking, feeling or sensing.

Trying to understand and interpret just what children are doing at play can be fascinating, but equally very boring at times. How can a parent maintain interest as the child tips the bricks out of the box and puts them back in for the twentieth time?

What is required is an empathic questioning approach, with the adult trying to put him/herself in the child's place. Careful attention to the facial expression and effort may give clues. Is it the sound of the bricks tumbling, the way in which they fall or the delight of being able to clear them all away and make the floor tidy again that makes the child repeat this action over and over again? The parent has to understand these kinds of questions before being able to comment appropriately or otherwise intervene.

Whatever the child is doing and at whatever age, parents taking time to understand what is happening is not only likely to facilitate the activity effectively, but will also enhance their own enjoyment, as well as giving the children a sense of value in what they are doing and who they are, raising their self-esteem, and enhancing their learning.

LETTING THE CHILD LEAD THE INTERACTION: Since play can be said to have no fixed goals apart from enjoyment, parents cannot set the agenda. To ensure they have fun, parents have to let children take charge of the play session and to determine what happens in large measure. This is analogous with the parent–helper partnership, where the helper follows the parents' lead in trying to understand their picture of the world, to clarify it and subsequently decide what to do. Parents should refrain from taking over the activity. This includes generally not giving instructions or directing what the child is doing. It might also include avoiding questions, since these are all likely to interfere with the child's game and may interrupt his or her thoughts. There may be times when a more active approach is required, but this should be tentative, sensitive to the intentions of the child, and preferably when invited by the child to answer questions, help with constructions or join in an imaginary scene.

COMMENTING: If parents feel a need to intervene, then the most helpful response in play can often be simply to comment on what the child is doing, thinking, feeling or experiencing. This is very much like the use of empathic responding, which requires parents to have attended carefully and to have tried to understand the child's current picture of the world. They should then be in a position to put into words or otherwise express what they think is happening. As with empathic remarks, this needs to be done at the right moment, so that it does not disturb the flow of the play or the child's concentration, and in a tentative way that invites the child to think about it and to respond if she/he wishes. It should be done in ways that are sensitive to the child's abilities, using language that is appropriate and understandable to the child.

As in the case with adults, the power of this kind of empathic responding should not be underestimated in terms of the child or the parent. If used appropriately it can be meaningful for the child through indicating that she/he is the centre of the parents' attention, is of interest and value to them, and possibly that they have understood what they are doing. This has considerable implications for the relationship and for the child's self-esteem. It might also provide a structure for the child, as well as an opportunity for further learning of words and ideas. For the parents, it might provide activity and interest, but more importantly the opportunity to test their hypotheses or understanding of the child, and therefore the chance to be corrected or develop these.

We would like to illustrate the points we have made so far about the skills of playing with children using an example. David, who was 3 years old, was is sitting at the table with paper and many different coloured crayons. He was clearly enjoying himself drawing, and was currently using all the colours to make lots of different spots on the paper. As he picked up the red crayon, his father, who had been sitting beside him and watching him carefully, said, 'Oh, you're using a red one now.' David looked up contentedly at his father, seemingly pleased that he had noticed. He held up the red crayon and said,

'Red one.' before happily continuing to cover the paper with red dots. His father then said, 'Now you're making lots of red dots'. David again appeared to be pleased about his father's interest, and responded by giving him a blue crayon and inviting him to join in.

Parents can find it difficult to restrain themselves from teaching or taking over in a situation like this, even though it might not be enjoyable to the child. For example, if the father took over and drew dots in a pattern or a particular picture beyond David's skills, then he might well feel discouraged. If the father had told David which colours to use and tried to ensure that he learned their names, it might not have been as the scene illustrated above. What his father did, however, was to make noticing comments, which were much less intrusive, but nevertheless gave David the opportunity to learn about colours and their names. He refrained, for example, from asking David to pick up the 'red crayon' in order to ensure that he could identify the colours correctly.

THE ABILITY TO USE IMAGINATION: Children have wonderful imaginations and parents will often find themselves drawn into games where they will have to put aside their adult persona and assume a different role. There is a clear relationship to empathy here. The parent needs to understand what it is that the child wants and respond appropriately. This means letting go of the desire to control the game and allowing the child full rein to let the story unfold as they wish. Again it means allowing the child to take the lead and to direct the adult and to tell them what they want them to do. In the example below Jenny's father shows his ability to let his daughter take charge, to put aside his own adult view of this play situation, and to allow his imagination to join with hers.

Four your old Jenny was sitting on the floor playing with her teddy bears. They were all sitting in a row and she was happily engaged in giving them their tea and telling them what was to happen after the 'pretend meal' was finished. Jenny's father was sitting on the floor with her. He joined in the game, eating the pretend meal and drinking the 'tea', while sitting alongside the teddy bears and letting Jenny tell him what to do. She was delighted to have her father's full attention in this way and felt very important as she gave him his instructions about what he should do when he had finished his tea.

Quite clearly Jenny's father was able to join in the imaginative game proposed by his daughter. He did not make alternative suggestions for play (e.g. 'Why don't we play with the doll's house?'), but went along with what his daughter wanted to do. He did not ask questions about what Jenny was trying to do, but simply became a part of the game. Although he did not try to teach her anything (e.g. about table manners or cooking), it was highly likely that she was learning a great deal. This might have included the fact that her father cared about what she wanted to do, that he valued this, and thought it important enough to give her his time. The relationship between them was being sustained or even strengthened, and Jenny was allowed to be the more powerful partner with likely effects on her confidence and self-efficacy.

ENCOURAGEMENT: There are many things that parents can do to encourage their children, including giving approval and praise, and showing pleasure in what a child is doing. It involves any actions that will enable children to continue with what they are doing and may be given not only for achievement, but also for their efforts and attempts. Paying attention to a child who is playing quietly is likely to encourage him/her to continue.

The skills of giving encouragement and praise are considered in the next section. What we will consider here, however, is how parents may be well-meaning but unintentionally discouraging during play. They may do this by ignoring altogether the child who is playing quietly or they may play competitive games with their children, which they feel they must win. They may provide toys and games that are beyond the child's developmental attainment, and, because parents are more skilled, they may also take over tasks with which children are struggling, instead of deliberately praising their efforts and otherwise supporting them. We will now look at these in more detail.

PLAYING COMPETITIVE GAMES WITH CHILDREN: Many games are competitive (e.g. football, chess) and are intended to entertain in terms of people struggling against each other with one person or a team winning. Although this can be highly enjoyable, the superiority of adults in terms of relevant skills and the grasp of rules makes it highly unlikely that children can win unless helped to do so. Since constantly losing can be very discouraging, one needs to consider such situations very carefully.

In effect, the principle for parents should be for games to be fun and not a bitter competition between them and their children (Webster-Stratton, 1992). Clearly games should be selected to be within the child's competence, or the rules altered to enable this. The process of playing together needs to be stressed and made enjoyable, but to encourage children the result needs to be tipped in their favour. This is not to say that they should win every time, since this would remove the essential enjoyment and function of competition, which is to encourage increasing effort and skill development. However, the end result should be tipped in favour of the child, but without it being so obvious that there is no point in the child making any effort.

Games lose their value if the results are totally predictable. Even in losing parents might give valuable examples to children of still having enjoyed the interaction and collaboration whatever the outcome.

ENSURING THAT PLAY IS AT THE CHILD'S PACE AND LEVEL: To be enjoyable, play must be pitched at the child's pace and level of competence. In general, allowing children to lead ensures this. If it is not pitched appropriately for whatever reason, then children's interest will be lost; they will not have fun, they will give up and they will lose the opportunity to develop competence, self-confidence and, most important, self-efficacy.

In the example below, Sarah, who was two years old, had no sense of achievement and was positively discouraged. She had found her older brother's jigsaw puzzle, had taken the box to her room and emptied the pieces on the floor. She was sitting down, piling the pieces up on top of each other, when her mother came into the room and saw her. However, with all good intention to help, she sat down beside her, said, 'That's not how you play with a puzzle. Look you do it like this.' And began to show her how to fit the pieces together. Instead of being interested and intrigued, Sarah simply screamed and threw a tantrum.

Sarah's mother misjudged her need to play with the toy in her own way, and interrupted the enjoyment she was getting from her own use of the jigsaw. The puzzle was in fact much too complex for Sarah's level of development, and, as might have been expected, her mother's attempt to teach Sarah how to play with it properly fell on deaf ears. The imposition of her mother's suggestions certainly discouraged Sarah, who may have felt pushed to doing something she could not achieve, and therefore screamed in frustration at having her own activity and possible learning curtailed. A more helpful approach might have been for Sarah's mother to notice the tower of pieces that she had made and to comment, saying something like, 'I see you're making a tower. It looks as if it will be very big.' This kind of response is more likely to encourage Sarah to continue with her game and to make her feel pleased and proud that her mother had noticed.

ALLOWING THE CHILD'S OWN LEARNING: Children are constantly learning new ideas and skills as they are playing without intervention from others, yet parents sometimes find it difficult to refrain from intruding and accomplishing tasks for them. However, this can be very discouraging for children. It stops them being successful on their own, but also fails to acknowledge the need for a degree of frustration in order to gain a sense of accomplishment and pride in achievement.

This is not to say that parents should not intervene, but should be sensitive to the degree to which children are becoming frustrated, to ask their permission to become involved, and then to make suggestions or otherwise add structure for the child to complete what they are doing and be successful on their own. When they are allowed to struggle and succeed with encouragement, foundations will be laid for them to try new tasks with belief in themselves and their ability to achieve.

Darren, who is six years old, has just been given a jigsaw puzzle for his birthday. He has tipped the pieces on the table and is struggling to put them together. He is clearly frustrated and beginning to loose interest. His mother, who is also sitting at the table watching him, takes the box with a picture of the completed puzzle and says, 'I wonder if this will help us to see what the puzzle looks like when it's finished. Perhaps we can see parts of the picture on the pieces and that will help us to know where they go.' This renews his interest and he starts to turn the pieces over, asking his mother to help him. Her response is to comment by saying, 'I see. We're turning them all over so that we can see the picture on each one. That's a good idea.'

Encouraged, Darren chooses a couple of pieces and starts to see if they will fit. Unfortunately, his first try is not correct. His mother says, 'What shall we do to see if we can find the right piece? Perhaps there is one with the same colours on it. That will give us a clue.' As a result, Darren looks and finds a similar piece, tries to fit it the wrong way at first, but is eventually successful and starts to look for the next piece. His mother praises him, saying, ' Well done, Darren. We'll soon be able to see the whole picture'.

At the beginning of this interaction Darren is clearly frustrated and on the verge of giving up; he is probably overwhelmed by the size of the problem and the extent of the options in front of him. His mother, who is an ardent fan of jigsaw puzzles, knows that the best way of starting is to work from the edges inward. However, she refrains from sharing this in order for him to find his own way of solving the problem. She encourages him, however, by suggesting the need to look at the completed picture, and this leads him to discover that he must be able to see the picture on the pieces. She praises this discovery and joins in only when asked, not taking over, but again following his lead. When he tries to join two wrong pieces, she does not discourage him (e.g. 'No! That's not right. Try this one.'). Instead she structures the search by suggesting a way in which Darren can find the right piece for himself. Although he does not fit it together correctly at first, she waits patiently for him to do it, allowing him a sense of accomplishment, increased by her subsequent praise. As a result, the chances of Darren feeling able to complete the task are likely to be increased, but certainly he will be left with the possibility of enjoying the challenge.

The Skills of Encouraging Children

Since encouragement has an important role in many situations other than play, we should like to explore the general skills involved in more detail. It is important in motivating children in many situations, it is likely to make a significant contribution to the parent–child interaction and relationship, and can be considered essential in raising children's confidence and self-esteem. Some authors (Quinn & Quinn, 1986) have made a distinction between praise and encouragement, while others suggest the distinction is difficult in practice and may reduce positive comments (Webster-Stratton, 1992). However, if encouragement or praise is to be meaningful and beneficial rather than a value-laden judgement of children, then some guidance on its use may be worthwhile.

Being genuine, honest and real: We have already explored the quality of genuineness earlier in the chapter, and it is particulary important here for parents to be genuine and mean what they say when encouraging or praising. If it is not said with real feeling, then it will be meaningless, for the parent, but more important in relation to the child.

Being specific about what is noticed: If encouraging comments or praise are to be meaningful as just suggested, then this is facilitated by them being specific. For example on being presented with the latest painting that the child brings home from playschool a parent might say, 'Oh, that's brilliant'. However, it might mean more to the child, if the parent says, 'Oh, I like the way you've used the red paint next to the yellow and let them mix to make that wonderful orange colour.' This clearly indicates that the parent is not only praising, but has really looked at the work and taken the time to think about it, but also to attempt to express her/his understanding.

Follow up the implications: If possible one should follow up on any implications of what has been done or said to further indicate the value of the child's work or effort. In the case of a picture, for example, putting it on the wall where it can be seen clearly demonstrates the value the parent has given to it. In the example above the parent is being specific about what they can see in the painting presented by the child.

Using body language, touch, hugs and cuddles: Touch is very important in enabling children to experience closeness or a sense of connection with adults in their lives. It is a very basic way in which they can know a parent's love, protection, empathy, security, concern and enjoyment. Touch can add emphasis and meaning to words of encouragement and show genuine enthusiasm and warmth for their child. Being hugged, cuddled, tickled, stroked, cradled, carried, swung round, or held by the hand, all give children the sense of being welcomed, enjoyed, safe and loved. There are, however, likely to be very real and positive effects on the relationship between the parent and child and his/her growth and development. As discussed in the last chapter, positive touch or massage can help the development of a sensitive parent–infant relationship (McClure, 2000), and babies born prematurely have been shown to develop more quickly and gain more weight when they are physically stroked (Field et al, 1986).

NOTICING THE EFFORT AND ACHIEVEMENT: In commenting encouragingly or praising, it is as important to notice effort as the achievement of a task. This is important, since their first efforts in doing a task will be less than perfect. Acknowledging effort will reinforce the child for trying and is therefore likely to lead to improved outcomes eventually. If parents look only for perfection, they will be disappointed, possibly indicating this in subtle but clear ways, or even being critical of the child's accomplishment. A fear of criticism is highly likely to discourage their efforts, especially if they are sensitive to failure or are low in confidence and self-esteem.

SHOWING CONFIDENCE IN THE CHILD'S ABILITY: If parents believe a child (or adult) can achieve a task and show confidence in them, they are not only likely to try harder, but also to succeed. This can be expressed both verbally and by non-verbal means (e.g. in the tone of voice), but it needs to be genuine as discussed earlier, and obviously truly believed to be within the child's competence. Asking children to take on tasks and responsibilities beyond their developmental level is counterproductive and will discourage effort by failure.

GIVING ENCOURAGEMENT IMMEDIATELY WITHOUT DELAY: Since young children have a limited sense of time, it is vital that encouragement should be immediate. To be effective, it needs to be spontaneous, and connected directly in time to the event or behaviour that is being noticed. What is also implied here, as will be discussed in the next chapter, is that care should be taken not to associate it unwittingly with unacceptable behaviour, which would of course be encouraged inappropriately.

THE SKILLS OF LISTENING TO CHILDREN
As indicated earlier in relation to the skills of helpers, just as listening is the essence of all communication in the adult context, so it is with children. As we have seen, it is very clearly involved in the skills of playing and it is the

basis of encouragement; simply listening is encouraging. Listening in the broadest sense is important in all contexts in dealing with children, as indicated, for example, in relation to the interactive cycle (see chapter 11). It is the most basic skill of all. Parents need to listen to children, in order to be responsive to them and their needs, whether this involves understanding the reasons for them being upset, an account of events in their lives, or even a direct attempt to say what they need, want and feel.

We have considered the skills involved in listening to parents in some depth earlier in chapter 5, and these are entirely relevant here. If parents take the time and trouble to listen properly, they will, for example, indicate respect for their children, be much more likely to understand them and their constructions or picture of the world, be more able to respond effectively, and enhance their relationship, which is the basis of the developmental processes. Children to whom parents listen, are likely to learn that what they have to say is of importance, to feel valued and to grow in self-esteem and confidence. They will be encouraged to communicate, to develop their language and social skills, and perhaps to share their troubles rather than acting them out through disruptive behaviour. Listening to children when they are small and maintaining this as they grow up is likely to keep open good lines of communication for adolescence, when the rapid growth towards independence may tax the relationship severely.

ATTENDING: As indicated earlier in the book, the most fundamental skill here is the parents' ability to concentrate and focus attention on their children; on what they say, show, do, and make them feel. However, this needs to be demonstrated in all aspects of the adult's behaviour. Parents may think they are attending to a child's story, but unless they can convey this clearly, its value is lost on the child. It is demonstrated in all aspects of the parent's behaviour, especially the non-verbal. We have previously discussed this at length, and will not repeat ourselves here, but should just note a few issues relevant to children.

Perhaps the most important way of showing attention is by looking at the other person and especially in the eyes. With children, however, this may not be quite so easy, as they may not show the same pattern of eye contact as adults. They may choose times to talk when they or the parent are engaged in other activities; they might be drawing, for example, or their parents driving. Even so, parents must be sensitive to the times when children need their whole attention. To make eye contact may require deliberate attempts to gain the child's visual attention, and this is likely to involve lifting the child to the parent's height or getting down to his/her level. As with adults, if one is to make a real attempt to be together and to listen, then they should be accorded the same respect and courtesy, and this is indicated clearly by taking account of the power differential that can be signalled by their difference in height.

Children may not look at the person when they are talking, but it is important to see their changing facial expressions, as it provides enormously important information about their feelings and their meaning. They are also likely to be much more active than adults when interacting, and this will need to be understood and either tolerated or possibly gently controlled.

ACTIVE LISTENING: The skills of active listening have again been previously discussed and apply equally to the situation with children. Parents are therefore involved in an active process of understanding what their children are saying, showing, meaning or feeling. However, since the child's constructions of events may be very different to the picture the parent has of the world, there is a clear need to test out their interpretations or to check them with the child.

Clear summaries, reflecting back to the child and empathic responding are all therefore as crucial here as they are in helping adults. They indicate close involvement, but they are also the major way in which parents can know that they have understood the child's constructions reasonably accurately. Additionally, if parents can recognise their child's feelings and name them, it may help the child understand and begin to put names to how he/she feels. It helps parents understand their children and their children to learn, including a trust in the relationship and a security that the parent is with them in understanding.

Lucy, aged four years, seemed out of sorts. She was restless and reluctant to settle to play with anything. 'What would you like to do Lucy?' her mother inquired in an effort to respond to her daughter's supposed boredom. 'Nothing!' Lucy snapped back. Surprised at her daughter's unusual response, she got down on the floor beside her and said, 'You sound grumpy and bored.' Lucy fell into her mother's arms and sobbed hard, 'I want to play with Jessica, but she has moved away.' Lucy's mother held her until the crying subsided.

In this example, the mother responded to her daughter's mood with an initial attempt to engage her. Lucy's uncharacteristic response alerted her to there being something wrong, which immediately made her more attentive and took her down to the same level on the floor. Her concern and an attempt to share her understanding as related to boredom was then indicated by an empathic comment, which was sufficient to stimulate Lucy into expressing her real feelings, both in words and in her crying, which her mother simply accepted and respected by cuddling her.

Although the mother's words were important, her physical contact was crucial. Touch is vital for young children, especially when they are distressed. Being held and cuddled can do more than anything else to contain feelings that seem overwhelming. Quietly holding children and calmly allowing them to cry is probably the most effective thing to do, since it indicates that you are with them in their pain or distress. As well as being soothing, it might also have the effect of teaching children not to fear emotion and that it is manageable and containable with other people involved.

Five-year-old Jake came running into the kitchen obviously upset with tears in his eyes. His mother bent down, took him into her arms and cuddled him. She said nothing while he just cried hard into her shoulder. Eventually when he had calmed, she learnt that the class pet hamster had died. Knowing how fond he was of the pet, she allowed him to cry, without attempting to stop him. She simply respected and acknowledged his feelings and remained with him, not attempting to make it better in any other way (e.g. by explanation, distraction, or promises of a replacement).

THE SKILLS OF EXPLORING PROBLEMS WITH CHILDREN

We have covered the skills of exploring problems elsewhere (Chapter 7), and have discussed this as the second stage in the overall helping process, which begins with relationship building and then continues with problem solving once a clear understanding of the situation has been gained. Although these models were presented in the context of helping parents, the ideas are equally applicable to parents exploring problems with children and going on to manage them as necessary (see next section).

Assuming that there is a reasonable relationship between the parent and child, then the process of exploration is: 1) to enable children to speak freely about their concerns and 'paint the whole picture'; 2) to focus them on the important aspects of the situation; 3) to help them identify everything that is relevant; and 4) to enable them to make sense of the problems in the context of their lives generally.

The skills that parents need to respond to their child's problems are the same as outlined in chapter 7. They include: attending, demonstrating empathy, questioning, making statements, reflecting, giving gentle commands, allowing pauses and summarising. However, these need to be adapted to children and we will discuss the differences to be considered.

TAKING THEIR CONCERNS SERIOUSLY: Perhaps the first thing to be said is that parents must take their children's concerns seriously, whatever they might be. To the adult their worries are likely to appear comparatively trivial, but of course to the child they are not by definition. However, by belittling them or denying their significance in any way will be of little help to the child. They should be acknowledged and respected, whatever their content, and explored like any other.

BEING SENSITIVE TO THE CHILD'S CONCENTRATION SPAN: As in all interactions with children their abilities and developmental level need to be taken into account. However, there is a relatively short period available for exploring problems with small children, because of limitations in their ability to concentrate. This means trying to grasp their situation as quickly as possible and focusing as quickly as possible on the most important aspects of their story.

SUSPENDING THE SEARCH FOR SOLUTIONS: We have discussed this before, but mention it here, because it may be very difficult for parents. Characteristically it may be difficult for them to allow their children to have problems. They are inclined to want to 'make things better' immediately and may not be able to delay this sufficiently to enable a careful understanding. Realistically, however, it is firstly necessary to have a good grasp of the situation before this can happen. Secondly, it will help the development of problem solving skills in the child if the process is undertaken properly, and thirdly the management of the issues are likely to be much more effective if the child is involved in the process at every stage, including goal setting and strategy planning.

QUESTIONING: As we have seen, the use of open questions are most likely to be effective in deriving a person's own picture of their problem and this is true for children. Closed questions may have a use, but have the danger of appearing like an interrogation. However, there is a place for multiple-choice questions in focusing children who might not quite know how to express the difficulty (e.g. Edwards & Davis, 1997). For example:

Parent: 'What is it that is troubling you?' (open question)
Child: 'I don't know.'
Parent: 'Is it the argument you had with your sister this morning or something that happened at school?' (multiple-choice).

The skill here is to ask one question, while supplying a limited number of possible answers within the child's memory span. This is not the same as asking multiple questions, where each may have a range of possible answers and could be very confusing for a child.

STRUCTURING: Young children may find it difficult to tell their story in a coherent and logical way, especially with respect to the sequence of events for example. This is likely to be made more difficult by distress and the limits to which they can see the events from another's perspective. It may help, therefore, if parents add the necessary structure, by slowing the child for example, and asking questions like, 'What happened first?' and 'Then what happened' so as to increase clarity (see Edwards & Davis, 1997).

OTHER STRATEGIES: There are many other strategies that might enable parents to explore problems with children. These include, for example, touch, play, or drawing (Edwards & Davis, 1997).

Touch: Since children might be distressed when they have a problem, the use of touch may help enormously to give them comfort and security. A hug or a cuddle will let children know that the parent loves and cares about them and will help to contain their anxiety. It is certainly important to be at the same level of the child and not to tower above him/her in this situation, so physically holding a young child on one's lap is likely to be very useful. It encourages intimate conversation in the knowledge that the child has the parent's full attention. Eye to eye contact can be made, but children should be able to look away easily, if they wish, so that they can think and talk. Being held, however, gives clear information that the parent is with them and likely to be listening carefully.

Play: Children may find it easier to talk while they are playing, since it can help them to be relaxed and less self-conscious. By playing they are not forced to make eye contact with the parent and can concentrate on the problem. This will help them to talk about situations that are more difficult or may even act out scenes with toys. It might indicate to the attentive parent what a child is really feeling concerned or worried about. For example, a three year old girl who threw the baby doll out of the toy pram because it was naughty gave her mother a clear indication of her powerful feelings of anger, jealousy and envy towards her new baby brother.

Drawing: Similarly, it may be easier for some children to talk while they are drawing. Like play it can help them to relax without them being quite so intensively the focus of attention. It can also be a useful way for them to explore the problem directly, with their picture illustrating the problem and being a talking point in terms of both its content and style.

THE PROCESS AND SKILLS OF PROBLEM SOLVING WITH CHILDREN

By working with children to help them to resolve their problems, it is hoped that as they grow up they will become more independent in learning how to do it for themselves. If they have learnt the skills in childhood by being helped themselves, then they may be more confident and effective in dealing with whatever befalls them in the future. We will, therefore, consider the skills that parents can use to encourage and empower children to begin to solve their own problems.

By helping parents with their problems and making the process explicit with them, it is possible that they will acquire an understanding of it in ways that will enable them to apply the same skills in relation to their children. We have already explored the stages and skills in Chapter 10, but will briefly consider the stages and skills of problem solving in order to illustrate this in the context of parents working directly with their children. Since the relationship is of paramount importance in the helping process, as we have stressed throughout the book, parents are likely to begin at an advantage. However, using the process and skills considered below can deepen this relationship and lead to a greater understanding and respect for each other.

We will use an example to illustrate the major points, trying to identify the skills being used at the different stages. What is crucial, however, is that parents are able to control their own anxieties sufficiently to enable them to be relatively objective, to involve the child completely, to listen to him/her, and to work in partnership.

CLARIFYING THE PROBLEM: Sally aged 7 years came home from school one day very upset and had obviously been crying. She told her mother that her best friend, Mary, would not play with her any more, because she had made some new friends and they had said that she was too little and silly. Sally's mother took her on her lap and said, 'I can see it's made you sad and upset.' Sally cried for a while, sitting with her mother's arms around her. When she was calm, her mother asked her to tell her what had happened. Sally repeated the story in more detail, with her mother asking a few further questions in order to try to see the situation clearly.

Skills: Sally's mother immediately gave her full attention to her daughter. She indicated her understanding with an empathic remark and demonstrated this clearly with a cuddle. She did not try to take the problem away or to find an immediate solution, but allowed Sally to cry without trying to minimise the situation in any way. She was responsive to her, and only questioned her about the problem, when she was calm enough to think about it. She then asked her to tell the story again and asked questions to enable her to be clear about what had happened.

SETTING GOALS: Feeling braver now she had talked about it, Sally said, 'I felt very lonely at playtime with no-one to play with.' Her mother responded by firstly saying, 'It was hard feeling on your own.' She then went on to ask what Sally would like to happen tomorrow. She replied by saying that she wanted them to let her join in with their games. Her mother said, 'Mary's upset you, but you still want to play with her?' and this led to Sally quite clearly nodding her head.

Skills: With her mother having listened to her carefully, and having given her plenty of time to talk, Sally herself identified that her central concern was loneliness. The mother indicated her understanding of this with an empathic statement, and allowed Sally to respond before continuing. Since it was evident from Sally's response that she had understood the major concern, she then went on to elicit a goal from Sally. She did not assume what it might be (e.g. to get a new friend). She did not respond emotionally to Mary's behaviour to try to diminish Sally's hurt (e.g. 'Mary's being a silly girl.'), nor did she suggest a solution (e.g. 'We'll go into school with Helen and her mother tomorrow.') which would have been unrelated to Sally's goal. She then checked it with her to be clear that it was what Sally really wanted, although she did challenge it tentatively. However, since Sally was definite about it and the goal was explicit, realistic, clear, specific, measurable and set in a time context, she accepted it as the basis for finding strategies.

PLANNING STRATEGIES: The mothers next question was, 'What do you think we could do about that?' and together they thought of some possible solutions. Sally suggested that her mother could tell Mary to play with her. Her mother suggested that Sally might try to make friends with Mary's new playmates. Sally then suggested that she could take her new skipping rope into school and invite Mary to play with her.

Sally's mother then said, 'Well we've got three possible solutions here. Let's look at each one to see what might work best. Number one, I should tell Mary to play with you. How do you think that would work?' They agreed that Mary might tell her mother that she would play with her, but then it might not actually happen, because she might not really want to. They also agreed that Mary might not like Sally's mother interfering. 'What about the second suggestion,' asked Sally's mother, 'that you try and make friends with Mary's new playmates?' 'That wouldn't work.' said Sally right away, 'They really don't like me, and they're horrible to me. I will take my new skipping rope to school and just ask Mary to play with me.' Her mother then asked if she would let Mary's new friends play as well, if they want to, and Sally replied, 'Only if they don't call me names.'

Skills: Once the goal has been agreed, the mother went on immediately to think about how it might be achieved. Since she felt that it was important for Sally to learn how to find solutions, she involved her immediately by asking for her suggestions about what she might do. She took Sally's suggestions, and added to them, but did not go on for too long, as it would have been too much for her to take in. She then went on to weigh up the relative merits of each, but structured this carefully. She took each suggestion in turn, summarised it, and then prompted evaluation with an open question. She stopped when Sally quite clearly decided what to do, but she hoped to help her explore possible obstacles by asking her quite a challenging question about involving the friends, given that Sally has expressed a clear dislike of them.

IMPLEMENTATION: The following morning Sally found her skipping rope and put it in her bag to take to school. Her mother encouraged her, saying, 'I see you've got your new skipping rope.' She then asked what Sally would do if Mary would still not play with her. Sally replied, 'I don't think she will be like that today. But I suppose I'll just be on my own again like yesterday. At least I will have my skipping rope to play with'.

Skills: Here Sally's mother notices and comments on her determination to carry through what she has already decided. This was intended as a way of encouraging her, but also to indicate that her mother was thinking about it. At the same time she wanted to add a note of realism to Sally's enthusiasm and to help her to think ahead to the possible outcomes of her actions. Again the conversation is short and the mother does not push it further, as Sally seems to realise the main implications.

REVIEWING THE OUTCOME: When Sally's mother met her from school in the afternoon, she was pleased to see her running out of school hand in hand with Mary. Nevertheless, later in the evening she asked Sally what had happened. It was slightly difficult because Sally was not bothered by the problem anymore, but her mother learnt that she had approached Mary, who had agreed to play, but only if the others could join in. She asked how Sally had handled this and was told that they had all played happily together, with Mary's friends teaching them a new skipping rhyme. She attempted to ask some more questions, but since Sally was not particularly interested in talking about it, she did not pursue it and simply praised her for dealing with the problem effectively.

Skills: Sally's mother waited until there was a convenient time and made sure that she reviewed Sally's strategy with her. Although it was clearly successful, she tried to explore what had happened in a little more depth to see what might be learnt about such situations for the future. However, she responded to Sally's lack of interest and quickly let the topic drop, but not without clear encouragement and praise for what she had achieved.

In Conclusion

In this chapter we have attempted to explore the situation of parenting in relation to toddlers and young children, in an effort to derive a framework to enable helpers to guide parents in being with their children and meeting their needs effectively. For simplicity, our general assumption is that the different aspects of the Parent Adviser model are directly transferable from helping parents to the situation of parents being with their children. Throughout we have assumed that the nature of the relationship is crucial and that this is should equate to a respectful partnership in which children are seen as people with a significant role to play in it. It is not possible for parents alone to determine the immediate, short-term or long-term outcomes for their children. This is to a large part in the hands of the children and the role to the parent is to take them into account and to try to respond as best they can to children as people with their own unique personality.

To enable this, we have outlined a set of qualities that directly parallel those of helpers generally, and have then considered how these might be put into effect via a set of parenting skills that might facilitate knowledge of children and their needs and effective responding. These include the skills of play, the more general skills of listening, providing encouragement, and then the skills related to the processes involved in exploring and finding solutions to children's problems.

Nothing we have said should be taken to imply that there is one way of dealing with children, nor that there is a perfect way to be with them. Being a parent is not easy and all that can be expected, as in any relationship, is that parents do their best in the interaction. Our contention is that if at least some of these ideas can be put into effect, then parents will be more able to relate to their specific children, to understand their needs and therefore to respond more effectively. Parents cannot be expected to demonstrate these qualities and to exercise appropriate skills all the time, but might be helped with such a model for guidance. If helpers are aware of the full range of skills and qualities that have been found to be helpful, then they may be able to share them with parents and hence facilitate the development of their children.

The points made here relate to parenting in general. However, since some aspects of children's behaviour is a major source of problems for parents, we will continue in the following chapter by considering a set of strategies specifically for managing unacceptable behaviour using positive and non-violent means.

CHAPTER 15
MANAGING BEHAVIOUR

Although we have so far considered qualities and skills for parenting in general, the problems parents have most difficulty with are related to situations in which their children's behaviour gives cause for concern. We will, therefore, complete the exploration of parenting with a look at this important topic. We will briefly define what we mean by difficult behaviour, describe a general model for its management, and then finally consider specific skills and strategies involved.

Difficult behaviour

Although difficult behaviour is hard to define in an absolute sense, we are referring here to any child behaviour that is problematic to the parents in terms of it being unacceptable to them or seen as naughty. No matter what the motivation of the child (e.g. curiosity, excitement, anger), it is the parents' (or carers') reaction to the behaviour that at least initially determines whether it belongs in this category. In general it is behaviour that they would like to stop. It includes a whole range of actions that are usually construed as deliberate on the child's part (e.g. tantrums), as antisocial in some way (e.g. being aggressive or destructive), or difficult to control, for example, disobedient, selfish, or dangerous.

Care needs to be taken in labelling childrens' behaviour as difficult, because it will depend upon the context in which the behaviour occurs, the age and ability of the child, and its appropriateness. Since it involves value judgements, parents may differ considerably in their views, as a function of their culture, personal beliefs, or even current mood. For example, differences in parenting style, as described in the last chapter, may lead to very different judgements. Authoritarian parent may expect total obedience from a child and view any questioning of this as a threat, whereas authoritative parent may accept it as part of the child's learning. The neglecting parent, on the other hand, might not even notice it.

Given such difficulties, where parents have problems with their children's behaviour, one of the first tasks of any helper in the exploration stage is to understand exactly what it is about the child that concerns the parents and to help them construe the behaviour differently where appropriate.

Managing Behaviour: General Principles

The parenting skills we have explored so far in the previous chapters can be viewed as facilitating children's development and well-being. The general assumption is that children will change and develop in a positive way and that parents need to provide the general context in which this can happen. In relation to difficult behaviour, on the other hand, there is a direct and immediate implication or requirement that the child's behaviour should change, because it is dangerous to the child, hurtful to others, or might otherwise interfere with his/her development. The focus for us here, therefore, is on how to bring about such change as quickly as possible and to describe methods that might be useful. Before this, however, we should like to examine the general principles of enabling this to happen.

APPLYING THE PARENT ADVISER MODEL

When children misbehave consistently over time, the parents' task is not only to find ways to produce behaviour change, but also changes in their children's constructions. The assumption here is that change is likely to be much more effective, if children understand why their behaviour is unacceptable and what is more appropriate. As a guide, we have found it helpful for parents to see the tasks involved as exactly the same as in the helping process outlined earlier in the book. Just as the helper works with them, parents may find it valuable to think of their task as: 1) relating to the child so as to; 2) exploring the behaviour and situation fully; 3) clarifying the problem in terms of understanding the behaviour if possible and particularly why it happens; 4) setting goals (e.g. to reduce the frequency or stop the behaviour in all or specified situations); 5) carefully planning strategies so as to achieve the goals; 6) implementing these strategies appropriately; and 7) reviewing the outcomes with appropriate adjustments to one's understanding, goals, strategies or implementation as necessary.

Possibly the most important task is for parents to understand what the child is doing and why. If this can be achieved, then a whole range of strategies might present themselves directly related to the explanation of the behaviour. The task for the helper is therefore to enable the development of a clear understanding of the behaviour in its particular context, to help parents formulate a goal appropriate to this understanding and to devise relevant strategies. For example, eighteen month old Jamie became very troublesome at his baby sister's feeding time, cuddling up close to his mother and trying to push his sister away from the breast. His mother would then push him away and Jamie would become even more distressed, with the result that his mother was considering abandoning breast feeding. Observation of this behaviour demonstrated a clear need by Jamie for his mother's attention. It was decided therefore, that she should encourage his proximity-seeking behaviour by having him sit close to her and look at a picture book together during feeding. It was also concluded that she should make a special time to give Jamie her undivided attention each day, engaged in something he enjoyed doing.

Adapting the parent adviser model in this way implies the need for the parent to work closely with the child and to explore the problem by any means possible, but particularly through discussion, if the child is verbal, and observation. Since communication between the parent and child is crucial to this, again the importance of the relationship is raised, and the notion of partnership applies just as much here as it does to the helper situation. The very first task, therefore, is a consideration of the relationship and its adequacy; the implication is that it might be necessary to work on it in order to improve the level and quality of communication. Improving the relationship is likely to have beneficial implications for the whole of the subsequent process, not only improvements in communication.

Without elaborating further, the relationship and other tasks are likely to be improved as a function of the qualities discussed in the last chapter (e.g. respecting the child as a person, being responsive). Empathy has a particular place here in that the task for the parent involves an attempt to understand the constructions of the child. Since children see the world so differently, this is not easy, but it is important that the parent tries to put themselves in their children's shoes and attempts to understand how they are making sense of the situation and what they are doing.

It may help if parents themselves understand that there is no certainty in doing this, and that the model they derive is actually a hypothesis. It may or may not be useful in suggesting solutions, but it is a beginning to the process, which in essence is a way of testing the hypothesis. This begins with goal setting on the basis of the hypotheses developed, followed by devising strategies, implementing them carefully, and then reviewing the outcomes (i.e. testing the validity of the hypothesis). Given the model of a child as a person and the relationship ideal as one of partnership, then it follows that all these tasks should be undertaken as far as possible together with parents consulting their children and involving them in the decision making process. This itself is likely to enhance the outcomes through the development of the relationship, but also through the use of the child's self-knowledge and expertise.

Applying the model of the helping process, assuming a partnership and using the qualities outlined earlier to foster the process, can in effect be understood as producing change by way of improved communication. It involves trying to understand how children make sense of the situation and then clearly communicating a different view, for example, about the rules of the situation, and the implications of their behaviour for themselves and others. It would be useful therefore if parents were to understand and use all the skills needed in the process (again as described earlier in the book), including those related to listening, exploring, challenging, for example, and problem management. We discussed this at some length in the previous chapter, and it is worth noting that the division we have made between this chapter and the last is artificial, since probably the best way of producing change even in relation to difficult behaviour is by giving positive, loving attention and understanding. Giving what Carl Rogers (1959) called 'unconditional positive regard' will have powerful effects upon children and their behaviour, nourishing their growth and self-esteem.

BEHAVIOURAL MODEL

Having stressed the application of the parent adviser model to the parenting situation and emphasising communication in dealing with difficult behaviour, there are other important models of value in this area. There are always situations where it is unclear or impossible to know what is going on in the child's behaviour, or where strategies have been tried and fail without it being clear why this should be. Perhaps the most important derive from the behavioural approach given prominence by Skinner (e.g. 1974) and others. Although there are severe limitations to using this approach, the central notion of trying to understand behaviour in terms only of what one can observe is attractive especially in relation to young children. This involves being very specific about observable actions (behaviours) and relating these to specific environmental events that precede the action (antecedents) or follow it (consequences).

These ideas have been developed by social learning theorists, most notably Albert Bandura (e.g. 1977) and have led to considerable developments in relation to severe childhood problems such as the treatment of autism and intellectual impairment (e.g. Newson & Hipgrave, 1982). It has also been central to the development of parent training programmes (e.g. Paterson, 1975; Quinn & Quinn, 1995; Sanders, 1992; Webster-Stratton, 1992). The basic behavioural principle applied within these approaches is relatively simple and states that the strength (e.g. frequency or likely occurrence) of a behaviour, in a given situation, is a function of its consequences. In other words, assuming that the behaviour of a child is specific to certain situations, an action that is followed by a positive outcome (e.g. reward) is likely to be reinforced or strengthened (i.e. is more likely to occur in future) in that situation, and an action that is not followed by a positive outcome is likely to be decreased in strength. This idea underpins almost all the strategies to be described later in the chapter and is extremely useful as a way of understanding behavioural situations and helping one devise methods of dealing with difficult behaviour or even serious behaviour problems.

A second principle, explored by Bandura (1977) particularly, is to do with imitation. From this work it has become clear that children learn a considerable amount by modelling what they see around them, so that anything parents do can be powerful determinants of children's behaviour, especially if the behaviour is then rewarded. This means that children are highly likely to imitate the behaviour of their parents or other powerful models (e.g. television characters) and may not discriminate between positive and negative behaviour. Research has shown, for example, that patterns of parenting may be acquired in this way (Huesman, Eron, Ledfkowits & Walder, 1984). Since children are highly likely to identify with their parents, if their parents used corporal or other means of punishment (e.g. shouting or withdrawing privileges), then it is highly likely that they will do the same with their own children in the next generation (Giles-Sims, Straus & Sugarman 1995; Henricson & Grey, 2001).

There are a number of implications of this approach for dealing with children's behaviour in the context we are discussing. The first is to do with how situations might be explored and the behaviour understood in its context, and the second relates to management strategies.

BEHAVIOUR ANALYSIS: As we have said throughout the book, exploration of a problem is crucial to dealing with it and the behavioural approach has led to a number of systems for analysing problematic behaviour (e.g. Sturmey, 2002) and these can be very sophisticated. What is also interesting is that the kinds of observations required are extremely useful in suggesting a variety of explanations for the behaviour and therefore a variety of possible intervention strategies. This approach can therefore be used on its own to help parents think systematically about their children's behaviour in context. For example, one might use an ABC analysis. This involves carefully specifying and observing the exact behaviour (B) of concern (e.g. its frequency and nature), the antecedents (A) or triggers for the behaviour (e.g. where and when it occurs, and where not) and the consequences (C) of it (e.g. the rewards or otherwise) (Sutton, 2000; Herbert, 1988). For example, parents may be completely unaware of the subtle cues they might be giving to their children to behave in a particular way, and the ways in which they might unintentionally reward inappropriate behaviour.

MANAGEMENT STRATEGIES: Having done a careful analysis of the situation before intervention, many possible strategies may be suggested, but the following are possible as general principles for reducing the frequency of difficult behaviour. These underlie much of what will be illustrated in detail in the remainder of the chapter.

The first principle in reducing the frequency of a behaviour is to be aware of the antecedents of it, and to avoid these. If an act occurs in a particular situation, then where possible avoiding the situation should have the effect of stopping or reducing the occurrence of it. If you know the triggers, then there is the possibility of avoiding the behaviour.

The second general principle is for parents to reward (i.e. reinforce) behaviour that they wish to encourage, especially by using positive attention and praise. By being immediately and consistently responsive to acceptable behaviours, they are likely to increase in strength and more likely to occur in the future. It is also worth noting that if these behaviours are incompatible with difficult behaviour, then the frequency of the problem behaviour is likely to decrease as a result.

The third principle is not to reinforce unacceptable behaviour. This may seem obvious, but parents often unintentionally reward difficult behaviour by attending to it. It is interesting to observe how much attention (even negative attention) is given to difficult behaviour, when many positive actions go completely unnoticed.

Another important principle is that parents should behave in ways they wish their children to act and not to do things that they do not want them to imitate. Young children learn rapidly and imitation is a central mechanism. Since parents are important models, all that they do is a possible source of material for their children as is illustrated in relation to punishment, for example.

A final point we should like to make is that the behavioural model was founded on a very strong scientific basis, emphasising measurement and experimentation. A number of valuable points might be learnt from this, but perhaps the most important for our purposes here is to try to establish a baseline against which to check the extent of change produced. If a parent is intent on changing the frequency of a child's behaviour, then it would be useful to have a measure of the frequency before intervening and to track it subsequently, so as to enable a judgement about whether and to what extent a strategy has been successful.

Punishment

A final principle we tend to endorse is to avoid the use of punishment as a way of helping children change, and particularly punishment that is violent or aggressive, such as smacking or otherwise using force. This comes from humanitarian views of it being morally wrong to use aggression in general, and especially with children. However, we are making the point clearly here, because of the prevalence of punishment in our society and its significance as often the first response to difficult behaviour. For example, a survey carried out in the UK (Department of Health, 2000) showed that 88 per cent of the public felt that it was sometimes necessary to smack a child. Two comprehensive reviews of research into physical punishment found that 90 per cent of children and 97 percent of four year olds had been punished in this way (Leach, 1999a; Leach 1999b).

However, there are also a number of other reasons why we would not advocate punishment in general, and these are largely to do with it: 1) not being effective; and 2) may have other undesirable consequences. We will list some of these points here:

- Although punishment may stop a specific difficult behaviour initially, it is not the most efficient or effective way of stopping it in the long term. Children may adapt to it, so that it quickly loses its effect.
- It gives a negative model to children (Waterston, 2000). Seeing a parent using physical means to get their own way is highly likely to be copied as a prime mode of interacting with others to get one's way, even though it will prevent the use of alternative strategies if it fails.
- Perhaps by modelling or other mechanisms, it has been associated with increased aggressive and antisocial behaviour (Cohen & Brook, 1995; Straus, Sugarman & Giles-Sims, 1997).
- Given that the parent–child relationship is crucial to the developmental process, physical punishment is likely to convey rejection and negative attitudes, and is unlikely to enhance the quality of the relationship in any way and may disturb it (Bee, 2000) by producing resentment and dislike.
- Punishment in itself is unlikely to communicate to the child what he is expected to do differently (Waterston, 2000; American Academy of Paediatrics, 1996).
- It may even disrupt the child's learning by generating anxiety. It has been associated with excessive anxiety in the child, leading to depression and suicidal tendencies in adulthood (Ghate & Daniels, 1997).
- It has also been related to impaired cognitive development in children (Straus & Paschall, 1998).
- It is not a method to be advocated in potentially abusive families, as children can habituate to it, with parents having to escalate its severity, leading to abusive consequences (Cleaver, Wattam & Cawson, 1998).

A recent survey suggests that parental attitudes towards disciplining children are changing (National Family and Parenting Institute, 1999). This indicates that most parents do not believe that punishment is the best way to socialise their children and would favour techniques that have been termed 'positive parenting.' There are also indications that parents regret the use of physical punishment, and that it is more to do with their own feelings (e.g. of anger), than it is to do with providing instruction for the child. However, even though disciplinary practices seem to have lagged behind these changes of attitude, it is reasonable to assume that parents welcome support for a more positive approach to the management of their children's unacceptable behaviour.

Specific Methods

We will now continue with a consideration of specific methods of behaviour management for use with behaviour that is undesirable and that needs to be reduced in frequency or eliminated altogether. All methods should be planned carefully with parents before they are implemented to ensure that they are effective. This will involve negotiation and partnership working as described in chapter 4. It will be necessary for the helper to acknowledge the parent's expertise in knowing their own child and what might or might not work for them. Negotiating in this way with parents will model how the parent should work with their children, involving them in planning and then communicating final decisions clearly.

The behaviour of concern should be clearly defined, and it is often helpful if parents spend a week or so observing what happens when the behaviour occurs and perhaps keeping a written note or diary of events. This often helps to clarify issues and contributes to the successful negotiation of an effective plan. It also creates a baseline against which to measure achievements.

Once goals have been agreed with parents and strategies carefully planned, they should be supported in implementing them in whatever way seems useful to them. Strategies are much more likely to succeed if they are supported by other family members. Both parents (or other carers) should be familiar with the decisions, should in general confirm each other's actions, and act consistently so that the child is not confused by conflicting messages.

All techniques used to manage inappropriate behaviour should always be paired with consistent reward for appropriate behaviour. All should be conducted respectfully using the guidelines for setting limits and boundaries, which we will now consider in more depth.

SETTING LIMITS

We saw in the last chapter that the authoritative style of parenting is associated with the most positive outcomes for children. This entails not only demonstrating high levels of love, warmth and acceptance of the child, but also high levels of control. Control may be interpreted as setting clear limits in relation to what is acceptable and unacceptable behaviour. This means parents having and communicating clearly defined rules, so that children know where they stand and what is required (e.g. seat belts will be worn at all times in the car; physical fighting is not the way to settle arguments).

This in itself does not necessarily produce acceptable behaviour, since, even if or perhaps especially if, children are living in a secure environment, their natural role or task is to learn, and this includes acquiring information about the rules. It is quite normal for them to test out these limits or rules, because it is in effect the only way to discover this information. They test the limits to see if they really do apply, particularly if parents have been inconsistent in the past.

The notion of partnership implies that these rules should be negotiated with children wherever possible (e.g. the time to be in from playing out with a friend). What can also be negotiated are the consequences of failing to comply. However, this is not always possible, particularly with younger children, and it is therefore important for parents to be sure what they want to happen. It is nevertheless worth reviewing the rules periodically, but certainly it is important to be clear about them in advance. This means that the situation can be handled more effectively, without having to make complex split-second decisions (which could be wrong) in the middle of a fraught situation.

Taking the example of a mother, who is visiting a friend with a child of the same age and would like to leave, but the children are still playing together, are oblivious of the time, and not listening to the parent's requests to tidy away the toys and leave. How should the parent handle this situation? How should she behave in order to communicate her decision (i.e. the rule) in this case, and to obtain the child's compliance with the minimum of fuss. Quite obviously, if she calls half-heartedly from a distance (e.g. the next room), the children are likely to remain absorbed in their play. The kinds of skills required are explored below.

- Parents are likely to be more successful, if they give their full attention to their children, moving close to them, looking at them, going to their level, and gaining their awareness and attention directly.
- This might be prefaced by attending to what the child is doing, joining him/her in the activity with encouraging comments, and then choosing the most appropriate moment to give the information about tidying and leaving.
- Again this might be even more effective, if the parent has already given a time warning of the end of an activity a few minutes in advance.
- All information or requests should be given **clearly** and simply (e.g. 'You need to stop now.....' or 'It's time to go home......').

- Parents should act and speak **confidently**, avoiding questions if possible.
- Verbal battles should be avoided, telling the child no more than twice before showing the child what is required (e.g. putting toys away).
- If possible parents should have decided in advance exactly what they require and stick to it.
- They should be realistic, however, in the demands they make and not enter into arguments that cannot be won. It is better to say, 'We need to go. I'll put the toys away' than to enter into an argument about it and then give in.
- Parents should communicate **clearly** in language that is appropriate to the age and understanding of the child.
- Communications are best if stated **concisely**, avoiding giving multiple commands that might tax the child's memory span.
- Parents should demonstrate **confidence** that the child will co-operate. This might be signally by saying, 'When ....., then.....' rather than 'If you don't ....., you can't.'
- It is likely to be most effective if parents behave **calmly**, remaining polite and respectful all the time.
- Any fussing or protest should be ignored.
- Parents should remain **consistent** in their approach, ensuring that their instructions are carried out. This also means that, where there are two parents, they should support each other's demands of their children.
- Any efforts by children to co-operate should be noticed and praised.

Although there are many general points to remember about gaining children's co-operation, parents might find it useful to simply think about the five 'Cs' in bold above (Bays, 2000) to be clear, concise, calm, confident and consistent. We shall see that these are particularly useful skills in all the behaviour management strategies we are going on to describe.

Positive Reinforcement
In chapter 14 we considered the skills of encouragement and saw how beneficial this might be, for example, in raising children's self-esteem and confidence. What we are going to do now is explore how aspects of encouragement, including parental attention and praise, can be harnessed to help support behaviour that parents want in their children, and hence to decrease behaviour that is unacceptable. We are talking here specifically about the second general behavioural principle discussed earlier in the chapter. This involves the use of positive reinforcement, which has been defined as any response or event that has the effect of increasing the probability of re-occurrence of the behaviour that preceded it. What we will describe here,

therefore, are the skills involved in using reinforcement to increase the likelihood of desired behaviour.

CLEARLY DEFINING THE BEHAVIOUR: In using positive reinforcement, it is important to be very clear about the desired or target behaviour to which it applies. As in setting limits, children might be involved in the decision, but certainly it should be communicated to them in age-appropriate language calmly and concisely. There should be a clear target and this means selecting only one or two behaviours at a time, so that it is manageable and the child is not confused.

CHOOSING A REWARD: There are many positive reinforcers and therefore these should be chosen as likely to be effective for the specific child. Making the choice with the child increases the likelihood of this. Rewards might include food, sweets, crisps, or drinks; access to activities such as games, music or television; or tokens in the form of stars, points or even money, which might be valuable to the child in themselves (i.e. indicating achievement) or exchangeable for other things that the child would like. This might even include a system in which the size or value of the eventual reward increases as the number of stars or points accumulate.

What is particularly important is that rewards be easy to use, and this is true of social reinforcers (e.g. attention, praise, smiles, thanks and affectionate touch), which are possibly the most effective of all under certain circumstances. Since they are so easy, they can actually be combined with any of the other reinforcers, which might be withdrawn slowly, leaving social approval to function as a reinforcer on its own. It is also wise to choose a range of possibilities for the same child, so that they can be varied if a particular option loses its appeal.

REWARD IMMEDIATELY: For positive reinforcement to be successful, the rewards must be contingent upon the target behaviour, follow it immediately without delay, and certainly when it first occurs and every time the behaviour is seen. If this does not happen, the power of the method will diminish as well as the speed with which change occurs, since it will be difficult for children, especially very young children, to detect the contingency. However, once the connection is clearly acquired and the frequency of the behaviour has increased, not reinforcing on every occasion has the effect of ensuring the behaviour is maintained for longer.

ASSESSING PROGRESS: Progress should be reviewed carefully at appropriate points, so that changes may be made, and this is aided by having a baseline of the frequency of the target behaviour and continuing to assess this while the programme is in place so that comparison can be made. However, an important aspect of success is to keep children actively interested and engaged in the programme and their progress. Parents should, therefore, involve them in the review, examining star charts with them for example, and praising success wholeheartedly.

REVISE AND RE-NEGOTIATE THE PROGRAMME AS NECESSARY: As a result of the review, parents should be prepared to revise the programme. This could be because the child's behaviour has changed successfully and the programme is no longer needed, or that the target behaviour should be altered to encourage further progress in the child. Alternatively, if little has been achieved within a week, for example, then the need for revision will be clear. It might be that the rewards are not appropriate, the target behaviour is unrealistic or the rewards are not being implemented properly. There could be any number of adjustments to make, but these should come out of a careful evaluation. As usual, however, any changes should be negotiated with children wherever possible, with parents remaining positive and confident in the child's ability to succeed.

PLANNED IGNORING

This strategy operates on the basis of the third principle described earlier, where parents may be inadvertently reinforcing difficult behaviour. Because it can be of such concern to parents, they will give difficult behaviour considerable attention, and this reinforces it. Even negative attention (e.g. as anger) from parents may have this effect. The strategy, therefore, is to remove the attention so that the difficult behaviour is not reinforced and will decrease or disappear. It is only suitable for use with behaviour that does not put the child or others in danger (e.g. temper tantrums, whining, swearing, and squabbling), especially as the immediate effect of planned ignoring is often a significant increase in the difficult behaviour. What we will describe here are a number of skills that are likely to increase the efficacy of this strategy.

LIMITING THE NUMBER OF BEHAVIOURS TO IGNORE: To avoid confusion and to make a programme practical, parents should again plan to deal with only one or two behaviours at a time. These should be clearly defined and communicated where possible to the child.

ACT IMMEDIATELY: As soon as the target behaviour occurs, parents must ignore it immediately, acting as though they did not know that it had occurred.

BEING CONSISTENT: The behaviour targeted should be ignored consistently each time it occurs. Ignoring a particular behaviour altogether may come as a great surprise to the child, who may redouble his/her efforts to engage the parents. This should be avoided at all costs, however, since attending even once will be strongly reinforcing, indicating to the child that she/he must be persistent and it will succeed. Parents who use this method must, therefore, be prepared to be tested and be well supported by family or others in order to remain consistent.

How to ignore: In one sense ignoring should mean not responding at all, just naturally continuing to do what one was doing at the time. However, this may be difficult, and parents might need to turn away from the child to enable them to ignore it effectively. No interaction of any kind should occur; parents should avoid doing or saying anything to the child with no eye contact whatsoever. On some occasions it might even be helpful to move away from the child physically. However, it is important to keep the child in sight, so as to ensure being able to respond positively at an appropriate point. However, if the child is physically demanding attention by clinging then leaving the room may be the only option.

Attend to appropriate behaviour: Ignoring should be for as short a time as possible; seconds or minutes. As soon as the difficult behaviour ceases, parents should immediately pay attention to the child in order to reinforce more acceptable behaviour. In fact, it may be useful to give lots of attention and praise generally to the child during this period, but only in association with good behaviour. Once the child quietens the parent may distract him or her to another area of interest. Alternatively with an older child it may be necessary to talk through what has happened.

Review and revise as necessary: Again the effects of the intervention should be monitored and reviewed, if possible with reference to the frequency of the behaviour before the programme began, and adjusted as necessary until successful.

Choices and Consequences

This strategy is slightly less easy to explain, but works on the principle that the unacceptable behaviour will not be reinforced, as the consequence of it will not be positive. Essentially what happens is that parents offer their children a choice of how to behave, with one of the options having consequences that are not positive, or even negative. The intention here is to indicate the child's control and to allow her/him to learn from the consequences. For example, a child may be given the choice of changing out of his/her school clothes and playing in the sandpit in the garden, or not changing and therefore staying inside the house. 'As soon as you have done your homework, you can watch television' is perhaps a better approach than, 'You can't watch television until you've done your homework', because it is framed positively, but it again gives the child a choice with different consequences; to finish his homework and then watch television, or not do his homework and not see television.

Where possible consequences should not be contrived and complicated. Where possible they should follow naturally from the particular option chosen, so that children can learn about taking responsibility for their own behaviour and learn from their mistakes. For example, if a child is arguing about wearing a coat to school, the parent might allow her/him to experience being cold rather than insisting she/he wears it. The coat might carried by the parent, in case it is requested by the child, but it is likely that he/she will learn that the consequence of not wearing a coat is to be cold. It is of course worth saying that consequences should never be dangerous, and parents should not act as though a punishment is being applied, since it is in the child's control entirely.

When helping parents to think through choices and consequences for their children it may be helpful to consider the following skills.

HELPING THE CHILD TO UNDERSTAND THE CONSEQUENCES OF THEIR BEHAVIOUR: Children have to be involved in this strategy and be clear about the options and consequences in advance. Parents need to communicate this information clearly and concisely, so that the child can take responsibility and make the choice. This might be done by a clear process of negotiation, so that children are as responsible as the parent in deciding the consequences. However it is done, parents need to be prepared for how to deal with the specific situation before it occurs. They need to have planned what they are doing, so that the choices and consequences are relevant, appropriate and understandable given the child's situation and ability. Using 'If ..., then...' statements may be helpful for younger children; for example, 'If you make a mess with your food, then I will take your plate away', or 'If you do not eat, then you will be hungry.'

ALLOWING THE CONSEQUENCE TO FOLLOW FROM THE CHILD'S CHOICE: It is not always easy for the parent to follow through with the consequences, because the child may be miserable and they might feel sorry for them. However, it is essential that parents do what they say, or children simply learn not to take their parents seriously. One might, for example, avoid statements like, 'If you won't get dressed, you'll go to school in your pyjamas', if this cannot be implemented.

TIMING: Where possible, the consequence of the behaviour should follow as soon as possible, and preferably immediately, so that the connection between the choice and the result is quite clear to the child. 'If you do that, then you will not get a treat tomorrow' is simply a threat, may be punitive, and will have little immediate effect on the target behaviour. However, the consequence should not last too long, as it would then become unnecessarily punitive and generate hostility and resentment. For example, going without television for a month is unlikely to be effective, for breaking something, whereas using pocket money to buy a replacement might be. If possible, one should also try to allow children to be reinforced subsequently for appropriate behaviour, by choosing, for example, to put their coat on when they do get cold and praising them for it.

TIME OUT

Time-out refers to any technique in which children lose the possibility of obtaining reinforcement for their difficult behaviour. It is related to the principle of not reinforcing unacceptable behaviour, but is used where it is not possible to ignore it, because it happens very frequently, or is dangerous to the child or other people. This might be used, for example, with aggressive or destructive acts.

Essentially the idea is that the child should be quickly and effectively moved into a situation in which there is no opportunity for reinforcement of any kind, social or otherwise. For example, the child might be quickly put into a small, but safe room with no one to interact with and nothing to do. It is best if the child cannot cause any damage or disruption in the situation. For younger children, the corner of a room might be used, where the parent can observe what the child is doing. It is not recommended as a first option in dealing with difficult behaviour, since it is comparatively drastic, does require direct control of the child, and can be seen as punitive. It is, however, extremely useful and effective if planned and carried out properly in relation to behaviours that parents find particularly difficult, and where their own anger may be running high. The following skills may be found to be useful when applying time-out.

LIMITING AND CLEARLY DEFINING THE BEHAVIOUR: As usual in all the methods, the target behaviour should be defined clearly and used for only one or two behaviours at a time. Using time-out with too many behaviours at one time is likely to be impractical for parents to manage, may confuse the children, and may become rather punitive by the frequency with which the method is used.

PLANNING AND NEGOTIATION: Again the programme should be planned carefully before being implemented, and this should include the children concerned. Plans should be made in consultation, with them helping to make decisions about all aspects. It is important that they know what is happening and why and this might need to be checked once time-out has been implemented.

CALM AND NON-PUNITIVE: All the procedures should be carried out calmly, without anger or aggression on the parents part. This is particularly important, as parents may become cross when dealing with the unacceptable behaviours involved, and the child may need to be physically controlled when put into the time-out situation. Parental anger may frighten children, but more important is to model emotional control for the child. Remaining calm conveys respect for the child, reduces the punitive element of the method, and enables the parent to act quickly and efficiently.

TIMING: Children should be put into the time-out situation immediately the behaviour occurs, preferably without threat, and left there for a maximum of 5 minutes or so. It is suggested by some that this be reduced by a minute per year of age for children younger than five, although one should think very carefully about using the method with very young children.

IGNORING THE CHILD: Interaction with children (verbal or non-verbal) should be minimised throughout the process of placing them in time-out and while they are there.

REMOVAL FROM TIME-OUT: Since it is important to reinforce appropriate behaviour, it is important to ensure that children are quiet and behaving reasonably well before they are removed from the time-out situation. Therefore, as soon as they are behaving well for a short time, they should be removed and given attention and praise for calming down.

CONSISTENCY: Time-out should be used very consistently if it is to be effective no matter how frequently the target behaviour occurs. A parent who uses it one day but not the next will create confusion in the child. It is also important that both parents support each others in the strategy, as the child could learn to take advantage of one parent against the other.

As with ignoring, it is possible that behaviour may increase initially, perhaps as a way of the child testing the limits, but parents should be aware of this and consistently respond as planned, even if this means the child going straight back into time-out within minutes of coming out. Consistency is the way that parents can give the clear message that they mean what they say and will stick to it. This may be difficult at the time, but will eventually provide stability for the child.

COUPLE THE METHOD WITH POSITIVE REINFORCEMENT: When using time-out, parents should also take care to introduce an additional positive element into the programme. This is most easily done by choosing an alternative, and preferably incompatible behaviour, to the target for time-out and to reinforce it consistently whenever it occurs.

In Conclusion

In this chapter we have explored the skills of managing behaviour that is unacceptable. In general our view is that parents can often avoid difficult behaviour by being in tune with their children, sensitive to what they are doing, and clear and positive in communication. However, when there is difficult behaviour, many parents in the United Kingdom, if not elsewhere, frequently resort to punishment, and particularly smacking. We have argued strongly against this on the grounds that it is not particularly effective and may have significant disadvantages (e.g. modelling aggression for the child). We have therefore outlined some general principles to guide ways of dealing with difficult behaviour positively and then described useful strategies in some detail.

The general principles derive firstly from the Parent Adviser model itself, applying it to the interaction between parent and child, in contrast to the interaction between helper and parent. In a general sense, this works on the relationship, with the aim of improving communication and modelling acceptable behaviour for children. It is certainly intended by this to help parents learn about and develop for themselves an understanding of their children and strategies for dealing with them that are related to possible explanations of the children's behaviour.

We have also included principles from social learning theory, as a second general model for helping parents to make sense of and deal with difficult behaviour. We have then provided an account of a variety of strategies that derive from this model, including setting limits, the use of positive reinforcement, planned ignoring, using choices and consequences, and time-out. These are powerful strategies if planned and implemented carefully. Using them will change children's behaviour, but also have more positive effects upon the parent–child relationship. However, they are not presented here as recipes for parents.

Our intention, in accord with the Parent Adviser model, is that these should be principles and strategies for helpers to develop with parents, if they are needed. The general style should not be that of an expert, but that of a thoughtful partner who begins with parents' own ideas, enables them to grasp general principles of management where necessary, makes the problem solving process explicit, and facilitates the parents in devising specific strategies themselves. This might involve prompting and even direct suggestions from the helper, but these should be minimised, with ideas being elicited from the parents wherever possible.

We should emphasise that, as discussed in Chapter 2, the aims of the helper include not only the management of individual problems with parents, but also the facilitation of their general understanding of their children and parenting, the enhancement of their ability to deal with future problems themselves, and the growth of their self-efficacy. The job of parenting is likely to become easier if they can take models from the helper and apply them; having general models in advance is more likely to be effective than just reacting to situations as they arise. Working in partnership with parents, communicating effectively, and making this explicit wherever possible, increases the likelihood that parents themselves will work in partnership with their children, listen to them and therefore understand them better.

Just as we have stressed involving parents in devising strategies, so children should be included at all stages as a model for their development. The strategies discussed in this chapter are concerned to a large extent with helping them to learn self-discipline, and to become increasingly responsible for their own decisions. Although the strategies will help, the parents' style is also important as a model for their children, hence the need for self-discipline, emotional control, clear communication and involvement of the child. Underpinning it all is the need to respect children as people and to attempt to empathise.

Although we are finishing our exploration of work with parents with a set of principles and strategies for managing children, we must just re-emphasise their context and note that these are not the only reasons for parents having difficulties. They frequently have to struggle with a host of problems, including depression, for example, poor living conditions, poverty, and relationship disharmony. General support is, therefore, always essential to facilitate their resilience and enable them to find their own personal and community supports to sustain them in both meeting their own needs and those of their children.

CHAPTER 16
FINAL ISSUES

We have reached the final chapter after an extensive journey concerned to explore the complexities of providing effective psychosocial care for parents and hence their children. We began by looking at their needs and the aims of helping in the broadest terms, taking account of the psychological and social context, and the importance of facilitating the ability of parents to manage effectively on their own. We continued by outlining a set of frameworks to be explored for their value in thinking about the processes of helping, including the importance and nature of the relationship with parents, and the qualities and skills required to enable the processes. Central to this, we presented a model of how people adapt psychologically, based upon construct theory. Although this has many implications for the task of helping parents, it was also used as the basis for thinking specifically about the task of parenting. In particular, it was used to present a model of the parent–infant interaction, which is the vital vehicle for knowing and meeting children's developmental needs. We finished our journey by looking at the qualities and skills involved in parenting in the early years and into middle childhood, including a number of specific strategies for promoting parent–infant interaction and dealing with difficult behaviour.

At the very least we hope the journey has been interesting. Our intention has been to challenge readers to think about communicating with parents more productively; enabling a collaborative enterprise that is to the ultimate benefit of parents and their children. We hope it has facilitated the development of clearer models for thinking about this work and has benefited readers in terms of the manner in which they relate and communicate.

Whether or not we have been successful, it is important to finish with a consideration of a number of issues relating to the application and implementation of the ideas in the book. We should like to think briefly about the need for training, before considering aspects of the system and the broader context within which the ideas presented have to fit. We will look at supervision, which is vital to effective intervention, and then consider resourcing, service coordination and soliciting further help for the family from other workers, including referring them where necessary.

Training
The ideas we have presented in the book are not definitive and do not provide absolute understanding of how to help parents. As we have said, we

have given them as food for thought, as a way of challenging the reader to think about the issues involved and therefore to be clearer about the tasks. We have also been describing complex skills. However, although reading the book may be useful, we have no doubt that there is a need for training courses to enable people to develop these ideas and skills and therefore their helping potential.

For each of us to develop, we need a context in which to present and explore our ideas, and to practise the skills involved in communicating with others. This requires circumstances in which we feel secure and trust the people working with us. We need to be able to try out our skills and to have clear and useful feedback on what we have done with positive and constructive suggestions for how to improve. Communicating is never easy and the more appropriate practice we have with feedback, the more effective we are likely to be, no matter what our level of expertise.

Simply applying the skills and strategies described in this book may be beneficial, but supervised practice with appropriate feedback will not only speed the learning process, but will increase the level of proficiency eventually reached. For maximum benefit, therefore, the reader is advised to seek practice opportunities, and there are a number of possible ways of doing this.

One might do it informally by meeting regularly with colleagues in a small group. This might involve detailed discussion of the kinds of ideas presented in the book, perhaps preceded by reading and presentations. It might also involve making, watching and discussing videotapes of people interacting in helping situations. Alternatives to this might include role play, in which individuals practise the skills of interacting and have feedback from a person in the parent role and from one or more observers. This might involve rehearsing very basic situations or even situations which members of the group have already experienced and found difficult. Soliciting the help of parents can enhance this kind of activity significantly, by, for example, involving them in the role play and feedback. Their expertise is invaluable, provided they are able to feel confident in the situation and valued for their candour. Although useful, such methods of practice can be stressful and do require a high level of trust in the group and clarity in relation to confidentiality, for example. There clearly needs to be respect for others and an emphasis upon improvement from one's own level, without competition and without a focus upon inadequacies.

As an alternative to peer collaboration, there are now a variety of courses offering training in counselling and counselling skills in most areas. These range from introductory courses training very basic skills to advanced postgraduate degrees. Provided they are of good quality, these are likely to be very useful to child and family workers, although it is not necessary to undergo the most elaborate and specialist courses to feel more confident and able to communicate more effectively with parents.

Since such course are not necessarily tailored to the specific needs of particular professions and services, one possible option is to approach local clinical psychologists and counsellors working in one's area and to elicit their help in facilitating training specifically geared to one's own requirements. Courses in the region of 30 to 60 hours over a period of ten to twelve weeks can have significant value for participants (e.g. Rushton & Davis, 1992).

This book is the text for the Parent Adviser course, which is now provided by the Centre for Parent and Child Support at Guy's Hospital. Courses are run regularly in London, and can be commissioned by organisations in their own locality (see website for further information:). The training involves a core component of 10 half day sessions, preferably taken at weekly intervals. To this can be added a selection of modules, each lasting about six half days. The modules include: 1) the facilitation of the parent–infant interaction beginning in the antenatal period; and 2) parenting toddlers and young children. We have also worked in the area of postnatal depression, but have not yet published the module formally.

The teaching methods are discussion based, entirely interactive and provide ample opportunity for the practice of the skills discussed in the book and for the provision of feedback. Two facilitators run each course and attempt to develop a partnership with the participants and to do so by demonstrating the qualities and skills addressed in the course. The overall aims are to help the participants to explore their current levels of knowledge and skill and to challenge them to change and develop, using an open seminar format and small groups of three for practising the relevant skills. The training is based upon a manual published in conjunction with this book (Davis, Day & Bidmead, 2002), and courses are also provided by the Centre for suitably qualified personnel to train as supervisors (see below) and trainers of the Parent Adviser approach.

Supervision

Learning and development does not and should not stop after basic training, and an important premise of the Parent Adviser approach is that all helpers need regular and on-going supervision. This is not only to maintain adequate performance, but also to continue to become ever more understanding and effective. There are many ways to ensure continuing professional development, and we would argue that high quality skilled supervision is the most essential requirement, using people who are trained specifically to do so. This is why we emphasised in Chapter 1 a tiered system of care for families, in that it provides Tier one staff (i.e. all those working directly with children and their families) with mental health specialists, who might not only provide training as discussed in the last section, but also subsequent consultation and supervision.

Supervision, as defined for example by Hawkins and Shohet (2000) essentially consists of an interactive interpersonal situation in which one person attempts to ensure that the other is as effective as possible in helping people. As stated here, the ultimate aim is to enable the person supervised to provide the most effective help for the recipients of the service, but there are a number of functions implied by this. These include, for example, allowing staff to: 1) explore the implementation of what they learnt in their training; 2) consider difficulties encountered in practice; 3) realistically evaluate their performance; 4) derive personal support, including a sense of belonging to the group or organisation; 5) continue to develop their ideas and skills; and 6) monitor the service model in practice, so as to maintain its integrity and ensure adherence to the model. Central to this is the endeavour of being able to learn something of value from each of the families with whom one works.

Hawkins and Shohet (2000) separate these functions into: 1) educative or formative; 2) supportive or restorative; and 3) managerial or normative. These overlap considerably, but may be given different emphasis according to the context, which might include, for example, whether the supervisor is the person's line manager or not, and the characteristics of the supervisor. Some would argue that clinical supervision and management should be separated, since the roles might conflict. For example, what is best for the service might not necessarily be in the best interests of the individual. Showing a difficulty or potential weakness to one's manager might have a very different outcome to sharing this with a clinical supervisor. However, this is more to do with the nature and quality of the relationship between the people involved and the skills of the supervisor/manager. One could, therefore, envisage both being conducted by the same person, which in reality is probably what happens in most services, where resources are never really sufficient.

Supervision in the sense we are discussing is not about providing a line manager, whose role is to ensure that the subordinate is directed appropriately and carrying out his/her duties properly. This may well be part of it, but our model is one of working alongside people, respectfully enabling them to use and develop their potential to the full and helping them manage any problems that inevitably arise as effectively as possible.

An implication of this is that the process of supervision might exactly parallel the process of helping parents, and as such, we have begun to see the models we have been discussing in the book as directly applicable to the supervision situation. For example, we see the process as including the need for a mutually respectful working relationship (ideally a partnership) as the vehicle for a careful exploration of relevant issues. Deriving a clear model of these issues provides the basis where necessary for problem management via goal-setting, strategy planning and implementation followed by review. We assume that the process is enabled by the qualities of the supervisor (e.g. respect, empathy, genuineness, humility, enthusiasm and integrity), underpinned by the skills of listening, exploring, challenging and problem management. The notions of construing are as relevant here as they are to the helper situation and the parent–child interaction. The supervisor is working on and through the constructions the person brings to supervision sessions in relation to the on-going work. Although all aspects of the process are important, support comes in large measure from the respect and understanding provided within the context of a relationship that has importance for the helper.

Our experience suggests that supervision in many of the helping professions is not as available as it should be, although it is as important for the physician, nurse, and social worker, as for the child care worker or teacher. Its significance increases wherever the job undertaken involves dealing explicitly with psychological and social issues, which are ever present, though often neglected in many of these roles.

Presumably one of the reasons for the lack of adequate supervision is the significant costs involved. It requires resources in terms of people to do it, training to enable them to function appropriately in the role, and the time and organisation for helpers and supervisors to meet regularly, when they are often overwhelmed with the demands of direct work. Nevertheless, it must not be regarded as optional, since it is likely to have the effect of ensuring quality of performance via support for the expertise of the helper, but also by their motivation, job satisfaction and stress management.

Given the complexity and responsibility of the role, we assume that in order to be effective, supervisors need to be carefully selected for the appropriate qualities and skills, trained to carry out the task, and then supervised themselves. For the Parent Adviser model, since we see the processes as parallel to the helping situation generally, the training involves a detailed understanding and application of all aspects of the core model. We have, therefore, developed at the Centre for Parent and Child Support a course, which is similar in style and format to the core module of the Parent Adviser training, but focused upon the supervision context.

Supervision is necessary on a regular basis, and the amount is to some extent dependent upon the individual's caseload. Taking into account the obvious practical and resource issues, we assume that newly trained Parent Advisers are best seen individually for supervision for about an hour and a half once every two weeks. Once every six weeks or so we also try to provide a time in which a number of Parent Advisers get together with a supervisor in a group setting. This adds to the one to one situation, by providing an opportunity to learn from one's colleagues, to derive peer support, and also the format for formal or informal training sessions on topics seen as problematic by members of the group.

Although economically attractive, we could not recommend group supervision as a substitute for individual sessions. This is largely because it does not allow sufficient time for each member of the group to deal with issues that are specific to them and the families on their caseload. Secondly, individual helpers may often have personal concerns, that are not appropriately discussed in a group setting. There are also implications for family confidentiality.

Other System Issues
RESOURCES

The question of supervision is only one of the issues to consider if one is seriously going to take on the frameworks and skills with which we have been dealing. All helpers need to communicate and may become more able to cope effectively with the psychosocial issues presented by families. However, this again does have resource implications.

Resources are severely limited in public services generally. They are currently insufficient to meet the needs of children and families in relation to education, health or social services. We traditionally run our services on the minimum resources available and they are rarely adequate to achieve the key tasks, which are mostly reactive. However, if they are to become preventive and promotional in relation to children's development, as well as reactive, then a considerable increase in resources is required. This is beginning to occur, for example in the UK and other Commonwealth countries such as Canada and Australia. Strategies such as Sure Start, On Track, and the Children's Fund in the UK are examples of note, where increased resources are being channelled into the early years and especially in deprived areas. An attempt is being made to prevent social exclusion and the gamut of developmental problems that pressage adult mental health problems, relationship difficulties, drug and alcohol problems, and crime.

However, there is a need for extra time with each family, if the helper's role is explicitly extended into the psychosocial arena, and if promotional and preventive work is to be taken seriously. We will exemplify this in relation to health visiting, but the same point is applicable to all (e.g. early years, school nursing, teaching). Health visitors in the UK may frequently have caseloads in the 100s, especially in the more deprived areas. It is not easy to add to an already improbable task the need to spent more time with families, especially as listening properly is almost certainly likely to involve further work in relation to the difficulties one hears. If one is to request increases in time from people, then they do need to be able to drop other tasks, or they need to be given extra resources to enable these other tasks to be done.

SERVICE COOPERATION AND CO-ORDINATION

Although increased numbers of helpers is one solution to the resource question, another is to share the extended role across all professions and people working with children and families, as was suggested at the beginning of the book in describing services organised into a tiered system. However, if personnel from all the relevant professions are to be involved in identifying and targeting families likely to have problems, there needs to be a way that enables diverse professions and organisations to cooperate and to coordinate their activities.

One might envisage a system where all families are visited before birth at home by midwives or health visitors, for example. This would enable relationships to be established with parents, as well as the identification of problems or risk factors predisposing the family and child to subsequent difficulties. Those likely to be at risk might then be provided with general support by the original visitor, or referred on to other workers, depending upon the particular nature of the difficulties identified. Whether referred or not, the helpers in either case would work as intensively as possible with the family to resolve current difficulties. They would also try to promote the parents' adaptation and particularly their interaction with their child, with the intention of preventing the escalation of problems and the occurrence of future difficulties. This is the kind of system envisaged within the European Early Promotion Project (Puura, Davis, Papadopoulou, et al, 2002) which fits very easily into the remit of Sure Start in the UK and other early home visiting schemes elsewhere (e.g. Olds, Hill, Robinson, Song & Little, 2000).

Such a system is highly dependent upon different services working together, sharing aims, skills and intervention activities, and coordinating their services to provide appropriate support that takes account of the needs and demands of families. Although this kind of organisation might be much more expensive initially, it is likely to reduce problems in the long term and therefore save resources that are currently needed to deal with problems that will otherwise become chronic, severe and entrenched.

Although not easy to achieve, to provide an effective system of care with broad aims requires all the different agencies and their personnel to work in partnership with each other as well as families. No profession has all the answers to the problems families face. Each has a potential contribution, although this is always dependent upon the relationship formed with families and the human qualities of the helper, whatever the profession. Just as we believe that partnership is the essence of support for families, so it is the basis for the integration of services.

Integration is important at all levels, but needs to be led by agreement between senior management levels and by policy. Successful implementation of change requires clear and agreed policy about a number of issues, because these impinge upon the work of all agencies. The first is to do with acknowledging the importance of psychosocial factors, which are involved in all aspects of the work of all agencies. The second is the importance of the parental role in relation to all aspects of the child's functioning; it cannot be ignored. The third is to recognise the need for extended work in some families, in contrast to most services where through-put seems the major concern and short-term intervention is the norm. Next there needs to be a deliberate emphasis upon promotional work and prevention, and finally, a need to recognise that all services can make a contribution to the psychosocial functioning of families, through the human qualities and skills of all their workers, whatever their technical expertise.

Endorsement of these points at a policy level might enable the issues to filter down service systems, such that integration is clearly permitted at the different management levels and on the ground. The different services would have to allow all workers the time and resources (e.g. training and supervision) to attempt to provide broader support for sets of families, in addition to the specialist support they would normally provide.

Policy might oil the system, but integration still requires close co-ordination of all those working directly with families. This actually means each person making the time and effort to meet and get to know all the relevant personnel in their area. This clearly requires knowledge of the services available and the people staffing them. The importance of this relates to the effectiveness of the work with families. Different helpers need to have agreed their respective roles, they need to be able to do joint visits where appropriate, to consult each other over a variety of issues, and then to be able to refer families when relevant for further effective help. The need for such integration is why we have adopted the tiered system described earlier in the book. If we assume overlap of the roles of all workers in terms of their mutual concern for the psychosocial functioning of children and families, then it is important that this be understood. People need to be very clear about their own roles in terms of what they can, cannot, or might not have to be able to manage, and the differences between roles.

REFERRAL AND ROLE CLARITY
Helpers working to the parent adviser model need to be particularly clear

about their role and expertise, because having a broader brief and being more skilled means that they are likely to hear about problems in many areas of a person's life. As a result of this, they might feel anxious about being out of their depth and going beyond their expertise. Although they should never assume knowledge or competence that they do not have, they are less likely to do this, if they follow the approaches taken in the book, have humility and are ready to express ignorance. To do otherwise would be of no value whatsoever to families.

An effective system of care should ensure that families have access to the most appropriate sources of help, and referring them on where necessary is an important role of all helpers. Although there should be no hesitation in referring a family (with their agreement), there is no reason why a helper should not discuss and explore any issues with them, even those directly relevant to another profession. If this helps the parents to think clearly about a problem, it can be to their advantage. It might, for example, enable them to make a clear list of symptoms for when they see a paediatrician, and to know what questions they need to ask. This may mean that they will be able to make the most effective and economical use of the referral. For example, a helper not trained in marital counselling may decide in conjunction with parents that a referral is appropriate. This does not, however, preclude the helper from exploring the relationship difficulties with the parents, enabling them to develop a clearer picture of the problems, and helping them to decide to whom they should be referred. There is also no reason why the helper should not continue to be in touch with the family when they are seeing the specialist.

The essential point to be made here is that one can provide basic help without having high level expertise in all areas. The frameworks and skills we have been discussing in the book are about relating to parents in ways that help them explore, derive clear models, and decide for themselves the most effective strategies for dealing with problems, including seeking appropriate expertise elsewhere. One can help by listening to what parents have to say and acknowledging their problems, whatever the issue, without being afraid of one's own limits. As we have seen, this may be extremely helpful psychologically. Where necessary the helper should explore each problem with the parents fully, not necessarily with the aim of finding solutions, but to enable parents to feel competent as problem managers, even if only in being able to decide for themselves the exact nature of their problems and the best sources of potential help.

If services are better coordinated, then the process of referral for more specialist help becomes easier. However, this does not take account of the fact that for whatever reasons some families will not approach the services they need. For example, health visitors and other Tier 1 personnel may relate to families who are difficult to engage but may not be able to facilitate a referral to child mental health services. Defining one's role in terms of problem type and content will not work in this situation. Help seeking is not simply determined by the most obvious problem; it depends upon the surrounding circumstances and is certainly very much related to the significant life constructions of the individuals involved. Even if prepared to be referred, waiting times may be so lengthy, that the Tier 1 helper has a role by default in problems that require specialised expertise.

However, even under these circumstances, well coordinated services improve the situation. For example, any information that may be of help to parents may become much more accessible via the helper, who can consult other professionals on behalf of parents. Secondly, closer coordination of services makes joint working more of a possibility, with helpers even taking on an advocacy role. This is also likely to be the case even if the family are seen by specialist centres, because in situations where long-term support is needed, dealing with one issue by referral does not necessarily remove the need for continuing help with the rest of life. Few services cater for this, and it is an intention within the Parent Adviser model that the general support for families is increased and a system of care provided.

Final Comments

We began the book by attempting to make very clear the high levels of psychosocial difficulties families and their children face, and the general absence of freely available, high quality support. The significant consequences of this make it quite clear to us, that much more help is needed. There should be a system of care universally available, that enables the promotion of child and family adaptation, the prevention of difficulties and very early intervention where necessary.

We have argued that such a system requires not only expertise in terms of knowledge, skills, strategies and techniques, but also high level understanding and skills in relating to and engaging families. An important aims is to foster and strengthen parents own resources in terms of, for example, self-efficacy and problem management. However, we hope to have made it clear that help is not just about what you do, but very much about the way that you do it.

We have explored these issues, and have attempted to provide frameworks that make it easier to understand the helping situation, to provide broad based psychosocial care and to promote and prevent. There are no absolute truths in this work and we have tried to communicate what amount to our best guesses at the moment. They are theories that are presented for the reader to test and elaborate. We sincerely hope that we have been able to engage you in this enterprise, and to encourage you to experiment with the ideas. In so doing, we hope you feel more confident and competent in listening to parents and their children respectfully, in working with them in partnership, in enhancing their dignity, and in making them feel good about themselves as people. Regardless of the physical and social problems they face, we hope you have learnt something about enabling parents to manage problems themselves and to elicit whatever extra help they need from the community and services around them.

Whether we have succeeded is for each reader to judge. There are skills to learn and processes to understand better, but no absolute rules. Each helper is different; each parent and child, each family is unique. The interactions between them are rarely routinely predictable. Nevertheless, we hope that each helper will come to realise the enormous influence they have as a person, and strive to harness the power of their own personality for the benefit of the families they serve. Communication is never easy, but it is worth practising and developing, as it is a very powerful way of enabling parents and hence their children.

REFERENCES

Ainsworth, M., Blehar, M., Waters, E. & Wall, S. (1978). *Patterns of Attachment*. Hillsdale, NJ: Erlbaum.

American Academy of Pediatrics. (1996). The short and long-term consequences of corporal punishment. *Pediatrics*, 98, 852–860.

Angold, A. & Costello, E. (1995). Developmental epidemiology. *Epidemiologic Reviews*, 17, 74 and 82.

Aronen, E. & Kurkela, S. (1996). Long-term effects of an early home-based intervention. *Journal of the American Academy of Child & Adolescent Psychiatry*, 35, 1665–1672.

Attride-Stirling, J., Davis, H., Day, C., Staveley, A., Farrell, L. & Sclare, I. (2001). Who needs psychosocial help? Characteristics of children and families in need. Unpublished manuscript available from Hilton Davis.

Attride-Stirling, J., Davis, H., Day, C. & Sclare, I. (2000). *An Assessment of the Psychosocial Needs of Children and Families in Lewisham: Final Report*. London: South London and Maudsley NHS Trust.

Attride-Stirling, J., Davis, H., Markless, G., Sclare, I. & Day, C. (2001). 'Someone to talk to who'll listen': addressing the psychosocial needs of children and families. *Journal of Community and Applied Social Psychology*, 11, 179–191.

Audit Commission. (1999). *Children in Mind: Child and Adolescent Mental Health Services*. London: Audit Commission.

Avon Premature Infant Project (1998). Randomised trial of parental support for families with very preterm children. *Archives of Disease in Childhood Foetal and Neonatal Edition*, 79, 4–11.

Bandura, A. (1977). *Social Learning Theory*. Englewood Cliffs, NJ: Prentice-Hall.

Bannister, D. & Fransella, F. (1986). *Inquiring Man: The Psychology of Personal Constructs*. London: Croon Helm.

Barlow, J. (1997). *Systematic Review of the Effectiveness of Parent Education Programmes in Improving the Behaviour of 3–7 Year Old Children*. Oxford: Health Services Research Unit, University of Oxford.

Barlow, J., Coren, E. & Stewart-Brown, S. (2002). Meta-analysis of the effectiveness of parenting programmes in improving maternal psychosocial health. *British Journal of General Practice*, 52, 223–233.

Bavolek, S. (1990). *Parenting: Theory, Policy and Practice: Research and Validation Report of the Nurturing Programmes.* Eau Claire, WI: Family Development Resources Inc.

Bays, H. (2000). *Priorities in Supporting Parents: A Training Pack for Health Visitors, School Nurses and Others Who Work with Families.* Slough: Wiltshire and Swindon Heath Care NHS Trust.

Beck, A. (1976). *Cognitive Therapy and the Emotional Disorders.* London: Penguin Books.

Bee, H. (2000). *The Developing Child.* Boston: Allyn and Bacon.

Bowlby, J. (1969). *Attachment and Loss.* New York: Basic Books.

Brazelton, T. (1992). *Touchpoint: Your Child's Emotional and Behavioural Development.* Reading, Mass: Perseus Books.

Brazelton, T. & Nugent, K. (1995). *Neonatal Behavioural Assessment Scale.* Cambridge: Cambridge University Press.

Brewer, S. (2001). *A Child's World.* London: Headline Book Publishing.

Brofenbrenner, U. (1979). *The Ecology of Human Development.* Cambridge, M.A.: Harvard University Press.

Brown, G. & Harris, T. (1978). *Social Origins of Depression: Study of Psychiatric Disorder in Women.* London: Tavistock.

Bryant, D. & Ramey, C. (1987). An analysis of the effectiveness of early intervention programs for environmentally at-risk children. In Guralnick (Ed.). *The Effectiveness of Early Intervention for At-risk and Handicapped children.* New York: Academic Press.

Buchan, L., Clemerson, J. & Davis, H. (1988). Working with families of children with special needs. *Child: Care, Health and Development*, 14, 81–91.

Buss, A. & Plomin, R. (1986). The EAS approach to temperament. In R. Plomin and J. Dunn (Eds.). *The Study of Temperament: Changes, Continuities and Challenges.* Hillsdale, N.J: Erlbaum.

Cadman, D., Boyle, M. Szatmari, P. & Offord, D. (1987). Chronic illness, disability, and mental and social well-being: findings of the Ontario Child Health Study. *Pediatrics*, 79, 805–813.

Carr, A. (1999). *The Handbook of Child and Adolescent Clinical Psychology: A Contextual Approach.* London: Routledge.

Caspi, A. (1998). Personality development across the life course. In W. Damon (Ed.). *Handbook of Child Psychology. Volume 3: Social, Emotional and Personality Development.* New York: John Wiley and Sons.

Cattel, R. (1965). *The Scientific Analysis of Personality.* Baltimore: Penguin Books.

Clarke, L. & Berrington, A. (1999). Socio-demographic predictors of divorce. In J. Simons (Ed.). *High Divorce Rates: The State of the Evidence on Reasons and Remedies.* Lord Chancellor's Department Research Series No 2/99, 1.

WORKING IN PARTNERSHIP WITH PARENTS

Cleaver, H., Wattam, C., & Cawson, P. (1998). *Assessing Risk in Child Protection*. London: NSPCC.

Cohen, P. & Brook, J. (1995). The reciprocal influence of punishment and child behaviour disorder. In J. McCord (Ed.). *Coercion and Punishment in Long-Term Perspectives*. New York: Cambridge University Press.

Coleman, P. & Karraker, K. (1997). Self-efficacy and parenting quality: findings and future applications. *Developmental Review*, 18, 47–85.

Cooper, P. & Murray, L. (1997). The impact of psychological treatments of postnatal depression on maternal mood and infant development. In L. Murray & P. Cooper (Eds.). *Postpartum Depression and Child Development*. New York: Guildford.

Cunningham, C. & Davis, H. (1985). *Working with Parents: Frameworks for Collaboration*. Milton Keynes: Open University Press.

Dale, N. (1996). *Working with Families of Children with Special Needs: Partnership and Practice*. London: Routledge.

Davis, H. (1993). *Counselling Parents of Children with Chronic Illness or Disabilities*. Leicester: British Psychological Society Books.

Davis, H. & Ali Choudhury, P. (1988). Helping Bangladeshi families: The Parent Adviser Scheme. *Mental Handicap*, 16, 48–51.

Davis, H., Cox, A., Day, C., Roberts, R., Loxton, R., Ispanovic-Radojkovic, V., Tsiantis, J., Layiou-Lignos, E., Puura K., Tamminen, T., Turunen, M-M., Paradisiotou, A., Hadjipanayi, Y., & Pandeli, P. (2000). *Primary Health Care Worker Training Manual*. Belgrade, FRY: Institute of Mental Health.

Davis, H. & Day, C. (2001). Using the Parent Adviser model to support parents of teenagers. In J. Coleman & D. Roker (Eds.). *Supporting Parents of Teenagers*. London: Jessica Kingsley Publishers.

Davis, H., Day, C. & Bidmead, C. (2002). *Parent Adviser Training Manual*. London: The Psychological Corporation.

Davis, H., Day, C., Cox, A. & Cutler, L. (2000). Child and adolescent mental health needs assessment and service implications in an inner city area. *Clinical Child Psychology and Psychiatry*, 5, 169–188.

Davis, H. & Fallowfield, L. (1991). *Counselling and Communication in Health Care*. Chichester: John Wiley and Son.

Davis, H. & Rushton, R. (1991). Counselling and supporting parents of children with developmental delay: a research evaluation. *Journal of Mental Deficiency Research*, 35, 89–112.

Davis, H. & Spurr, P. (1998). Parent counselling: an evaluation of a community child mental health service. *Journal of Child Psychology & Psychiatry*, 39, 365–376.

Davis, H., Spurr, P., Cox, A., Lynch, M., von Roenne, A., & Hahn, K. (1997). A description and evaluation of a community child mental health service. *Clinical Child Psychology and Psychiatry*, 2, 221–238.

Davis, H., Stroud, A., & Green, L. (1989). Child Characterization Sketch. *International Journal of Personal Construct Psychology*, 2, 323–337.

Day, C. & Davis, H. (1999). Community child mental-health services: a framework for the development of parenting initiatives. *Clinical Child Psychology and Psychiatry*, 4, 475–482.

Day, C., Davis, H. & Hind, R. (1998). The development of a community child and family mental health service. *Child: Care, Health and Development*, 24, 487–500.

Department of Health. (2000). *Protecting Children, Supporting Parents: A Consultation Document on the Physical Punishment of Children*. London: Department of Health.

Dorman, C. & Dorman, H. (2002). *The Social Toddler*. Richmond: The Children's Project.

Dryden, W. (1999). *Rational Emotive Behavioural Counselling in Action*. London: Sage Publications.

Earls, F. (1994). Oppositional-defiant and conduct disorders. In M. Rutter, E. Taylor and L. Hersov (Eds.). *Child and Adolescent Psychiatry: Modern Approaches*. Oxford: Blackwell Science.

Edwards, M. & Davis, H. (1997). *Counselling Children with Chronic Medical Conditions*. Leicester: British Psychological Society Books.

Egan, G. (1990). *The Skilled Helper: A Systematic Approach to Effective Helping*. Pacific Grove, CA.: Brookes/Cole.

Eiser, C. (1990). *Chronic Childhood Disease: An Introduction to Psychological Theory and Research*. Cambridge: Cambridge Unversity Press.

Elkan, R., Kendrick, D., Hewitt, M., Robinson, J. J. A., Tolley, K. et al. (2000). *The Effectiveness of Domiciliary Health Visiting: A Systematic Review of International Studies and a Selective View of British Literature*. HTA, 4(13).

Ellis, A. & Dryden, W. (1987). *The Practice of Rational-Emotive Therapy*. New York: Springer.

Emde, R. (1989). The infant's relationship experience: developmental and affective aspects. In A. Samaroff (Ed.). *Relationship Disturbances in Early Childhood*. New York: Basic Books.

Field, T., Grizzle, N., Scafidi, F., Abrams, S., Richardson, S., Kuhn, C. & Schanberg, S. (1996). Massage therapy for infants of depressed mothers. *Infant Behaviour & Development*, 19, 107–112.

Field, T., Schanberg. S., Scafidi, F., Bauer, C., Vega-Lahr, N., Garcia, R., Nystrom, J., & Kuhn C. (1986). Tactile/kinesthetic stimulation effects on preterm neonates. *Pediatrics*, 77, 654–658.

Finch, J. Hill, P. & Clegg, C. (2000). *The Health Advisory Service Standard for Child and Adolescent Mental Health Services*. Brighton: Health Advisory Service and Pavillion Publishing Ltd.

Fundudis, T. (1990). A survey of health visitors views on the relevance of behavioural techniques for their casework. In J. Stevenson (Ed.). *Health Visitor Based Services for Pre-school Children with Behaviour Problems. Association for Child Psychology and Psychiatry Occasional Papers, No. 2.*

Furneaux, B. (1988). *Special Parents.* Milton Keynes: Open University Press.

Galboda Liyanage, K. (2000). *A Community Study on the Association Between Parent–Child Joint Activity and Behaviour Problems of Pre-School Children.* Unpublished PhD thesis, University of London.

Ghate, D. & Daniels, A. (1997). *Talking About My Generation: A Survey of 8–15 Year Olds Growing Up in the 1990s.* London: NSPCC.

Gibran, K. (1926). *The Prophet.* London: Penguin Books.

Giles-Sims, J, Straus, M. & Sugarman, D. (1995). Child, maternal and family characteristics associated with corporal punishment. *Family Relations: Journal of Applied Family and Child Studies*, 44, 170–176.

Gomby, D., Culross, P., Behrman, R. (1999). Home visiting: recent programme evaluations – analysis and recommendations. *The Future of Children*, 9, 4–26.

Goodman, R. (1994). Brain disorders. In M. Rutter, E. Taylor and L. Hersov (Eds.). *Child and Adolescent Psychiatry, Modern Approaches.* Oxford: Blackwell Science.

Graham, P. (1998). *Cognitive-Behaviour Therapy for Children and Families.* Cambridge: Cambridge University Press.

Hardy, J. & Street, R. (1989). Family support and parenting education in the home: an effective extension of clinic-based preventative health care services for poor children. *Journal of Paediatrics*, 115, 927–931.

Hawkins, P. & Shohet, R. (2000). *Supervision in the Helping Professions: an Individual, Group and Organizational approach.* Buckingham: Open University Press.

Hay, D. Pawlby, S., Sharp, D., Asten, P., Mills, A. & Kumar, R. (2001). Intellectual problems shown by 11 year old children whose mothers had postnatal depression. *Journal of Child Psychology and Psychiatry*, 42, 871–889.

Henricson, C. Katz, I. Mesie, J., Sandison, M. & Tunstill, J. (2001). *National Mapping of Family Services in England and Wales: A Consultation Document.* London: National Family and Parenting Institute.

Henricson, C. & Grey, A. (2001). *Understanding Discipline.* London: National Family and Parenting Institute.

Herbert, M. (1988). *Working with Children and Their Families.* Leicester: British Psychological Society.

Herbert, M. (1988). *Psychology in Action.* Leicester: British Psychological Society.

Holden, J., Sagovsky, R. & Cox, J. (1989). Counselling in a general practice setting: controlled study of health visitor intervention in treatment of postnatal depression. *British Medical Journal*, 298, 223–226.

Home Office. (1998). *Supporting Families: A Consultation Document*. London: Stationery Office.

Huesman, L., Eron, L., Ledfkowits, M. & Walder, L. (1984). Stability of aggression over time and generations. *Developmental Psychology*, 20, 1120–1134.

Kazdin, A. (2001). Treatment of conduct disorders. In J. Hill & B. Maughan (Eds.). *Conduct Disorders in Childhood and Adolescence*. Cambridge: Cambridge University Press.

Kelly, G, (1991). *The Psychology of Personal Constructs: Volume 1: A Theory of Personality*. London: Routledge.

Kline, P. (1984). *Psychology and Freudian Theory*. London: Methuen.

Kurtz, Z., Thornes, R. and Wolkind, S. (1994). *Services for the Mental Health of Children and Young People in England, a National Review*. London: Department of Public Health South Thames Regional Health Authority.

Lambert, M. & Bergin, A. (1994). The effectiveness of psychotherapy. In A. Bergin & S. Garfield (Eds.). *Handbook of Psychotherapy and Behaviour Change*. New York: John Wiley & Sons.

Lea, D., Clarke, M. & Davis, H. (1998). Evaluation of a counselling skills course for health professionals. *British Journal of Guidance and Counselling*, 26, 159–173.

Leach, P. (1999a). *Physical Punishment of Children in the Home*. London, National Children's Bureau.

Leach, P. (1999b). *The Physical Punishment of Children: Some Input from Recent Research*. London: NSPCC.

Ley, P. (1988). *Communicating with Patients: Improving Communication, Satisfaction and Compliance*. London: Croom Helm.

Maccoby, E. & Martin, J. (1983). Socialisation in the context of the family: parent–child interaction. In P. H. Mussen (Ed.). *Handbook of Child Psychology Vol. 4*. New York: Wiley.

Malphurs, J., Larrain, C., Field, T. Pickens, J., Pelaez-Noguras, M. Yando, R., & Bendell, D. (1996). Altering withdrawn and intrusive interaction behaviors of depressed mothers. *Infant Mental Health Journal*, 17, 152–160.

Maughan, B. & Yule, W. (1994). Reading and other learning disabilities. In M. Rutter, E. Taylor and L. Hersov (Eds.). *Child and Adolescent Psychiatry: Modern Approaches*. Oxford: Blackwell Science.

McCain, M. & Mustard, J. (1999). *Reversing the Real Brain Drain: Early Years Study Final Report*. Toronto: Ontario Publications.

McClure, V. (2000). *Infant Massage: A Handbook for Loving Parents, Third Edition*. New York: Bantam Books.

Meltzer, H., Gatward, R., Goodman R. & Ford, T. (2000). *Mental Health of Children and Adolescents in Great Britain*. London: The Stationery Office.

Mental Health Foundation (1999). *The Big Picture: Promoting Children and Young People's Mental Health*. London: Mental Health Foundation.

Murray, L. & Andrews, L. (2000). *The Social Baby: Understanding Babies' Communication From Birth*. Richmond: The Children's Project Ltd.

Murray, L., Kempton, C., Woolgar, M. & Hooper, R. (1993). Depressed mothers speech to their infants and its relation to infant gender and cognitive development. *Journal of Child Psychology and Psychiatry, 7*, 1083–1101.

Murray-Parkes, C., Stevenson-Hinde, J., & Marris, P. (1991). *Attachment Across the Life Cycle*. New York: Tavistock/Routledge.

National Family and Parenting Institute. (1999). *The Millennial Family*. NFPI: London.

Nelson-Jones, R. (2000). *Introduction to Counselling Skills: Text and Activities*. London: Sage Publications.

Newson, E. & Hipgrave, T. (1982). *Getting Through to Your Handicapped Child*. Cambridge: Cambridge University Press.

NHS Advisory Service. (1995). *Together We Stand: The Commissioning, Role and Management of Child and Adolescent Mental Health Services*. London: HMSO.

Oates, M. (1994). Postnatal mental illness: organisation and function of services. In J. Cox & J. Holden (Eds.). *Perinatal Psychiatry: Use and Misuse of the Edinburgh Postnatal Depression Scale*. London: Gaskell.

Offord, D., Boyle, M., Szatmari, P., Rae-Grant, N., Links, P., Cadman, D., Byles, J., Crawford, J., Blum, H., Byrne, C., Thomas, H. & Woodward, C. (1987). Ontario Child Health Study: II. Six month prevalence of disorder and rates of service utilization. *Archives of General Psychiatry, 44*, 832–836.

Olds, D., Eckenrode, J., & Henderson, C., et al. (1997). Long term effects of home visitation on maternal life course and child abuse and neglect: fifteen year follow-up of a randomised trial. *Journal of the American Medical Association, 278*, 637–643.

Olds, R., Henderson, C., Tatelbaum, R., & Chamberlin, R. (1986). Improving the delivery of prenatal care and outcomes of pregnancy: a randomised trial of nurse home visitation. *Pediatrics, 77*, 16–28.

Olds, D., Hill, P., Robinson, J., Song, N. & Little, C. (2000). Update on home visiting for pregnant women and parents of young children. *Current Problems in Paediatrics, 30*, 109–141.

Olds, D. & Kitzman, H. (1993). Review of research on home visiting for pregnant women and parents of young children. Future of Children, 3, 53–92.

Onozawa, K., Glover, V., Adams, D., Modi, N. & Kumar, C. (2001). Infant massage improves mother-infant interaction for mothers with postnatal depression. *Journal of Affective Disorders*, 63, 201–207.

Parr, M. (1999). Integrating infant observations skills into parent facilitator training. *Infant Observation*, 3, 33–46.

Patterson, C. (1986). *Theories of Counselling and Psychotherapy*. New York: Harper and Rowe.

Patterson, G. (1975). *A Social Learning Approach to Family Intervention*. Champaign Ill.: Research Press.

Pearce, J. (1991). *Families and Friends, How to Help Your Child Enjoy Happy Relationships*. London: Thorsons Publishers.

Pless, I. & Nolan, T. (1991) Revision, replication and neglect in research on maladjustment in chronic illness. *Journal of Child Psychology and Psychiatry*, 32, 347–365.

Pless, I. & Satterwhite, B. (1972). Chronic illness in childhood: selection, activities and evaluation of non-professional family counselors. *Clinical Pediatrics*, 11, 403–410.

Pugh, G., De'Ath, E. & Smith, C. (1994). *Confident Parent, Confident Children: Policy and Practice in Parent Education and Support*. London: National Children's Bureau.

Puura, K, Davis, H., Papadopoulou, K., Tsiantis, J., Ispanovic-Radojkovic, V., Rudic, N., Tamminen, T., Turunen, M-M., Dragonas, T., Paradisiotou, A., Visakou, S., Roberts, R., Cox, A. & Day, C. (2002). The European Early Promotion Project: a new primary health care service to promote children's mental health. *Infant Mental Health Journal*, 23, 606-624.

Quinn, M. & Quinn, T. (1986). *What can a Parent Do? Practical Skills to Help Parents be more Responsible and Effective*. Newry: Family Caring Trust.

Quinn, M. & Quinn, T. (1995). *From Pram to Primary School – Parenting Small Children from Birth to Age Six or Seven*. Newry: Family Caring Trust.

Roberts, R., Loxton, R., Campbell, J., Frame, M., Kirkum, M., Lake, M., Wood, M. & Ross, T. & Davis, H. (2002). The European Early Promotion Project: promoting the transition to parenthood and preventing psychosocial problems in children. *Community Practitioner*, 75, 464-468.

Rogers, C. (1959). A theory of therapy, personality and interpersonal relationships as developed in the client centered framework. In S Koch (Ed.). *Psychology: A Study of a Science*. Vol. 3. New York: McGraw-Hill.

Rushton, R. & Davis, H. (1992). An evaluation of the effectiveness of counselling training for health care professionals. *British Journal of Guidance and Counselling*, 20, 205–220.

Rutter, M. Giller, H. & Hagel, A. (1998). *Antisocial Behaviour by Young People.* Cambridge: Cambridge University Press.

Sanders, M. (1999). Triple P – Positive Parenting Programme: towards an empirically validated multi-level parenting and family support strategy for the prevention of behaviour and emotional problems in children. *Clinical Child and Family Psychology Review,* 2, 71–90.

Sanders, M. (1992). *Every Parent: A Positive Approach to Children's Behaviour.* Sydney: Addison-Wesley.

Schaffer, R. (1977). *Mothering.* London: Fontana/Open Books.

Scott, S., Knapp, M., Henderson, J., Maughan, B. (2001). Financial cost of social exclusion: follow up study of antisocial children into adulthood. *British Medical Journal,* 323, 191–194.

Skinner, B. (1974). *About Behaviourism.* London: Cape.

Skynner, R. & Cleese, J. (1994). *Life and How to Survive It.* London: Methuen.

Smith, C. (1996). *Developing Parenting Programmes.* London: National Children's Bureau.

Sokolov, I. & Hutton, D. (1988). *The Parents Book.* Wellingborough: Thorsons.

Stevenson, J. (1990). Health visitor based services for pre-school children with behaviour problems. *Association of Child Psychology and Psychiatry Occasional Papers,* No. 2. London: ACPP.

Straus, M. & Paschall, M. (1998). *Corporal Punishment by Mothers and Child's Cognitive Development: a Longitudinal Study.* Montreal: World Congress of Sociology.

Straus, M., Sugarman, D. & Giles-Sims, J. (1997). Spanking by parents and subsequent antisocial behaviour of children. *Archives of Pediatrics and Adolescent Medicine,* 151, 761–767.

Sturmey, P. (2002). Treatment interventions for people with aggressive behaviour and intellectual disability. In G. Holt and N. Bouras (Eds.). *Autism and Related Disorders: A Basic Handbook for Mental Health, Primary Care and Other Professionals.* London: Royal College of Psychiatrists.

Sutton, C. (2000). *Child and Adolescent Behaviour Problems.* Leicester: British Psychological Society.

Sutton, C. (1992). Training Parent to Manage difficult children: a comparison of methods. *Behavioural Psychotherapy,* 20, 115–139.

Taylor, D. K. & Beauchamp, C. (1988). Hospital-based primary prevention strategy in child abuse: a multilevel needs addressment. *Child Abuse and Neglect,* 12, 343–354.

Thomas, A. & Chess, S. (1977). *Temperament and Development.* New York: Brunner/Mazel.

Tsiantis, J., Dragonas, T., Cox, A., Smith, M., Ispanovic, V. & Sampaio-Faria, J. (1996). Promotion of children's early psychosocial development through primary health care services. *Pediatric and Perinatal Epidemiology*, 10, 339–354.

Van Ijzendoorm, M. & Kroonenberg, P. (1988). Cross-cultural patterns of attachment: a meta-analysis of the Strange Situation. *Child Development*, 59, 147–156.

Waterston, T. (2000). Giving guidance on child discipline. *British Medical Journal*, 320, 261–262.

Webster-Stratton, C. (1992). *The Incredible Years: a Trouble-shooting Guide for Parents of Children Aged 3 to 8*. Toronto: Umbrella Press.

Webster-Stratton, C. (1994). Advancing videotape parent training: a comparison study. *Journal of Consulting and Clinical Psychology*, 62, 583–593.

Webster-Stratton, C. & Herbert, M. (1994). *Troubled Families - Problem Children*. Chichester: John Wiley & Sons.

Wickberg, B. & Hwang, C. (1996). Counselling of postnatal depression: a controlled study on a population based Swedish sample. *Journal of Affective Disorders*, 89, 209–216.

Yates, A. (1970). *Behaviour Therapy*. New York: Wiley and Son.

Zeanah, C., Boris, N. & Larrieu, J. (1997). Infant development and developmental risk: a review of the past ten years. *Journal of the American Academy of Child and Adolescent Psychiatry*, 36, 165–178.

INDEX

D

depression, 21–22

directives, 95

disruptions of parenting process, 2–3

distractions, 70, 75–76

divorce, 23–25

drawing, 243

E

early play

See play activities

empathy, 63–64, 95–97, 112, 122, 224–225, 251

encouragement, 234, 237–238

endings, 44–45, 81–83, 145–146

enthusiasm, 65–66, 112, 225

European Early Promotion Project, 13–14,
190–192, 194–195, 273

expert model, 47–49, 88

exploration

areas of exploration, 88–90

behaviour analysis, 253

definition, 85–86

duration, 90

first meeting, 79–80

helping process, 37–38

observation techniques, 98–99, 201–203

parent-child interactions, 241–243

parent-helper relationship, 86, 196–198

parent-infant interactions, 196–198, 202–205

partnership model, 88

personal construct theory, 112–113, 125–126

play activities, 210–216, 229–236,
239–240, 243

skill development, 90–98, 241–243

solution suggestions, 86–88, 242

See also challenging skills

F

facial expressions, 67, 202, 239–240

family support

care strategies, 3–5

helping process, 26–29

need assessment, 194–195

Parent Adviser Model, 9–16

prevention programmes, 192–198

promotion, 187–192

relationship issues, 24–25

See also parenting; problem management

first meeting

contract formulation, 80–81

endings, 81–83

exploration, 79–80

greeting, 76–77

introductions, 78–79

location, 74–75

orientation, 77–78

personal construct theory, 110

preparations, 73

G

games, 212, 234–235

genuineness, 60–61, 111–112, 225–226, 237

goal setting, 40–41, 113, 133–139, 244–245

H

helping process

aims, 26–29

clarification, 38–39, 244

cooperative efforts, 273–274

early intervention strategies, 198–200

endings, 44–45, 81–83, 145–146

evaluations, 43–44, 113, 144–146, 246

exploration, 37–38

Q

questioning, 93–94, 242

R

referrals, 274–276
reflections, 94–95
respect, 53, 58–60, 111, 222–223
responsiveness, 157–160, 204–205, 223
rewards, 259
rhymes, 210–212
risk and resilience factors, 181–185, 194, 196
role-play, 129–130

S

self-constructions, 13, 22
self-disclosure, 121
self-esteem, 22–24, 36–37, 220–223
sensitivity, 223
setting limits, 256–258
skill development
    challenging skills, 115–124
    exploration, 90–98, 241–243
    infancy, 173–178
    parenting, 22–23, 27–29, 228–246
    supervision, 269–272
    training, 267–269
    See also communication skills
songs, 210–212
spontaneity, 60–61
statements, 94
strategy planning, 41–44, 113, 139–143,
    198–200, 245–246
summarising, 97–98, 120–121, 240
supervision, 269–272

T

theory of personal constructs
    See personal construct theory
tiered system of care, 5–9, 13
time-out, 263–265
touch, 205–209, 237–238, 241, 243
training, 267–269
transplant model, 49–50
trust, 36